EXPLORATIONS

Senior Author
William K. Durr

Senior Coordinating Author
John J. Pikulski

Coordinating Authors
Rita M. Bean
J. David Cooper
Nicholas A. Glaser
M. Jean Greenlaw
Hugh Schoephoerster

Authors
Mary Lou Alsin
Kathryn Au
Rosalinda B. Barrera
Joseph E. Brzeinski
Ruth P. Bunyan

Jacqueline C. Comas
Frank X. Estrada
Robert L. Hillerich
Timothy G. Johnson
Pamela A. Mason

HOUGHTON MIFFLIN COMPANY   BOSTON

Atlanta   Dallas   Geneva, Illinois   Lawrenceville, New Jersey   Palo Alto   Toronto

Acknowledgments

For each of the selections listed below, grateful acknowledgment is made for permission to adapt and/or reprint original or copyrighted material, as follows:

"Best Friends," adapted from *Felita*, by Nicholasa Mohr. Text copyright © 1979 by Nicholasa Mohr. Reprinted by permission of Dial Books for Young Readers, a Division of E. P. Dutton, Inc., and the author.

"The Boy Who Drew People Upside Down," by Jean Friedman. Copyright © 1980. Originally appeared in *Cricket* magazine. Reprinted by permission of the author.

"The Case of the Golden Opportunity," adapted from "The Case of the Golden Opportunity," by William and Loretta Marshall. *Highlights for Children*, December 1982. Copyright © 1982 by Highlights for Children, Inc., Columbus, Ohio. Reprinted by permission of Highlights for Children, Inc.

"The Cat and the Golden Egg," adapted from *The Town Cats and Other Tales*, by Lloyd Alexander. Copyright © 1977 by Lloyd Alexander. Reprinted by permission of the publisher, E. P. Dutton, Inc., and Brandt and Brandt Literary Agents, Inc.

"Catalogue," by Rosalie Moore, from the May 25, 1940 issue of *The New Yorker* magazine. Copyright © 1940, 1968. Reprinted by permission of The New Yorker Magazine, Inc.

"The Crow and the Pitcher," from *The Fables of Aesop*, retold by Joseph Jacobs. Copyright © 1950. Reprinted by permission of Macmillan Publishing Co., Inc.

"Emergency Please!" adapted from *The Revenge of the Incredible Dr. Rancid and His Youthful Assistant, Jeffrey*, by Ellen Conford. Copyright © 1980 by Ellen Conford. Reprinted by permission of Little, Brown and Company and McIntosh and Otis.

"Gramp," text abridged from Chapters 4 and 5 of *Gramp*, from *Luke's Garden and Gramp: Two Novels*, by Joan Tate. Copyright © 1971, 1979 by Joan Tate. Reprinted by permission of Harper & Row, Publishers, Inc., and Pelham Books, Ltd.

"The Heroine of Kapiti," by Shirley Climo. Copyright © 1983. Originally appeared in the June 1983 issue of *Cricket* magazine. Reprinted by permission of the author.

"Home from the High Meadow," from *The MacLeod Place*, by William H. Armstrong. Copyright © 1972. Reprinted by permission of the author.

"How Nameless, Tennessee, Got Its Name," from *Blue Highways*, by William Least Heat Moon. Copyright © 1982 by William Least Heat Moon. Reprinted by permission of Little, Brown and Company in association with the Atlantic Monthly Press.

"I Never Asked for an Allergy," adapted from "I Never Asked For No Allergy," by Bette Greene. Published in *Philip Hall likes me. I reckon maybe.*, by Bette Greene. Text copyright © 1974 by Bette Greene. Reprinted by permission of the publisher, Dial Books For Young Readers.

"In Winter," by Robert Wallace. Copyright © 1968 by Robert Wallace. Reprinted by permission of the author.

"Lovable Ladybug," adapted from *Never Pet a Porcupine*, by George Laycock. Copyright © 1965 by George Laycock. Reprinted by permission of Grosset & Dunlap, Inc./Paul R. Reynolds, Inc.

"Making a Friend," from *O Sliver of Liver*, by Myra Cohn Livingston. (A Margaret K. McElderry Book). Copyright © 1979 by Myra Cohn Livingston. Reprinted with permission of Atheneum Publishers.

"Making Dreams Come Alive: The Art of Marc Chagall," from *Marc Chagall*, by Ernest Raboff. Copyright © 1982. Reprinted by permission of Gemini Smith, Incorporated.

Printed in the U.S.A.

ISBN: 0-395-37610-6

FGHIJ-KR-943210/8987

Continued on page 575.

Contents

4

Magazine Three

Magazine Four

Explorations
Magazine One

Contents

EMERGENCY PLEASE!

by Ellen Conford

Jeff was glad to baby-sit with the Winchell boys for a few hours. After all, what could happen?

"Oh, Jeffie, thank goodness you're home!"

"Mrs. Winchell?"

"Listen, Jeff, this is an emergency. My husband won't be in till six and our regular baby sitter has a stomach virus and no one in the world seems to be home and I have a midterm exam in *half an hour* ——"

"You want me to stay with the kids?"

"Oh, please, Jeffie, if you can. You've always done such a good job of it before. I'll pay you — I should have left by now ——"

"No problem. I'll be right over. And you don't have to pay me."

"We'll talk about that later. Just *come!*"

"On my way."

I hung up the phone, grabbed my jacket from the closet, and ran out the front door and down the steps. It was four o'clock, and my mother had left a note saying she'd be late and we'd go out to eat when she got home.

It was raining lightly when I got to the Winchells' house down the block, and Mrs. Winchell was standing at the door, holding it open for me.

"You're a lifesaver, honey," she said. "I'll only be two hours, but Dave should be home first, and you can leave when he gets here." Dave is her husband.

"Don't worry about it," I said. She really looked frantic. Mrs. Winchell is going to college, and with her three kids and classes and the house, she's probably got her hands full.

"Don't worry about a thing," I said. "Good luck on your exam."

"Thanks, dear." She patted the air near my head — I think she meant to pat me on the head, but she was in a hurry. She waved to Matthew, Mark, and Fletcher, who were lined up in the hall behind her. "Be good for Jeff, now, boys." She ran out the door.

The Winchell kids are good kids and young enough to look up to me as one of the "big kids." Matthew is eight, Mark is six, and Fletcher is four. They look a lot alike, all with straight blond hair and blue eyes. Standing there lined up in size place, they were really sort of cute.

I herded them into the family room, and we sat down in a circle on the floor.

"Okay, men," I said briskly, "what'll we do? Who wants to watch TV?"

"ME!" yelled Fletcher, as if he hardly ever got the chance to watch TV.

"Let's play basketball," Matthew said.

"No, it's raining out. It's no good playing in the rain."

"I want to play Uncle Wiggily," said Mark.

"Isn't there something you all like to do?" I asked.

They looked at each other thoughtfully. Matthew's eyes lit up.

"Yeah! Make concoctions."

"Yeah! Coctions!" Fletcher yelled.

Mark nodded. "We all like that."

"What's making concoctions?" I asked.

Matthew smiled happily. "We go into the kitchen and mix up a whole lot of things and add some food coloring and maybe some soap so it bubbles."

"Then what do you do with it?" I asked nervously.

Matthew shrugged. "Flush it down the toilet."

"I don't think your mother would like that too much."

"That's why we should do it now," Matthew said.

Very logical.

"No concoctions," I said sternly. "Now, what else do you all like to do?"

"Watch *The Flintstones!*" yelled Fletcher.

"Play Uncle Wiggily," Mark insisted.

"Make a cake," said Matthew.

That didn't sound like a bad idea. If Mrs. Winchell had any cake mix around, it should be pretty easy; and think how pleased she'd be when she came back to find a nice, homemade cake waiting for her.

"I'll tell you what. We'll mix up the cake and then, while it's baking, we'll play Uncle Wiggily. How's that, Mark?"

Mark thought about it for a minute. "Okay."

"Come on, Fletcher. We're going to make a cake and then play Uncle Wiggily."

"Don't know how to make a cake," said Fletcher. He turned on the television and plopped down on his huge stuffed turtle in front of the screen.

"*The Flintstones!*" he yelled. "*The Flintstones* is on!" He bounced up and down on his turtle.

"Oh, let him watch," Matthew said. "He'd just be in the way anyhow."

"Okay, you watch *The Flintstones;* but *don't move.* Okay, Fletcher?"

Fletcher was staring at the set. He didn't look as if he'd ever move.

"Don't worry," said Matthew. "He'd stay there all night if you let him."

We went into the kitchen, and Matthew found a box of cake mix. He got out a bowl and the eggs. They each got to break one egg into the bowl.

We were picking eggshells out of the cake mix when there was a horrible scream from the family room.

I raced in there and found Fletcher holding his mouth and crying.

"Fletcher, what happened?" I grabbed his hand away from his mouth. I thought my heart was going to stop. Blood seemed to be gushing out of his mouth.

"Fletcher, what happened? What did you do?" He just kept screaming and crying.

I was panic-stricken. How much could a little kid like that bleed before he lost too much blood? How had he hurt himself so badly? What was I going to do? My mother wasn't home, and Mrs. Winchell said *nobody* was home ——

"Matthew," I said, trying to sound calm, except that my voice was shaking, "get me a clean handkerchief."

Matthew ran upstairs and was back down again in a minute with a handkerchief. I tried to press it against Fletcher's lip, but he twisted around and screamed right through it.

"It's okay, Fletcher," I said. "It's okay. This'll make it better."

But it didn't. He seemed to bleed even more.

I picked him up. I remembered that three blocks away, on Staunton Road, there was a house with a doctor's name sign

on the front. We don't go to her, but it was close; and at the moment, that was the only thing I could think of to do.

"You two, get your raincoats and umbrellas, if you have them. Hurry up, we're taking Fletcher to the doctor."

"What doctor?" asked Mark.

"MOVE IT!" I yelled. "Get Fletcher's coat too."

They ran. Even Mark didn't dawdle.

My heart pounding, I carried Fletcher into the kitchen. I washed off the handkerchief and put it against his lips again. He was only crying now, not screaming anymore.

There was a blackboard in the kitchen with *yogurt, milk, coffee,* and *granola* written on it. Under that I wrote *I took Fletcher to the doctor. Don't worry. Jeff.* If Mr. or Mrs. Winchell got back before we did and saw the blood on the floor in the family room and kitchen, at least they'd know I had the situation under control.

Sure I did. I was shaking so hard I could have homogenized Fletcher.

Matthew and Mark were back in an instant. We put Fletcher's coat on and ran down the front steps.

It was raining much harder now. "You guys walk under the umbrella," I said, "and let's go."

We jogged the three blocks to the doctor's. Fletcher is not a particularly heavy kid, but neither am I, so by the time we reached the door my arms were aching. I rang the bell and walked in.

The waiting room was full of people. I staggered up to the nurse at the desk and gasped, "Emergency. *Please.*" She looked at the four of us. Mark was holding the open umbrella and dripping all over the carpet.

"What kind of emergency?"

I held out the bloody handkerchief for her to see.

"All right, take a seat please. I'll have the doctor see him right away."

We didn't take a seat. We just stood there. She went somewhere down a hall and came back a few minutes later.

"Come with me, please." I followed her, and Matthew and Mark followed me.

"You boys," she said, "wait out there, all right?"

"He's my brother," Matthew said.

"Don't worry. We'll take good care of him. Just wait in the reception room."

"Go on," I told Matthew. "You watch Mark."

I carried Fletcher down the hall. The nurse led me into a small room with an examining table. "Just put him down there," she said.

Fletcher looked around. He must have finally realized he was in a doctor's office, because he began to wail.

"No shots! No shots!" The bleeding didn't look so bad now, but his chin and mouth were a mess of red smears.

"Is this the patient?" the doctor asked pleasantly, putting her hand on Fletcher's head.

"No shots!" yelled Fletcher. "No shots!"

"Well." The doctor smiled. "He sounds in pretty good shape."

"This really was an emergency," I said. I didn't want the doctor to think I shouldn't have bothered her. "I was baby-sitting with him and all of a sudden he yelled and he was bleeding all over the rug. His mouth."

"Yes. Open your mouth, son."

"No shots!" Fletcher yelled. The doctor ducked her head down and grabbed a peek at Fletcher's mouth.

"What happened to him?"

"I don't know," I said miserably. "We were making a cake. He was in the other room watching television. I shouldn't have left him alone."

"Let's get this cleaned up and take a look. Why don't you wait outside?"

"He's just a little kid. He'll be scared."

The door opened and another nurse walked in.

"Not with Jeannie here," the doctor said. She looked at Fletcher. "You're not scared, are you?" Fletcher looked at Jeannie.

Jeannie smiled. "And what's *your* name?"

"No shots," Fletcher said, but more quietly now.

"What a nice name, No Shots. What's your last name, No Shots?"

Fletcher giggled.

I was so relieved. I left him there with the doctor and Jeannie and went into the waiting room.

Matthew and Mark were sitting in the middle of the reception-room floor, their slickers still dripping little puddles around them. The umbrella was open, and Mark was twirling it upside-down in front of him, like a top.

"He'll be okay," I said. "The doctor's taking care of him. Close the umbrella, Mark."

"I don't know how."

Matthew reached for it and closed it. "Did they find out why he was bleeding like that?"

I shook my head. "No, but the doctor'll take care of him."

I slumped down into a chair and tried not to show the boys how upset I was. I didn't know what the doctor would have to do to Fletcher, but whatever it was, I knew it was my fault for leaving him alone. How would I ever explain this to Mrs. Winchell?

The nurse at the desk called me over. "I'll need some information about him. He's not a patient of ours, is he?"

"I don't think so. I'm his baby sitter. Those are his brothers," I said.

"Some baby sitter," I thought. She was probably thinking the same thing.

I gave Fletcher's name and age, and Matthew gave the nurse his parents' names, address, and telephone number.

"Do you have any relatives in the vicinity?" she asked Matthew. He looked at her blankly.

"Does any of your family live around here?" I asked him.

"My mother and father," he said.

"Besides them," the nurse said.

He shook his head.

I began to get even more worried. "You mean, next of kin?" Why did they need to know the next of kin? That was what you had to know when someone was *dying*. "Is it that serious?" I tried to keep my voice down so I wouldn't worry the kids, but my heart began to pound like a hammer.

I thought I would keel over before she said, "Of course not. We just like to know if there's an adult relative to sign forms and things if necessary."

"Why would it be necessary?" My voice shook.

Before she could answer, Fletcher came trotting down the hall, one hand in Jeannie's, proudly waving a wooden tongue depressor.

"He's fine!" the nurse said. "And he was *so* brave. Weren't you brave, No Shots?"

Fletcher laughed delightedly.

"The doctor wants to see you for a minute." She pointed down the hall.

I practically ran down the hall and found the doctor washing up in the little room where Fletcher had been.

"What happened?" I asked breathlessly. "What did you have to do? Is he okay?"

"He's fine. All it was, really, was a cut upper lip. It looked a lot worse than it was. You know, those mouth and lip cuts bleed like crazy. They really scare most parents."

I breathed a loud sigh of relief and slumped against the wall. "He doesn't need stitches or anything?"

"I don't think so. I didn't want to do anything too much without his parents here. The bleeding is stopped, so it ought to be okay."

"Did you find out how it happened?"

"The nearest I could figure out," the doctor said, drying her hands, "is that he got into a fight with a turtle."

"Ohh. He must have been wrestling with his stuffed turtle."

"Then he probably just bit his lip hard. But since we don't know for sure, tell his parents to call me. If he's not up to date on his shots, his own doctor should give him a tetanus shot. Have them call me when they get home, all right?"

"All right," I said. "Thanks a lot."

I went back into the waiting room. Fletcher was standing on a chair, waving his tongue depressor around like a symphony conductor.

"Let's go, guys. Come on, Fletcher. We'll get your coat on and go home."

"No Shots," said Fletcher. He jumped up and down on the chair. "Name is No Shots."

I grabbed him and got his coat on. "No jumping, No Shots. No jumping, no running, no turtle wrestling."

Three people in the waiting room tittered.

Very funny.

It wasn't until we trudged back to the Winchells' house that I realized that I had no key and we'd locked ourselves out. So we went to my house, and Matthew kept watch at the front window till he saw his father's car pull into their driveway.

My stomach jerked crazily. I was not looking forward to explaining this.

I got Fletcher's slicker back on, and we went down the block to the Winchells'. Mr. Winchell had just opened the front door when we reached the house.

"Hey, what's up, kids? What are you doing out in this rain?"

Fletcher waved his tongue depressor as he trotted into the house. "My turtle bit me and I was bleeding and the doctor gave me this because I was so brave."

"*What?*"

With my heart sinking into my stomach, I explained.

Mr. Winchell looked stunned for a moment. Then he bent down in front of Fletcher. "Let's see where your turtle bit you."

Fletcher opened his mouth.

"Oh, that doesn't look so bad," he said.

"It was bad," said Fletcher. "It was *very* bad. I was *bleeding*. It *hurt*. Is *The Flintstones* on?" Still wearing his raincoat, he wandered off into the family room.

"I'm really sorry, Mr. Winchell. I left him alone in there, and I shouldn't have. It's all my fault."

"Jeff, I'm very grateful you were here. You can't watch him every minute. This could have happened anytime. You were terrific the way you handled the whole thing. You should be very proud of yourself."

I shook my head. I think he was just being nice. There wouldn't have been anything to handle if I had kept my eye on Fletcher.

I gave him the doctor's card, which the nurse had given me before we left the office.

"I'd better go call her. Listen, Jeff, thanks a million. Thanks for *everything*."

"Sure. So long, Matthew. So long, Mark."

"Bye, Jeff," said Matthew.

Mark didn't say anything for a minute. Then, as I was halfway out the door, he called, "Jeff? You promised to play Uncle Wiggily."

I was still feeling pretty upset when my parents got home, and even dinner out at Cliff's Shore Manor didn't do a thing to make me feel better.

My parents kept asking me why I was in such a bad mood, but I didn't want to tell them. I was somehow hoping they'd never find out about the whole thing. I could imagine how proud of me they'd be if they knew that while I was supposed to be responsible for the Winchell kids I had let one of them practically bleed to death.

A few minutes after we got back from the restaurant, the doorbell rang.

My father went to open it, and there was Mrs. Winchell, her hair damp and frizzing, not even wearing a raincoat. She was breathless.

"Oh, Jeff!" She headed right for me. "Liz, Spence, did you hear what happened? Did you hear what Jeff did?"

I wanted to shrink into the wall. I was stunned when she grabbed me and hugged me so hard I couldn't breathe for a minute.

Then she told them the whole thing — very dramatically.

"Jeff, you were just — just ——" She grabbed me and hugged me again. "You should be proud of this boy," she said to my mother. "He saved the day. I don't know what would have happened if he hadn't been there."

I was getting more and more embarrassed by the minute. When Mrs. Winchell pressed some dollar bills into my hand, I cringed.

"No!" I tried to hand them back, but she wouldn't take them.

"Please, Mrs. Winchell. I don't want any money. I'm just sorry that Fletcher got hurt when I was supposed to be watching him."

"Are you serious, Jeffie? He gets hurt while *I'm* watching him. You keep that money. It's not nearly enough for what you did. You just better know how grateful we are, that's all."

My parents were standing there looking dazed, and she let herself out the front door.

"Why didn't you tell us?"

"Jeff, I'm so proud of you," my mother said.

"You really come through in an emergency." My father was beaming at me, as if I had won the hundred-yard dash or something.

What was the matter with everybody? Why couldn't they see what I saw? I had loused things up, and everyone was praising me like I was some kind of hero or something.

I stuffed the money Mrs. Winchell had forced on me into a pocket. "It was my fault in the first place," I muttered. "Nothing to be proud of."

But they kept beaming at me and carrying on about it for the whole rest of the evening. So by the time I went to bed, I was beginning to let myself feel just the tiniest bit like a hero.

Author

Ellen Conford has written many humorous and realistic books for children. Among them is *The Revenge of the Incredible Dr. Rancid and His Youthful Assistant, Jeffrey,* from which the story you have just read was taken. Mrs. Conford says her ideas and characters come from her own life, influenced also by adults and children she has known.

Comprehension Questions

1. What happened while Jeff was baby-sitting?
2. What did Jeff do to help Fletcher?
3. Why was Jeff surprised when Mr. and Mrs. Winchell thanked him for helping Fletcher?
4. Why were Jeff's parents proud of him?

Vocabulary

The answer to each of the following word puzzles is a compound word that appears in "Emergency Please." Figure out each word part, then write the compound word, and use it in a sentence.

Example: place of residence + produced = **homemade**
terror + struck =
showers + outer garment =
to operate a vehicle + path =
infant + to occupy a seat =

List other compound words found in "Emergency Please." Make up your own word puzzles for two of them.

Writing an Interview

At the end of the story, Jeff said that he was beginning to feel "just the tiniest bit like a hero." Pretend that you are a reporter and have been assigned to interview Jeff. Ask him about his adventures baby-sitting for the Winchell boys. Write the questions you would ask him.

Alliteration

Lots of lazy lions.

A **million** mischievous
monkeys
A **billion** bellowing burros
A **zillion** zigzagging zebras

There are many words that stand
for numbers or amounts — *lots,
million, billion,* and *zillion* are just a
few of them. See how many num-
ber words you can list. Here are
some to get you started:

few	**dozen**
more	**pair**
many	**heaps**

Look at the picture at the top
of the page. The group of words
lots of lazy lions shows the use of
alliteration. Alliteration means repeating the same beginning sound
in a group of words. Writers and
poets sometimes use alliteration to
create humor or to make their writing sound musical.

The group of words *lots of lazy
lions* repeats the sound that the
letter *l* stands for. Look at the
three groups of words at the top
of the left-hand column. Does each

one use alliteration? What sound is repeated in each of these groups of words?

Choose two or three words from your list of number words. Make a list of adjectives and a list of nouns that have the same beginning sounds as your number words. Then use your lists to write alliterations. Here is an example:

	Adjectives	Nouns
A pair of	purple	plums
	pale	pandas
	playful	ponies
A dozen	dancing	daffodils
	dandy	ducks
	discontented	dinosaurs

When you have made your lists, try mixing and matching. You might end up with a *pair of purple ponies!* Compare with your classmates. See who can come up with the funniest and most fabulous phrases. Choose your most colorful alliterations, and draw pictures to go with them.

A pair of playful pandas.

A Zillion Stars

by Yoshiko Uchida

Rumi was certainly not looking forward to spending the weekend at the Haradas' farm. What happened during the weekend to make her feel differently?

When Mama first told me we were going to spend a weekend at the Harada farm in Livingston, I didn't want to go.

"Aren't they the ones with the two boys?"

Mama nodded. "That's right. Danny and Jimbo."

"How old are they?" I asked cautiously.

"Oh, Danny must be almost twelve now, and I guess little Jimbo is seven."

I groaned. Now I *knew* I didn't want to go. Danny would probably be mean and bossy, and Jimbo would be a pest.

It was too late, though. Papa had saved up enough to buy a secondhand Model T, and he'd already put up a sign in the window of our grocery store saying it would be closed over the weekend.

"Maybe my tonsils will swell up again," I thought. "Then I'll have to go to bed with a temperature and not have to go." When I opened my mouth and looked at my tonsils, though, they were just sitting there, two small, pink, healthy-looking lumps, not a bit swollen like they'd been last Christmas when I didn't want them to be.

"You'll enjoy the farm, Rumi," Papa said to me. "They have acres of vineyards and a pair of mules, some chickens, and a dog."

It was only the dog that interested me. I was dying to have a dog, but Mama said we couldn't have one while we lived in the small flat above Papa's store.

"Wait until we can move to a real house someday, Rumi," she said.

"I could be an old woman by then," I thought.

Well, anyway, we went to Livingston.

Papa was feeling so good, he was whistling and singing almost from the minute we left Oakland. He drove carefully while we were on the main highway, but when he turned off onto the narrow dirt road that led to the farm, he stepped on the gas and made the dust billow up behind us like a small tornado.

"Papa, aren't you going too fast?" Mama asked nervously.

Papa only rolled up the window to keep out the dust and told her everything was under control.

I could see rows and rows of grapevines now, stretching out in neat, straight lines on either side of the road. When I saw the water tower off to our right, Papa said we were almost there.

"There's the barn," he said, pointing to a sloping brown roof. Then I saw the Haradas' small white house sheltered near a cluster of trees.

"We're here!" Papa shouted, and he began to honk his horn.

That was when I smelled burning rubber.

"Papa, something's burning," I yelled at him.

Mama sniffed and said, "Rumi's right. I think the car's on fire."

"Nonsense," Papa scoffed, but he turned around just to make sure.

"Look out!" Mama screamed. But it was too late. The car crashed into the doghouse and came to a screeching stop only a few yards from the Haradas' house. The doghouse was smashed and tipped over on its side.

The chickens fluttered and squawked all over the yard, and an old brown collie barked furiously at us. Danny and Jimbo were right behind him, charging toward us like a couple of wild boars. They were barefoot, brown as toasted almonds, and wearing faded wool swim trunks.

By the time we jumped out of the car, Mr. and Mrs. Harada had rushed from their house.

"Your wheels are smoking!" Mr. Harada shouted.

He and Papa threw quick handfuls of dirt and sand at the smoke that billowed from the rear wheels.

33

"I guess I had the brakes tightened too much," Papa said sheepishly. "I don't know too much about cars yet."

The smoke cleared in a few minutes, but Jimbo kept throwing fistfuls of dirt at the tires and then at his big brother, until Danny wrestled him to the ground and made him say he was sorry. I didn't wait around for Jimbo to start pelting me next. I just ran and caught up with Mama and Mrs. Harada, who were walking toward the house. They were already talking as though they'd never stop.

Mama and Mrs. Harada had sailed together from Japan a long time ago when they both came to America to get married. They had been good friends ever since. They wrote long letters to each other, but this was the first time we'd ever come to visit them in Livingston.

Mrs. Harada kept telling me how nice it was to have a girl around the house for a change, and I helped her serve the ice-cold lemonade and the pale yellow sponge cake that was still warm. I could tell that Mrs. Harada had put her best cloth on the dining room table, because it looked just like the big white crocheted cloth Mama used when we had company.

I watched Danny and Jimbo from the corner of my eye while I ate my cake, and once I caught Danny eyeing me back. The minute they'd swallowed the last of the lemonade, though, they went slamming out the back door. Their mother was so busy talking that she didn't even notice.

I knew the grownups would be talking for hours about the farm and the grocery store and how it had been back in Japan. They were getting swallowed up in times and places I didn't know about. So pretty soon, I slipped out the back door too.

I looked at the small vegetable garden behind the house where Mrs. Harada was growing corn and beans and tomatoes, and then I walked toward the barn.

The barn was nice and cool, and it smelled of fresh hay and animals. I looked for the mules and found them outside

standing in the hot sun, swishing flies with their tails. I lured them over to the fence with some weeds I pulled from the ground, but when they got close and sniffed the weeds, they just bared their huge yellow teeth at me as though I'd been mean for having made them come to the fence for nothing.

I finally found Rick, the old collie, lying in the shade of the walnut tree, and he gave me a friendly wag of his tail, even though it was my papa who'd smashed up his house. His nose felt cool and wet even in all that heat, and when I scratched his head, he thumped his tail again. I loved him so much that I just ached to have a dog of my own.

I walked out a little way after that, right up to the edge of the vineyards. They looked as though they went on forever, curving clear around the entire world, and I could feel the sun beating down on them and on my head like a silent drum. There were no sounds of streetcars or rumbling delivery trucks. I felt as though somebody had put a huge glass bowl over my head that shut out all the sounds of the world, and suddenly I wanted to make some noise.

"Hey, Danny, Jimbo!" I shouted as loudly as I could. "Where are you?"

I knew they wouldn't answer even if they could hear me. I just wanted to hear my voice hollering out there in all that space, so I hollered again. Nobody answered.

The boys didn't turn up until it was almost time for supper, and Mr. Harada had already begun barbecuing chicken over hot charcoals. They came running down the dirt road, grinning and covered with dirt and grime.

"Just look at yourselves," Mrs. Harada scolded, as she heaped fresh beans and corn and tomatoes into big serving bowls. She sent the boys off to wash up at the pump outside, still talking to them after they'd gone.

"You could at least have invited Rumi to go swimming with you," she grumbled into the tomatoes.

I really didn't care that much. I didn't know how to swim anyway.

We ate outside sitting on mats spread out beneath the trees, and when we'd finished, old Rick came to lie down beside me instead of by either of the boys. That made me feel good, but I guess it bothered Danny because after a while he slid over next to me and showed me how to pick fleas from Rick's back.

"You've gotta be real quick," he explained, "'cause those fleas can jump about three or four feet." He parted the long hair on Rick's back and looked carefully for the tiny black specks that burrowed in the dog's pink flesh.

When he caught one, he squeezed the flea between his two thumbnails, making a tiny popping sound. Then he showed me the smear of blood left on his nail, saying, "That's most likely *my* blood." He pointed to the ring of red welts around both his ankles. Just seeing them made me feel itchy over my entire body, but I kept looking until I finally caught a flea of my own.

We stayed outside until long after the sun went down, and Mr. Harada brought out a kerosene lamp that I think attracted every bug around for a hundred miles.

I was surprised when Mrs. Harada got up and said it was about time to begin the baths. I knew there was no bathroom in their house. I wondered if we were all going to have to take turns standing under the cold-water pump, but Mr. Harada brought out a square tin tub, which he set over a small pit beyond the pump. He filled it up with water and then built a small fire beneath it. Then he strung up a rope between two trees and hung a couple of blankets across it.

After a while he called, "Well, the water should be just right now. Who takes the first bath?"

Mrs. Harada said it should be me. I was afraid I was going to get cooked alive in that hot tin tub, but she showed me that the fire had been banked and brought me a bucket of cold water in case the bath water was too hot.

I washed and rinsed myself on the wood platform beside the tub and then climbed onto the wood float and felt it sink beneath my feet. There was a rush of warm water gurgling all around me, and I let myself sink down until I could feel the water tickle my chin.

I turned around so I could look out at the vineyards and the lemon wedge of a moon that sat in the star-filled sky. I held my breath and listened to the nighttime sounds of the crickets and all the other creatures that lived in the fields. They were all talking like crazy, and I could even hear some frogs having a friendly conversation somewhere out there.

I was beginning to like Livingston and could have sat there all night in watery splendor, but I had to get out when Mama came to tell me to hurry because the others were waiting.

The next morning, Mr. Harada let me pitch some hay down to the mules with an enormous pitchfork bigger than I was.

He told me all about how he grew his grapes, about how they had to be irrigated and weeded and watched carefully until they were ready to be harvested. He also told me how it had been in the early days when he first came to Livingston from Japan.

"Oh, what a barren, desolate place it was then, Rumi," he said, growing serious. "It was the kind of land nobody else wanted because nothing would grow on it. Each time we planted our small seedlings, the wind would rip through the fields tearing them up by the roots or covering them with dust that smothered and killed them."

"Then why didn't you just leave?" I asked.

Mr. Harada looked at me as though he couldn't believe I could ask such a question. "And give up?" he asked. "We were determined, Rumi. We would never give up. Every time those seedlings were torn from the ground, we all went out there in those hot, dry fields and planted new ones, again and again, year after year, until one day we finally conquered the wind and the dust and even the sun. And now look at what we have!"

I could just feel how proud he was of his land, and I wanted to say something nice to him. I didn't know what to say, though, so I just worked even harder at pitching the hay, even though my arms ached so much I thought they'd drop off.

We had a picnic lunch by the Merced River, with rice balls and leftover chicken. Papa tried to teach me how to swim, but I kept breathing water up my nose and sinking to the riverbed like a sack of sand.

"You're never gonna learn how to swim," Jimbo scoffed.

Danny just said, "Aw, leave her alone, Jimbo. She comes from Oakland where they don't have any rivers or irrigation ditches to swim in."

We didn't have wagon rides in the moonlight either, and Mr. Harada said he thought that might be a nice thing to do.

That night I couldn't wait for the mules to get hitched up, and I was the first one to be hoisted up onto the big flat wagon. There wasn't any hay to sit on, but Mrs. Harada spread out a couple of old blankets, and we went bouncing along over the bumpy dirt roads that cut through the dark vineyards.

After a while, Papa and Mr. Harada began to sing some old Japanese folk songs they knew. When they stopped, I started singing "Old MacDonald Had a Farm," and Danny and Jimbo pitched right in with me.

We must have sung all five verses at least four times, until finally Mama said, "I think that's enough, Rumi."

Danny's father let him take the reins for a while, and I almost fell off the wagon when Danny offered to let me hold them too.

"It doesn't matter much who's got the reins," he said, not wanting to give me too much credit. "The old mules know where to go."

It was true. They just plodded along, their heads bobbing up and down, as though pulling us through the nighttime fields was the most natural thing in the world for them to be doing. It made me feel proud just to hold the reins as though I were really driving them.

When Mr. Harada took the reins again to head for home, Danny and Jimbo and I went to the back of the wagon and sprawled out on our backs to look up at the sky. I never knew before that there were so many stars up there. Back home in Oakland, I couldn't even see the sky from my bedroom window.

Out there in the country, the stars were so bright and seemed so close. It was almost as if they were talking to us in clear shining voices, like crystal bells.

"I'll bet there are a hundred million stars up there," Jimbo said suddenly.

"Naw, more like a hundred billion," Danny corrected.

"You're both wrong," I said. "There're at least a million, billion, *zillion* stars up there."

I was waiting for Danny to tell me I was crazy, but he surprised me again.

"Yup," he said in a faraway voice, "I guess maybe there *are* a zillion stars up there all right."

It was funny how that trip to Livingston turned out to be just about the best vacation I ever had.

Sometimes, even now, when I lie in bed and close my eyes, I can still see those zillion stars blinking across that dark night sky. Sometimes, I even think a little bit about Danny Harada and how he turned out not to be so bad after all.

Author

Yoshiko Uchida was born in California. Her parents had come there from Japan. In her story "A Zillion Stars," the author recalls a childhood trip with her family to visit friends in the California countryside. Besides short stories, Yoshiko Uchida has written more than twenty children's books, including collections of Japanese folktales and realistic stories about Japanese or Japanese-American children.

Comprehension Questions

1. What caused Rumi to change her mind about going to the Haradas' farm for the weekend?
2. What was the one thing that interested Rumi about the farm? Why?
3. Why were Rumi's parents excited about the trip?
4. How did Rumi expect Danny to act? How did he surprise her?

Vocabulary

Rumi hoped that her **tonsils** would swell up so that she wouldn't have to go to the farm.

In order to pronounce the word *tonsils,* where would you divide it into syllables? Divide each of the following words from the story into syllables. Then write a sentence for each word.

barren
silent
crochet
splendor

Writing a Story

At the end of the story, Rumi said that the weekend at the Haradas' farm turned out to be the best vacation she ever had. What was the best vacation you ever had? Write a story about it to share with your classmates.

Organizing Study Time

Tonight is the night! Your favorite movie is going to be on television. Then you remember: The assignment that your teacher gave the class two weeks ago is due tomorrow, and — as usual — you have not yet started.

Problems such as the one described above can be avoided by planning and organizing your study time. This lesson will help you to learn some ways to make the best use of your study time. Good planning will help you to do better in your schoolwork. It will also leave more time for other activities, like movies and sports.

When to Study

When it's time to go to bed and you haven't done your homework, you may find yourself saying, "I didn't have time!"

To find out if it's true that you don't have time to study, try keeping a chart of how you actually spend your after-school time.

The chart shown below is for one day — Tuesday — but you can make one for a few days or even a week to see how your time was really spent.

How I Spent My Time Tuesday

3:00–5:00 P.M.	Soccer practice
5:00–6:00 P.M.	Bus ride home
6:00–7:00 P.M.	Dinner
7:00–8:00 P.M.	Homework
8:00–9:00 P.M.	Free time

When you look at your chart, or at the one on page 44, you will probably find some activities, such as riding the school bus and eating dinner, that are done at the same time every day. It is a good idea to make study time one of these regularly scheduled activities.

Deciding to have a regular study time is the first step in making a study plan. If you stick to the time that you schedule, you may not have to pass up your favorite movie for last-minute studying.

Where to Study

Once you have decided when to study, the next step is to plan where to do your work. Just as it is helpful to plan a regular time each day for studying, it is also helpful to study in the same place each day. If possible, the place you choose should be comfortable, with a table or desk and good lighting. It should be a place where you will not be tempted to do something other than study. A place that is quiet is best. Keep your paper, pencils, and other things that you use often near your study place, and put them away when you are through.

What to Study

You will make better use of your study time if you know exactly what you must complete in that time. When your teacher gives an assignment, you should write it down in a notebook, not on a scrap of paper that you might throw away. Do not count on being able to remember the assignment.

Read directions carefully. Time spent reading the directions may save you from having to do an assignment over. Be sure you know what books and other materials you will need.

Suppose that your teacher gave the following homework assignment.

Read the chapter about Japan in your social studies text-book. Write down important ideas and facts so that you can take part in a class discussion.

The first thing that you should do is write the assignment down in your notebook. Read it over and make sure you understand it. Then plan the steps you will follow to complete it.

What are the most important directions in this assignment? First of all, you are to read a chapter about Japan. Then you are to write down important ideas and facts. Finally, you are to be ready to use what you read about in a class discussion.

How to Study

It is now your regularly scheduled study time. You are sitting in your comfortable study spot with all your materials in front of you. The next step is planning *how* to study.

Begin with a short review of the lesson that was presented in class, and reread the directions for the assignment.

If you have a reading assignment, like the one at the top of this page, there is a way to study that will help you to understand what you read and remember it longer. It is called S Q R R R.

There are five steps in the S Q R R R study method. The next part of this lesson will explain the five steps and how you can use them to help you plan *how* to study.

Step 1: *S* stands for *survey*. To *survey* means to "look over." Many articles have titles and headings. They may also have pictures and captions. Look at the article on Japan on page 47. It has a title and three headings, a picture, and a caption. Before you start to read, survey the three headings. Look at the picture and read the caption.

Surveying an article gives you some idea of what you will be reading about. You do not have to take a lot of time to survey.

Japan

An Overcrowded Country

Japan is a country in the Pacific Ocean made up of four large islands and many smaller ones. Although all of these islands put together are only as large as the state of Montana, over one hundred million people are crowded onto them. Japan's cities are overcrowded because the mountains that cover Japan take up so much land.

Mountains That Attract Tourists

Most of Japan is mountainous. The highest mountains are called the Japanese Alps. The mountains are beautiful and attract many tourists each year. The most famous peak is Mount Fuji. In winter, it is a skiing spot, and in summer, people climb to the rim of its crater.

Scarce Farmland

Because of these mountains, there is very little land suitable for farming. The Japanese need to use every bit of their precious land carefully. Rice, the main crop, can be grown on the hillsides, as can tea. Wheat, barley, fruit, and vegetables are also grown in Japan.

Mount Fuji.

Step 2: *Q* stands for *question*. When you read to answer a question, you are more likely to pick out and remember important information. You can change the headings in an article into questions. In the article about Japan, the heading *An Overcrowded Country* could become the question *Why is Japan an overcrowded country?* Write down your questions so that you will remember them.

Step 3: The first *R* stands for *read*. Read the information under the first heading in "Japan" to answer the question you made from that heading. Read carefully and try to get as complete an answer to the question as you can.

Step 4: The second *R* in the SQRRR study method stands for *recite*. To *recite* means to "repeat from memory." When you have finished reading the information under the first heading, recite to yourself in your own words the answer to your question. When you recite the answer in your own words, you are more likely to remember it. What answers did you find to your question about the first heading? Recite them to yourself. You might say something like, "Japan is overcrowded because it has over one hundred million people in an area only the size of Montana. The mountains take up so much space that people are crowded in the cities."

Steps 2, 3, and 4 must be repeated for each heading. That is, for each heading, you must think of a question, read to answer that question, and recite the answer to yourself. Your second question for this article might be *Why do the mountains attract tourists?*

Step 5: The third *R* stands for *review*. To *review* means to "go back over." When you have finished reading the entire article, recite to yourself once again the answers to the questions you asked in Step 2. If you do not remember an answer, go back and find it again. You may want to write down the answers after the questions.

Using the SQRRR Study Method

Read the article "Japan," applying the SQRRR study method, to complete the assignment on page 46 of this lesson. Remember to do these things.

- Survey the headings.
- Turn the headings into questions and write the questions down.
- Look at the question for the first heading. Read the section after that heading to find the answer.
- Recite the answer to yourself. Write down the most important ideas and facts.
- Go on to the next heading and do the same thing. Continue this procedure until you come to the end of the article.
- Review your work by reading the questions again and saying the answers to yourself to see if you have understood and remembered the information.

Skill Summary

Planned, regular study periods will help you to do better in your schoolwork and will leave more time for other activities. Choose a comfortable, quiet place as your regular study spot. Always write down assignments and read directions carefully. Use SQRRR (survey, question, read, recite, review) when you have a reading assignment. It will help you to understand better and remember longer.

Teaching Snoopy to Dance:

Bill Meléndez and the Art of Animation

by Valerie Tripp

When you watch a cartoon show, the characters seem to move like real people. How does Bill Meléndez help to make this happen?

Pictures That Move

Have you ever watched the scene in a Charlie Brown television special where Lucy holds a football for Charlie Brown to kick? Lucy holds the football on the ground with one finger. Charlie Brown gets ready to run. A flicker of doubt crosses his face; but he lifts up his elbows, leans forward, and runs. His feet move so fast they are a blur. His arms pump up and down. He gets to the football, and *WHOOSH!* Lucy grabs it away. "ARRGH!" Charlie Brown flies up into the air. *WHOMP!* He hits the ground so hard the dust rises.

Without a word spoken, the scene tells a story that is both funny and sad. Lucy has done it again. She has fooled poor Charlie Brown.

Charlie Brown is not the only one who was fooled. You were too. Charlie Brown and Lucy are not people. They are drawings. They are made up of lines, circles, and colors on flat pieces of paper. They can't move. Yet, as

Left: Animator Bill Meléndez works on a drawing of Snoopy. Right: Lucy and Charlie Brown are two of the many characters Bill Meléndez has animated.

you watched that scene, you saw Lucy and Charlie Brown move. You saw expressions on their faces. You saw them make movements as smooth and as natural as your own hand when it turns the pages of this book. Who fooled you? The animator who drew those pictures that seemed to move. In this case, the animator's name is Bill Meléndez.

Forty-Five Years in Animation

Charlie Brown and his friends are only a few of the cartoon characters Bill Meléndez has animated during his forty-five years in the business.

Bill Meléndez started out at Walt Disney Studios as an assistant animator on Mickey Mouse and Donald Duck cartoons. He also worked on the films *Bambi, Dumbo,* and *Fantasia.*

"I never planned to be an animator," Bill explains, "but when I finished school, Disney Studios was the only place that had jobs. The Mickey Mouse cartoons were so successful, they needed lots of animators. They were hiring anybody who could draw a straight line! Now I had never really studied art, but in school I was always doodling. I was drawing, drawing, drawing, just for the fun of it, all the time. So, when I was hired by Disney I thought, 'What a fun job!' It was fascinating to me. I learned animation by watching what the people around me were doing."

After Mickey Mouse, Bill worked on Bugs Bunny, Mr. Magoo, Porky Pig, and Daffy Duck cartoons. He has won hundreds of awards for his work on thousands of projects from television commercials to animated films. Bill says, "The most rewarding thing is that after forty-five years, I still love it. I still look forward to going to work."

What Animation Is

Today, Bill spends his time not only drawing animated characters, but also talking to people about animation. He has taught animation at college and has led workshops at children's museums. At the workshops, Bill explains what animation is and how it works.

"Animation is a simple, forthright talent," says Bill Meléndez. "It is the ability to create the illusion of movement. You do it by illustrating the movement in a series of still drawings."

To illustrate a movement, you must study it carefully. Many

animators keep a mirror next to their drawing boards so they can check how they make simple movements. How does a hand look when it is waving? How does a mouth look when it is laughing?

You cannot illustrate a movement in one drawing. You must divide the movement into parts. Then you must draw each part separately to show the beginning, middle, and end. The picture at the top of the page shows how you could illustrate the flapping of a butterfly's wings.

A flap of a butterfly's wings, divided into five parts (top) and nine parts (bottom). Notice that the drawings in the series of nine change more slowly. What do you think would happen if you divided the action into fifty parts?

Once you have "stopped" the movement in a series of still drawings, you make it "go" again by moving the drawings. If you moved the series of nine drawings shown above, it would look as if the wings flapped. The more drawings you made, the smoother the action would look. That's what animation is.

Animated Cartoons

Now, what is an animated cartoon? It is a series of still drawings each slightly different from the one before. The drawings are photographed one at a time, and the film is projected like a movie.

Look at the two pieces of film shown on the left. When you run either piece of film through a projector, it looks as if the figures or objects are moving. This is because the pictures are rolling by so smoothly that you don't notice the separate frames. You can't tell that you are really seeing twenty-four frames a second.

The only difference between the two pieces of film is that in the animated film the pictures in the frames are of a drawing, not real people. That's an important difference. With a drawing, anything is possible. Bugs Bunny can be shot out of a cannon, squashed flat by a steamroller, or bounced like a ball. No matter what happens, Bugs Bunny always comes up laughing,

On the far left is a piece of an animated cartoon film. The film is a series of still drawings in small boxes called frames. Next to it is a strip of regular movie film. It, too, is a series of still pictures in frames. However, these pictures are of a real scene.

chewing a carrot, asking, "What's up, Doc?"

The next time you see Bugs Bunny chewing that carrot, remember that you are really seeing 1440 drawings every minute. In a half-hour television show, you are seeing 43,200 drawings, each one only slightly different from the next. Animating sounds like dull work, doesn't it? Bill Meléndez doesn't think it is. "Animators don't think of it as drawing one drawing after another after another. We think of it as illustrating *action*," Bill says.

Illustrating even a simple action can take dozens of drawings. Hundreds are thrown away because they are not quite right. Bill says, "You can tell if you are making a good drawing as you go along. Experience tells you if it is convincing."

For an animated action to look real, it should take as long as the same action would take live. The characters should move in the same way live actors would move, as in the example shown below.

Bill Meléndez says the most important thing he tells animators is, "You must keep the overall action in mind, not think of it as drawing one, two, three, four, five little drawings, or you will make it mechanical. You'll make the movement without the emotion. The joy of it is that with a light and fun touch, you can create the feeling that these are real people."

People lean forward when they walk. To look convincing, animated characters should lean forward when they walk too.

An animator can use flourishes, or extra touches, to make actions convincing. Some of these are shadows (top, left); dust clouds (top, right); speed lines (bottom, left); and water splashes (bottom, right).

Sparking an Idea for a Peanuts Special

Bill Meléndez has made Charlie Brown, Lucy, and Snoopy seem real to millions of television viewers. The Charlie Brown characters started out in a comic strip called "Peanuts," created by Charles Schulz. When Bill animated some of the Peanuts characters for television commercials, his work showed Charles Schulz that the characters could move. The Peanuts gang entered a whole new world. Bill has animated more than thirty Charlie Brown specials over the last twenty-five years, including "It's the Great Pumpkin, Charlie Brown" and "A Charlie Brown Christmas."

How does a Charlie Brown television special come to be?

It begins with an idea thought up by Charles Schulz. Bill Meléndez calls Charles Schulz "Sparky." It seems like a good name for someone who sparks so many wonderful stories and characters.

"Sparky comes up with a story situation, or premise. We get together and talk about it. I scribble down notes and sketches as we talk," explains Bill. "Then I roar back to my studio and put the story together like a comic strip. I draw a few key pictures and write captions under them. That's called a story board. I bring the story board to Sparky, and he suggests changes. Then I roar back to my studio and make the changes we decided on. If we're on the right track, if we have a good premise, our work usually goes very fast. In just a few days, Sparky's idea is developed into a whole story."

From Story to Script

Scriptwriters turn the story into a script that shows actors what they are supposed to say.

"As soon as the script is ready, we gather actors to record the narration, musicians to record the music, and technicians to record the sound effects." The recording of the voices, music, and sounds is called the sound track. Doing the sound track is fun for Bill Meléndez because he gets into the act. He is Snoopy's voice. "I do Snoopy's growls, grunts, and howls," he explains. "*AAOOOOOO!* Recognize that howl?"

First the Sound Track

The sound track has to be recorded first, because the animator draws pictures to match the sounds. If Charlie Brown says "G-O-O-D G-R-I-E-F!" the animator has to know when he says it in the story; for how long he says it; and if he is happy, sad, or mad. The animator has to draw the face and body expressions to match what the characters say and do. Snoopy has to dance for as long as the music lasts. Charlie Brown's mouth has to be in the correct position for every syllable he speaks.

To help the animator, the sound track is put on movie film, which is divided into blank frames. A machine called a sound reader counts how many blank frames go by as one syllable is heard. If twenty frames go by as Charlie Brown says "Good," then the animator has to fill those twenty frames with pictures of Charlie Brown looking as if he's saying "Good."

Next the Drawings — Thousands of Them

When the animator knows what action must be pictured in each frame, he draws key drawings called extremes. Extremes show how the scene moves from the start of an action to the end.

They do not show every drawing needed to illustrate an action. Assistant animators called in-betweeners draw the illustrations that go in between the extremes.

There are ways to cut the number of different drawings from 43,200 for a half-hour show to twenty or thirty thousand. Drawings are usually shown for at least two frames; otherwise, the action looks jerky. Sometimes a character will stand still, so the

The first and last drawings are the same. This series could be repeated over and over to show the woman hopping on the pogo stick as long as needed.

same drawing can be shown for several frames. Those drawings are called holds. Often, actions are repeated. Look at the drawings on page 58 showing a person hopping on a pogo stick.

Finishing Touches

When the drawings are finished, they are traced by people called inkers onto clear sheets called cels. The inker traces each line carefully. People called opaquers then color in the outlines.

The colored cels are placed over backgrounds. Backgrounds are drawn separately from figures so that figures can be moved separately. Sometimes the background will be still while the characters move. Other times, the background will move and the characters will be still.

When the colored cels and the backgrounds are ready, they are photographed. An editor matches the film to the sound track, and the animated cartoon is then complete.

"Nothing Is Impossible"

It takes time and talented people to make an animated film. One half-hour show takes four to six months from start to finish. There are sometimes as many as sixty people working in Bill Meléndez's studio. He wouldn't have it any other way. "I tried working alone at home — it just made me nervous! At the studio there's a team of us, a whole bunch of people laughing over this and that, giving each other feedback. It makes work fun and easier."

Wouldn't it be *easier* to make a live movie? "The best animation does what can't be done in live action," Bill Meléndez says. "Nothing is impossible in animation. That's the magic of it!"

Author

Valerie Tripp has traveled to every state except Alaska, meeting and talking with people in all parts of the country. A writer for ten years, she especially enjoys writing for children. The best part of writing about Bill Meléndez, she says, was learning that, like herself, he has found work that he loves to do. Valerie Tripp has received degrees from Yale and Harvard.

Bill Meléndez working with an editor
and a layout person at a Moviola. They
are checking characters' movements.

An assistant animator carefully tracing
one drawing at a time to make the
characters "move."

An animation checker working on inked
cels before they are painted. She
wears a glove to prevent smudges.

Comprehension Questions

1. How does Bill Meléndez make cartoon characters appear to move?
2. How did Bill Meléndez get started in his job?
3. What is an animated cartoon?
4. Besides the animator, who are some of the people involved in making an animated cartoon? What does each of these people do?
5. Why does Bill Meléndez like his job so much?

Vocabulary

Copy the puzzle spaces and boxes shown at the bottom of the page onto a sheet of paper. Write the word or words for definitions 1–4. Choose from the words in the list. Start with the first space and write one letter in each space. If there are two words (for example, *story board*), skip a space between the words. When you have finished, unscramble the letters in the boxes to fill in the last word.

Writing a Script

Write a script for a cartoon show of your own. You may use familiar cartoon characters, such as the Peanuts gang or Donald Duck and his friends, or you may make up characters of your own.

WORD LIST

premise	inkers	opaquers	story board

PUZZLE

1. story situation
2. a few key pictures put together like a comic strip
3. people who trace the drawings onto cels
4. people who color in the outlines

5. a howling good dancer

Suffixes

Look at the picture above. That contestant really knows her suffixes. She knows that a suffix is a word part that is added to the end of a base word. A suffix changes the meaning of the base word.

Read the chart at the bottom of the page. What does each of the following words mean?

farm**er**   magic**ian**
animat**or**   pian**ist**

Some suffixes name people or things that *do* something.

break	+	er	=	"something that breaks (such as a wave)"
sail	+	or	=	"someone who sails"
music	+	ian	=	"someone who plays music"
novel	+	ist	=	"someone who writes novels"

Other suffixes mean "in a certain way," "full of," or "like."

luck	+ y	=	"full of luck"
calm	+ ly	=	"in a calm way"
thunder	+ ous	=	"full of thunder"
child	+ ish	=	"like a child"

Read the chart at the top of the page. What does each of the following words mean?

gloom**y**   mysteri**ous**
sudden**ly**   fool**ish**

Knowing these two kinds of suffixes can help you understand many words that you find in your reading.

Read the following words and divide them into two lists. Make one list of words that name people or things that do something. Make a second list of words that tell what something is like or how something is done.

shiny	**actor**
stylish	**famous**
typist	**busily**
humorous	**reporter**
bicyclist	**comedian**

Now it's your turn to play the Great Word Play Game. Use words from your first list to complete the following questions. Then use words from your second list to complete the answers. Write the questions and answers on a sheet of paper. Be careful! Each word has to be in exactly the right place for all the words to fit.

1. Q. Who can write stories about _____ new clothing?
   A. A fashion _____
2. Q. Who may become _____ by playing a role?
   A. An _____
3. Q. Who can win a _____ trophy by pedaling fastest?
   A. A _____
4. Q. Who works _____ at a machine in an office?
   A. A _____
5. Q. Who can make people laugh by being _____?
   A. A _____

Rustytoes

by John Cunliffe

Garlick Rustytoes had an unusual name — but his name wasn't the strangest thing about him. What changed him from the worst neighbor in the village to the best friend the farmers ever had?

There was a farmer who lived in a good country of rich and easy land, and it was bad luck to his neighbors when he died, for he was the best farmer, and his was the best farm, in all those parts.

"Who will buy the farm, now Grimble's gone?" they said. "There's none will be able to make it thrive as he did."

None of his neighbors had the money to buy it, so it went to a stranger. They were all keen-eyed to see what kind of man the new owner would be, but not a soul saw him arrive. He came at the dead of night, with his great cart rumbling along the lane, disturbing people in their sleep. But the word soon went round: "The new man's come to Grimble's farm. No one saw his coming. They say he came by night. There's a strange thing."

There was a shaking of heads, and worried faces everywhere, but for some days no one had a sight of him. There was smoke from the chimneys and a sound of hammering at Grimble's farm. There were strange roars and rumblings, but no sign of man or beast in the lanes or fields. But when the mail carrier knocked on Farmer Rice's door on Friday morning, he said, "Good morning, Farmer Rice. And how do you like your new neighbor?"

"I cannot tell you that, Billy, for I've never seen him," said Farmer Rice crossly. "I don't even know his name. What kind of neighbor is that? He'll come round soon enough when he wants to borrow a thresher."

"As to his name," said Billy, "I can tell you that. I've just taken him a letter. He's called Garlick Rustytoes!"

"Garlick Rustytoes?" said Farmer Rice. "What sort of name is that? Not an honest one. Certainly not a name of our valley. Perhaps he's from the mountains, or beyond?"

"I cannot say," said Billy, "but his name isn't the worst thing about him."

"Well, tell us what is the worst of him," said Mrs. Rice. "If this outlandish fellow's to live along by us, we'd better know his worst; his best will be no hurt to find out for ourselves. Now sit you down, Billy, and tell us what you know."

"Outlandish is right," said Billy. "Aye, that's the word. *Outlandish*. Right well outlandish! Well . . . I'm walking into the stackyard with this letter for him, when I hear this awful loud snorting and gurgling coming out of the barn. Something like an elephant snoring, it was. Then I creep nearer, and I nearly fall over myself for simple fright. Sticking out of the barn was this pair of feet."

"There's nothing frightening about a pair of feet, Billy," said Farmer Rice.

"There was about *this* pair of feet," said Billy. "I've not told you their size. You see, they were the size of your kitchen table! And they were on the end of legs as thick as a tree! And I'm standing there trying to believe the truth of what I can see, when the toes begin to wriggle. I didn't wait to see more. I threw the letter on the ground and ran for it."

"But, Billy, be sensible," said Farmer Rice patiently. "Our kitchen table is four feet long. You couldn't have seen feet that size."

"I could, and I did. Not ten minutes ago," said Billy indignantly.

"But if those feet were that size . . ." said Mrs. Rice.

"How big would the man be on the other end of them?" demanded Farmer Rice. "Are you trying to tell us . . ."

"I'm only telling you what I saw," Billy grumbled.

"But a man with feet so big would be anything up to twenty feet tall!" cried Mrs. Rice.

"Are you trying to tell us we have a *giant* for our new neighbor?" asked Farmer Rice.

"Make what you can of it," said Billy, "but I swear I'm telling you the truth of what I saw."

"We cannot have giants living about here," said Farmer Rice. "This is a peaceful valley. Oh, it's different in those mountainous places — all sorts of things go on there. But it's five hundred years or more since giants were known in these parts. We're too settled and comfortable now for such goings on — and on the next farm too. No, Billy, you must have been dreaming. You must have been."

"My granny used to say . . ." began Mrs. Rice.

"She was another dreamer," retorted Farmer Rice.

"You'll see for yourself soon enough," said Billy. "I must get on with my letters, or I'll never be finished today." And off he went.

What Farmer Rice didn't see was a huge hairy arm coming over the hedge and a great hand picking up his best cow and whisking it away. Three more cows disappeared in the same way before dinner time. Poor bewildered creatures, they found themselves in a new home with a fearsome master. Garlick Rustytoes had stolen them. When it came to milking time, there was a great to-do. The cow-man came running, shouting, "Master, master, four of our beasts are gone."

"Gone? Gone? What do you mean, man? They cannot be gone. We have the best hedges and fences in the valley. There's no way my beasts could be gone," shouted Farmer Rice.

"But they are, master. Come and see!"

So they went together, all round the farm. There was no gap in hedge or fence. No gate was open. They counted the cows again, and yet again. They even brought Mrs. Rice to count them. There was no mistaking it — four were missing, and the best milkers too.

"Whoever could have taken them knew what they were about," moaned Farmer Rice.

"But all your gates are locked," said Mrs. Rice. "There's no way they could have been taken, unless . . . unless . . ." She looked in the direction of Rustytoes's farm.

"Unless *what,* woman? What do you mean to say?" cried Farmer Rice.

"Well, if that mail carrier were right. I mean, if this Rustytoes *is* a giant . . ." said Mrs. Rice.

"Oh, I'll not believe such tales," Farmer Rice snapped, and he stamped out of the house.

At all the farms bordering on to Rustytoes's land, strange things began to happen.

Ten sheep disappeared at Apple Tree Farm. A horse and three pigs vanished from Hill Top Farm. A hut full of hens was whisked away at night at Mill Farm so swiftly and smoothly that not a single hen wakened on its roost to give a warning. Farmer Rice even lost a barn, and all the hay and oats in it, from an outlying field. There was only a pale square of grass to show where it had been!

"Now what did I tell you?" said Mrs. Rice. "There's only one sort of person could do a thing like that, and that's . . ."

"Now I'll not have you frightening people with talk of giants," grumbled Farmer Rice. "There are lots of ways these things could happen. Have you never heard of thieves? They did a lot of mischief in the old days. Who knows — they may have come back again."

"Thieves, indeed," snorted Mrs. Rice, but she said no more, seeing the mood her husband was in. She attacked her pastry with the rolling pin, as if to say, "There's for your thieves!"

But things got worse. Heavy footsteps shook the country roads by night, and things began to disappear from more distant farms up and down the valley. A plow and a cart disappeared from as far away as Windmill Farm. Mysterious shadows fell across bedroom windows in the moonlight, and people trembled in their beds. Though the dogs barked, no one dared to go out to see what was stirring. The whole valley was afraid, and no one knew what to do — until the mail carrier called again at Rice's farm, and Farmer Rice had an idea.

"Pass the word round, Billy," he said, "to every farm you visit. Tell every farmer who has had anything stolen to meet on Crompton Village Green at ten o'clock on Wednesday morning. Then we'll all visit Rustytoes. We'll have to get to the bottom of this, and I can think of no other way."

"That I will," said Billy. "It's the best idea I've heard yet." And off he went to carry his message about the valley.

Billy did his work well. At ten o'clock on Wednesday morning, there was a large and angry crowd of farmers on Crompton Green. There was someone from almost every farm for ten miles around. Each person carried a pitchfork or a stout stick.

"Friends," shouted Farmer Rice, "you all know why we're here, don't you?"

"Aye, we do," murmured the farmers.

"Everyone here has had stock and machinery stolen in the last two weeks," went on Farmer Rice. "And no ordinary thief could carry off cows in broad daylight, with no sight or sound of their going. Besides, we're honest folks in this valley. There's been no thieving here for hundreds of years. But we have a new neighbor — this Garlick Rustytoes; and I cannot help noticing that his fields are suddenly full of cattle and sheep, when he's not once been to market since he came here.

Indeed, nobody has so much as seen his face. So, I suggest we all pay a call on our new neighbor and ask him a few questions!"

"But, Farmer Rice," called Jim Dobson, "some say this Rustytoes is nothing less than a giant!"

"There's no need to upset people with wild talk of giants," said Farmer Rice. "Nobody's set eyes on the fellow yet, so how can anyone say?"

Luckily for Farmer Rice, Billy was away with his letters, for his story of Rustytoes's enormous feet could have scared these angry farmers away.

"To Rustytoes's farm, then!" shouted Farmer Rice. "Come on, let's rouse him!" And he led the way, with the buzzing mob of farmers following, their staves and pitchforks jaunting at the ready.

There seemed to be no one about at Rustytoes's farm. As they approached the house, the farmers grew more and more excited as they spied their stolen property. Cries went up on all sides: "There's my sheep! There's my Daisy and her two

calves! Bless me, there's my barn, and all the hay still in it! So that's where my thresher went to!" And so on, all the way up to Rustytoes's door. By then they were so angry that they hammered on the door ready to break it down.

"Come out, you thief!" they shouted. "We've come for our property! It's no good hiding; we've got eyes to see. Come on, hand it all over!"

Some looked in the windows but couldn't see anyone. Then, a thunderous voice boomed out of the sky at them, "Little midgets, do you dare to come and trouble Rustytoes?"

They all looked upwards. A great grinning face loomed above them. Rustytoes was leaning on the farmhouse roof, as though it were a log gate, and leering over at them.

"I'll take what I want, and none can stop me, so take yourselves off before I squash you!" he roared. Then he came stamping round the house to show his full height. Not one of them stayed to argue. You cannot argue with an angry giant, for that is what he truly was, twenty or thirty feet high. They all scampered off as fast as they could go, with Rustytoes's laughter bellowing after them.

They didn't stop until they reached Crompton Green again. Then they all flopped onto the grass to get their breath back.

"What are we going to do?" moaned Farmer Rice. "Billy was right, and Rustytoes *is* a giant. I was right, and he *has* stolen our things and means to go on stealing. But we cannot send a giant to prison, and we cannot fight him. What can we do?"

"He'll take what he wants, until we're all too poor to go on farming," said Jim Dobson gloomily. "He'll take our land next, and we'll have to go and live in the mountains."

"Oh, it cannot be as bad as that, surely," said Farmer Rice, but he couldn't convince even himself. They all fell into a gloomy silence and drifted off home one by one.

Things did get worse — much worse. Rustytoes took what he wanted, and the farmers of the valley grew poorer and poorer. Rustytoes was so big and strong that no one could stop him.

Soon Rustytoes began to make the other farmers do all his work too. He had his bed in the big barn, and he lay there all day eating sweets. He lay on the straw, laughing at the little people as they hurried about to do his work. Rustytoes grew rich and fat and lazy, but he was as strong as ever, and everyone feared him.

"Can't you think of a way of overcoming this Rustytoes?" Mrs. Rice demanded of her husband.

"I cannot," said Farmer Rice. "He's just too big and strong to be defied."

"Then what will become of us?" moaned Mrs. Rice.

"I cannot tell, my dear, but it's a bleak outlook," said Farmer Rice, and he went gloomily off to bed.

But something did overcome Garlick Rustytoes. Something quite simple. Something natural.

One morning, the neighborhood woke to a strange sound. A roaring, moaning, bellowing sound that came and went with the wind and sighed amongst the trees. There it was again, louder.

"What in the world is that?" exclaimed Mrs. Rice at breakfast.

"Bless me, I don't know," said Farmer Rice. They went outside to listen.

A yowling and howling echoed across the fields.

"What a dreadful noise," said Farmer Rice. "It will turn the milk sour."

"It's coming from Rustytoes's Farm," said Mrs. Rice.

"It's some new trick of his," said Farmer Rice.

"No, it sounds like someone in pain," said Mrs. Rice. "Come on. We must go and see. It sounds so pitiful."

So they crept up to Rustytoes's farm and fearfully approached the big barn from where all the noise seemed to be coming. Great roars and yells, low moans growing to a sound like thunder, thumpings and gaspings, and sighing and weeping issued from the open door. Rustytoes's feet, sticking out, threshed about. Trembling, Farmer Rice and his wife looked in. There was poor Rustytoes, lying on the straw with the side of his face all swollen.

"Oh, help me. Please help me," he moaned, seeing them.

"Why, you great fellow, what's happened to you?" asked the astonished Mrs. Rice, who had never seen him before.

"Toothache. I've got a toothache," moaned Rustytoes. "Oooooooh, and it does hurt."

"A giant toothache too," said Mrs. Rice. "The pain's as big as he is, and it must be dreadful. It's laid him low, great as he is. Poor fellow, he has an abscess on that tooth the size of a cow, and nothing hurts more."

"But he's bad, and he's a giant, and it serves him right," whispered Farmer Rice.

"Bad he may be, but we must help him. You cannot let anyone suffer so and not help," protested Mrs. Rice. To Rustytoes she said, "Now lie still, and I'll make you a poultice, and I'll gather some herbs that will ease your pain. Then we'll bring the dentist from the village and see if he can get that tooth out of you."

"You're a kind woman, Mrs. Rice," said Rustytoes, groaning between his words. "Oooh! Ouch! If only you'll help me, I'll promise to be good and kind to you and all the farmers. Oooh! I cannot bear the pain. I've been awake all night with it. It's too much for me. I'll die if you don't take this pain away! I'll give back all that I've stolen, if only you'll help me. Please help me, good people."

"Do you promise?" said Farmer Rice. "Do you promise to give back all that you have stolen? Everything?"

"Yes. Yes. Everything."

"Do you promise to be good to all your neighbors and never steal or frighten anyone again?"

"Yes. I promise. All you say," moaned Rustytoes. "Anything to be rid of this pain."

"Then we'll do all we can to make you better," declared Farmer Rice.

"Oh, stop your talking, and let's see to the poor fellow," said Mrs. Rice, and she got quickly to work.

There never was such a busy scene. More people arrived, and Mrs. Rice set them to work. They gathered herbs and made a giant poultice with two bedsheets. Farmer Rice excitedly told all the farmers about Rustytoes's promises. The dentist was sent for, and he climbed bravely into Rustytoes's mouth to examine the bad tooth. He came out looking dazed, saying the tooth was the size of a loaf and that it would have to come out. A big rope sling was made to pull the tooth. Ten horses were brought and harnessed to a long rope fastened to the sling. All the while, Rustytoes moaned on, though Mrs.

Rice's herbs had soothed his pains. At last all was ready. The sling was around the tooth, and the horses were ready to pull.

"Take the strain!" called Farmer Rice. The ropes tightened as the horses tensed their muscles.

"Pull!" shouted Farmer Rice, and all the people urged their horses on.

"Heave! Come on, my beauty! Pull, my girl! Come on, now!" So they coaxed them on, and the horses pulled with all their strength. The ropes creaked and cracked with the great strain. All eyes were on the tooth. It didn't move. More horses were brought — fifteen, then twenty. They all pulled again, and the great tooth moved slightly. Then the people took the ropes and pulled with the horses.

"All together!" called Farmer Rice. "One. Two. Three, and pull." Horses and people pulled and pulled with all their strength. There was a loud crack. The tooth shot out, releasing the rope, so that the horses galloped off down the lane, and everyone fell over in a heap. Amid all the noise and muddle, there was Rustytoes, sitting up and smiling all over his face.

"It's gone!" he exclaimed. "It's gone. Oh, what a wonderful feeling." They all looked at him. "What good people you are," he said. "I've been as bad as I could be to you, and yet you all came to help me when I was in pain."

"But you made us some promises," Farmer Rice reminded him.

"I'll keep them," said Rustytoes happily. "Better than that, I'll be the best neighbor you ever had, from this day on. I'll help you with your work and protect you from your enemies. Whatever you want doing, I'm your giant; at your service, good friends."

Rustytoes kept his word. He gave everything back. He worked hard to help anyone who asked him. He moved barns and uprooted trees. He dug new roads and dammed a river.

79

He helped to build houses and farms. No one ever dared to attack the people of the valley with a giant to defend them, so there was peace as never before. The people of the valley became happy and prosperous, and they grew very fond of their giant. Everyone knew him as Dear Old Man Rustytoes, and they all loved and trusted him. Even so, Farmer Rice kept an eye on him.

"You can never be sure with giants," he said.

"Never fear," said Mrs. Rice. "Old Man Rustytoes has a great many more teeth in his head, and he might need another one pulled one of these days."

Author

John Cunliffe, who loves telling stories, has been a librarian and an elementary school teacher in England, where he was born. He says, "Children are the most avid, attentive, and enthusiastic audience anywhere in the world." The story you have just read is from his collection of giant tales, *Giant Kippernose and Other Stories*.

Comprehension Questions

1. What changed Garlick Rustytoes from the worst neighbor in the village to the best friend the farmers ever had?
2. Before they saw Rustytoes, what clues did the farmers have that he was a giant?
3. Whose idea was it to go out to Rustytoes's farm? Why did the farmers decide to go?
4. When did the farmers know for sure that Rustytoes was a giant?
5. What did Rustytoes do that caused him to get an abscessed tooth?

Vocabulary

You can often discover the meaning of a word by using the context clues in the story. Find each of the following words in "Rustytoes," and write the clues to its meaning that are given in the story. The page number next to each word tells you on which page of the story it can be found.

outlandish (page 66)   **keen-eyed** (page 65)
defied (page 74)   **to-do** (page 67)
issued (page 75)   **bleak** (page 74)

Writing a Story

How did Rustytoes's personality change at the end of the selection? Write a story that features the villagers and Dear Old Man Rustytoes.

The Mystery of Bird Migration

In the fall, many types of birds migrate to their winter homes, where the weather is warm and food is plentiful. How do they know when to go? How do they find their way? Bird migration has long been one of the mysteries of nature.

Something Told the Wild Geese

by Rachel Field

Something told the wild geese
   It was time to go.
Though the fields lay golden
   Something whispered, — "Snow."
Leaves were green and stirring,
   Berries, luster-glossed,
But beneath warm feathers
   Something cautioned, — "Frost."
All the sagging orchards
   Steamed with amber spice,
But each wild breast stiffened
   At remembered ice.
Something told the wild geese
   It was time to fly, —
Summer sun was on their wings,
   Winter in their cry.

Science

When you read a good story like "Rustytoes," you probably read it as quickly as you can, eager to find out what's going to happen — but careful to not peek ahead and spoil the surprise. Now think about how you read a chapter in a science textbook. Do you read it the same way? Probably not. By now, you probably know that when you read science, it *isn't* a good idea to read quickly, and it *is* a good idea to look ahead. This lesson will give you some more tips for getting the most out of a science textbook chapter.

Use SQRRR

You should use SQRRR when you read anything that has been written to give you information. *Survey* the lesson to get some idea of what it's about. Read each heading. Look at all of the pictures, and read the captions that go with them. If there are diagrams or maps, study them, and read the captions. Think of a *question* you want to be able to answer as you read each part of the lesson. Then *read* to find out the answer to your question. After you have finished reading the chapter, *recite* the answers to your questions as well as to the questions given at the end. This will serve as a *review* and help you to remember what you've read. If you have trouble with a question, reread the part of the chapter that you expect will give you the answer.

Get the Meaning of New Words

Since a science textbook is teaching you new things, there will probably be words that are new to you as well. Most of the time, new words are printed in boldface or in another way that makes them stand out. The author often tells you the meaning of new words or makes sure you can get their meaning from the sense of the sentence or paragraph. If you can't get the meaning of a word from the text, you should use some other way to find out what it means. Look it up in the glossary, if the book has one. If the book doesn't have a glossary, or if the word isn't listed there, you should look it up in a dictionary.

Answer the Questions *What? Who? Why? When?* and *How?*

A science book often answers the questions *What? Who? Why? When?* and *How?* about a subject. The next selection, "Bird Migration," will answer these questions. It will tell you *what* migration is and *who* migrates, as well as *why, when,* and *how* birds migrate. Keep the questions *What? Who? Why? When?* and *How?* in mind as you read any science lesson, and write down the answers to them.

Look for Cause-Effect Relationships

When a science lesson tells you *why* something happens, it is showing you a cause and an effect. An author may use clue words to tell you that one thing causes another thing to happen. These are words such as *because, since, due to,* and *so.*

Study Diagrams

Take the time to understand the information given in a diagram. Read the caption. It will tell you what you should learn from the diagram. As you read a part of a lesson that has a diagram, look at the diagram often so that you will understand what you are reading. A diagram may even tell you things that are not told elsewhere.

Summary

This lesson gave you some more tips for getting the most out of a science textbook chapter:

- Use SQRRR.
- Look up new words in the glossary or in a dictionary.
- Keep the questions *What? Who? Why? When?* and *How?* in mind as you read, and write down the answers to them.
- Notice cause-effect relationships.
- Study diagrams.

Preview

The next selection, "Bird Migration," is presented in the form of a science textbook chapter. When you read it, use the methods explained in this lesson.

Bird Migration

What Migration Is

Have you ever seen a large flock of birds flying in a V-formation? Did you see them in the spring or in the fall? Did you wonder where they were going?

The birds you saw were probably **migrating**. To migrate, in science, means to move from one place to another in large numbers — and then to return.

Who Migrates

Birds are not the only animals that migrate. Many ocean fish move to freshwater streams to lay their eggs. Then they return to their homes in the sea. Eels, on the other hand, live for most

A flock of Canada geese flies over Horicon Marsh, a National Wildlife Refuge in Wisconsin.

of the year in freshwater lakes and rivers. In the fall, they head for the ocean to lay their eggs.

Elk, moose, and caribou move back and forth between summer and winter feeding grounds. Seals and whales swim great distances and return. But the migrators that people see and admire and wonder about most are the birds.

Why Birds Migrate

In the fall, as cold weather approaches, insects begin to disappear. Plants wither and die. Weed seeds are being blown away. The berries and food crops have all

A herd of caribou at Denali National Park in Alaska migrates to its winter home.

been picked or eaten. Fish are moving down to warmer, lower depths. There will not be much food left for birds who live where the seasons change. But the birds' bodies seem to know all this. As the days grow shorter, they prepare for winter.

Almost a third of the world's birds leave their homes each fall and return in the spring. Migrating birds store extra fat in their bodies for the journey. Some birds travel thousands of miles without stopping. They burn the stored fat for energy. The longer the distance a bird has to travel, the more fat it will store before it leaves.

The American golden plover lives in eastern Canada. It flies two thousand miles over the Atlantic Ocean to northern South America before stopping for food. Then it continues on. Its Alaskan cousin does the same thing on the West Coast, but its first stop is Hawaii, three thousand miles away.

This golden plover is resting in its nest in Manitoba, Canada, its summer home.

When the golden plover starts its flight, it weighs about six ounces. It weighs just over three and a half ounces at the end of its flight. The plovers replace the fat quickly before they start out again for their winter homes in Argentina.

Most birds fly north to south to reach a place where the weather is warm and there is plenty of food. They stay in their wintering places until spring comes back to their northern homes. Since the seasons are reversed below the equator, migrating birds have two summers and no winters.

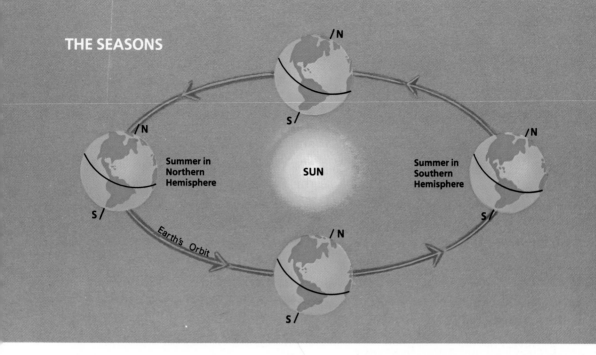

Summer in
Northern
Hemisphere

SUN

Summer in
Southern
Hemisphere

Earth's Orbit

How Birds Know When to Go

The change of seasons is one reason why birds migrate. As fall approaches, the days become shorter and the nights longer. Do you know why this is? Look at the diagram. Because the axis of the earth is tilted, different parts of the earth receive more direct sunlight as it revolves around the sun. This causes the seasons.

Scientists believe that the length of the days tells the birds when it is time to migrate. Scientists also know that this is not enough to explain what starts the birds moving.

The earth turns around an imaginary line called its axis. Notice that the axis is tilted. This causes the seasons to change.

Experiments have shown that birds in cages move to the part of the cage that corresponds to the direction in which they usually fly. No matter how the cage is turned, or how the number of daylight hours are disguised, the birds move to the correct corner and flutter their wings. Something inside is telling the birds that it is time to go.

Many changes take place in birds' bodies before they migrate. Birds store fat to give them enough energy for the long trip. Their feathers drop, or **molt** (mōlt), and they grow a new set. In spring, changes occur that prepare the female bird to lay eggs. All these changes within the bird, together with the seasonal changes outside, seem to trigger the urge to migrate. Scientists believe that birds have an inner clock that works together with the outer clock of the solar system.

The Arctic tern holds the migrating birds' record for long-distance flying. Its powerful wings carry it between the Arctic Circle and Antarctica twice a year. The map shows the routes followed by the Arctic tern.

How Far a Bird Can Travel

The distances that some birds travel are astonishing. The bird that makes the longest journey is the Arctic tern. Look at the map and trace the route the tern travels. Its flight from the Arctic to the Antarctic is a journey of ninety-six hundred miles or more. And the Arctic tern flies that distance twice a year.

The Arctic tern is a large and powerful bird. However, there are tiny birds that also make amazing journeys. The ruby-throated hummingbird is one such flyer. This three-and-a-half-inch bird migrates between Texas

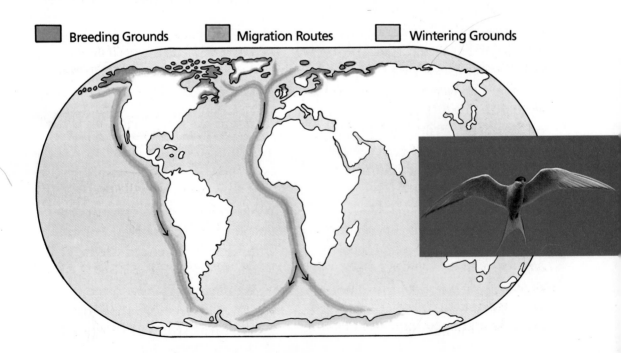

Breeding Grounds   Migration Routes   Wintering Grounds

and the Yucatan Peninsula in Mexico. It flies five hundred miles across the open waters of the Gulf of Mexico without stopping to eat or rest. It makes the journey in about ten hours.

How Birds Find Their Way

Perhaps more astonishing than the great distances birds migrate is their ability to find their way back. How do birds keep from getting lost?

Birds have very keen eyesight. Those that fly by day use landmarks to guide them. They follow the coastline. They recognize mountain ridges and rivers. When they are close to home, they may recognize fields, groups of trees, or even buildings. But this is not enough to explain how birds blown off their course, or those flying over water, keep from getting lost.

Do you know what a compass is? People use a compass to tell direction. Scientists think that birds have an **internal compass** — a compass inside their heads. Birds that fly by day use the sun to steer by. When the angle of the sun changes, the bird adjusts its course. Birds that fly by night use the stars. They follow a star that points them home.

The ruby-throated hummingbird may be small, but it manages to fly five hundred miles nonstop twice a year.

How Migrating Birds Are Tracked

How do we know how far birds travel when they migrate? How do we know which routes they take? One way of tracking birds is by **banding** them. Light metal strips, or **bands**, are placed around the legs of millions of birds. (Some banders use nets to capture whole flocks of birds at one time.) A serial number, the place, and the date are stamped onto the band. The birds are released. Anyone who finds a banded bird can tell how far the bird has traveled and how long the trip has taken.

The route taken by the Arctic tern is known because of banding. Over the years, banded terns have been found in various places around the world. Scientists have thus been able to piece together the tern's travel path. Each recovered bird added another piece to the puzzle.

Banding is done in almost every country on earth. From banding, scientists have learned

- which birds migrate
- what their flight paths are
- how long they live
- if and when flocks move to new nesting places
- how many of the group survive the flight

People who watch birds as a hobby can be very useful to

A tool called a bird-banding plier is being used to measure and then band the leg of this burrowing owl. The band will help scientists keep track of the bird's travels.

scientists who study birds. Bird watchers help to collect information about birds that live in their area.

How You Can Help

If you should ever find a banded bird that is not a pigeon, you can help too. Write the serial number and the address that you find on the band on a post card. Also tell where, when, and how you found the bird. Send the post card to

Fish and Wildlife Service
Bird-Banding Section
Laurel, Maryland 20810

You will be sent a reply telling about the bird. The information you supply will be added to the record. This information will give scientists one more piece of the bird migration puzzle.

Every year for all their lives, many birds fly hundreds or thousands of miles to their wintering grounds. Then they fly back home. Each time they return, they build nests or grow bright new feathers, lay eggs, and wait for the chicks to be born. Then when the young birds are strong enough and the days grow short, they set out for their winter homes again.

Scientists have learned many facts about how and why birds migrate, but there are still many mysteries to be explained. Perhaps you can be one of the people who will help to find some of the answers.

Comprehension Questions

1. What happens to the food supply of birds as winter comes?
2. What happens within a bird's body that triggers the urge to migrate? What happens outside the bird's body?
3. How do migrating birds find their way back home?
4. Describe how scientists learn about the migration routes of birds.

Activity

Do you see birds where you live? Are they around in winter as well as summer? Your library has guides with pictures of American birds. Use one to identify some of the birds you have seen. Choose one kind of bird and find out:
   a. what it eats
   b. what size it is
   c. if it migrates
   d. where it nests

The Whimbrel

by Colin Thiele

The whimbrel would never fly again without help from Tessa and Axel. What did they do to help?

About a hundred people lived in the little town of Snapper Bay in southern Australia. Some of them were young, and some were old, and some of them were in-between.

Axel Jorgensen was seventy-two, with a mop of white hair, and a cotton-wool beard, and legs that bowed outward like bananas.

Tessa Noble was twelve, with brown-and-green-speckled eyes, a mop of brown hair, and legs that bowed inward at the knees like bent sticks. She lived in a white house in the main street of Snapper Bay. There was only one street in the whole town, so it had to be the main one anyway. She lived with her father and mother and her grown-up brother, Jody, and Jody's wife, Bridget.

Axel Jorgensen lived by himself in a wooden hut far around a curve of the bay, away from the town. It was the place where the sandy beach ended and the first rocks reared up near the start of the Hammerhead Handle. He was a fisher and a forager, a sailor and a beachcomber, a talker and a teacher. He taught Tessa many things. When they walked along the coast together, he taught her about seashells and albatrosses, and when they walked inland by the lakes and marshes, he taught her about summer sedges, snails, and spoonbills in the wildlife sanctuary. She thought he was one of the Wise People of the World.

She had called him Uncle Axel for as long as she could remember, even though they were not related. He often came to have a meal in Tessa's house, and Tessa's father went fishing with him whenever he could.

She spent as much time pottering about near his shack as she did in her own little street in Snapper Bay. The shack was filled with things that Tessa's mother called junk. There were oars and rusty oarlocks, bits of rope, rudder pins and grappling hooks, boxes, chains, and old craypots that seemed old enough to have come out of Noah's Ark. For Axel had been a

sailor as well as a beachcomber, a lighthouse keeper as well as a fisher. He had known Tessa since the day she was born.

One morning when Tessa walked around the long curve of the beach to Axel's hut, she found him busy and excited. He was working at the vise on his bench near the door of his shack.

"What are you doing?" she asked. "What's up?"

"You'll never guess, Tessa girl," he said. She knew that something had happened, because he never called her Tessa girl unless he was excited.

"What is it, then?"

"Look inside." He nodded at the shack. "But move slowly."

She was suspicious and walked very carefully. "Is it a snake?"

"Not a snake. Come and see."

At first she couldn't see anything at all in the shadows. She opened her eyes wide and then puckered them quickly to get a clearer view.

"I can't see a thing."

"Not very smart, are you?" He chuckled. "Wouldn't take you out to see things in the marshes."

"Is it a . . . Oh!" Suddenly she saw it. There was a little silence while she took a breath and looked at it. Axel went on working at the vise on his bench.

It was a bird with a long curved beak, lying on its side in a large wire cage, panting. It was streaked brown and buff over the wings and body, but its breast was white, and its crown had long white stripes above the eyes. It was beautiful — lovely mottled feathers and bright frightened eyes, and a long slender downward-curving bill.

"What is it?" Tessa asked at last.

Axel straightened up and stopped his filing at the vise. "A whimbrel," he said.

"A whimbrel." Tessa tasted the name on her tongue. "I like that. It's a name with meanings in the sounds."

"Yes," Axel answered. "Speed and distance, and lonely faraway cries in the night."

Tessa looked at it again. "Is it hurt?"

"Yes."

She sensed something in his voice. "Is it very bad?"

"Pretty bad."

"Wings?" she asked.

Axel took the thing he was making out of the vise, examined it, put it back, and turned toward her.

"He's lost a foot, Tessa. He can't stand up properly."

She was horrified. "A foot? How on earth could he have lost a foot?"

"Who knows?"

"A fish? Do you think maybe a barracuda bit it off?"

Axel shook his head. "It would have happened on the land — or in the air. He likes the inlets and the mud flats."

"A sharp piece of iron, then? Or a piece of wire — a power line he didn't see when he was flying fast?"

Axel's big mop of white hair trembled as he shook his head again. "No. A bullet, more likely."

Tessa was appalled. "Not a bullet!" she said quickly. "Nobody — nobody would shoot at a whimbrel!"

"No?" Axel rubbed angrily with a file. "Have you seen the way Tiny Herbert and Joe Zucci handle a rifle around here? Like maniacs!"

"But not at a whimbrel. Surely they wouldn't shoot at a whimbrel."

"They'd shoot at anything. At a stilt or a curlew or an ibis or a pelican, at a spoonbill or a snipe or a swallow or a swan, at a post or a tin or a light bulb or a tank. They ought to be locked up."

"That's awful." She was silent for a while. "What's going to happen to him?"

Old Axel looked up sharply. "What do you think? He can't live as he is, can he? He has to fly all the way to Siberia or Canada in a few weeks' time."

"But that's on the other side of the world!"

"Yes. Big enough trip to tackle with two legs."

She sat on an old box near the door and glanced back and forth from Axel to the whimbrel. "Can he land on one foot and take off again?"

"Most birds can stand on one foot — if it's not too windy. But his other foot is hurt too — the claw."

"Can't he stand at all, then?"

"He can tumble about and hop and flap and flop. But how could he live like that? How could he get enough food? It would be better to put him away than to let him starve to death."

Her eyes opened wide. "Put him away?"

"Yes. Kill him kindly."

"No," she said quickly. "Oh no, you wouldn't do that." She paused for a second and looked at the old man shrewdly. "You couldn't do that, could you?"

He seemed to be so busy at his vise that at first she thought he hadn't heard her. But after a while, he went on without looking up. "Sometimes things have to be done even when you don't want to do them. Even when it's very hard."

"I know you wouldn't do it," she said confidently, "even if you could." She stood up and went over to him. "What are you making?"

He unfastened something very small from the vise and held it up. It was a foot. A tiny wooden foot — for a whimbrel.

Tessa held the whimbrel while Axel tried to fit the artificial foot. It was not an easy thing to do, even though the little piece of wood was carefully made, with three carved toes and a hollow stem to fit over the stump of the leg.

Fortunately the whimbrel didn't struggle. Axel showed Tessa how to hold him firmly and gently with the wings wrapped against his body. Although he was frightened, he seemed to know that they were trying to help. His dark eyes blinked and flashed, and when his head moved jerkily, his long bill darted about like a probe. Tessa was spellbound.

"It must be four inches long," she said.

Axel didn't even look up. "Four!" he said. "More like sixteen; nice streamlined bird, the whimbrel."

"Not the bird. The bill."

"What about the bill?"

"It must be four inches long."

"The bill is, yes. Not the bird."

"No, the bill, the bill."

"Well, why didn't you say so in the first place?"

Tessa snorted. "Oh, really, Uncle Axel!" She was about to say much more but decided to hold her peace. She looked down at the whimbrel again, at the great curving beak, as black as ebony, at the white breast, the mottled back, and the light stripe running above the eyebrows and over the curve of his head.

"Oh, you're a beautiful fellow," she said. But the bird suddenly struggled, and she had to tighten her grip.

"Hold still, Willie," said old Axel gently. "We're nearly finished with you."

"Is that his name — Willie?"

"Suits him, I reckon. Will-he walk? Or won't he?"

"*Will-he* walk! That's a dreadful joke, Uncle Axel."

"Well, we'll soon know."

"Finished?"

"Finished."

Axel put his pliers and other tools aside and straightened up. "Put him down in his pen."

The whimbrel fluttered for a minute, but he settled down quickly and began to pace up and down in the cage. At first he lifted his leg with a high awkward step, like someone learning to walk on skis, but before long he grew used to it and stomped about happily. Tessa had her nose pressed against the wire. "It works, Uncle Axel," she said excitedly. "It actually works."

"Of course it works," he answered haughtily.

"Do you think he'll be able to fly now and land without somersaulting?" Tessa asked.

"Give him a day or two to get used to it," Axel said. "It's not every day that a bird has to learn to fly with a wooden leg."

It was wise to wait. Two days later the wooden leg was useless. After Willie had walked in his tray of water a few times, the light wood grew soggy and began to break up.

"Fat lot of use that was, Willie," said Axel. "Wouldn't have lasted you to Mount Gambier, let alone to the other side of the world. We'll have to do better than that."

So he worked at his bench for another whole day and made a metal foot — of aluminum. It was beautifully shaped, but it was too hard to fit to Willie's leg.

"Won't work," Axel admitted at last. "Might hurt him; probably do more harm than good."

Tessa was downhearted. "Whatever are we going to do, then? He looks so helpless when you take his foot away from him."

"We'll win yet. I've still got bags of ideas."

This time he made a plastic foot, cutting the shape carefully to match the real one and melting out a hollow stem with a red-hot skewer. It fitted beautifully. But Axel was still not satisfied. He experimented for another two days, making more and more little feet and varying the length and diameter of the hollow stem until he had one that was perfect. It fitted snugly over the whole of the stump of Willie's leg and extended a half inch or so beyond it so that the two legs — the real one and the artificial one — were of exactly the same length. Then Axel fastened a tiny clamp around the stump to be doubly sure.

"Now, Willie," he said, "you ought to be able to dance."

Willie walked as if he was marching in a brass band. He looked so pleased that Tessa thought his big bill would break into a long downward-curving smile.

"He's all right this time," she said. "Now he really can look after himself."

Axel kept him for another week, checking the foot carefully every day. By now Willie was quite tame, standing quietly when they came near him and even eating out of their hands. Tessa could see that Axel was becoming so fond of him that soon he would not be able to part with him.

"Are you going to keep Willie?" she asked slyly one day. "Or are you going to set him free?"

Axel looked at her quizzically.

Tessa was very uncomfortable. She knew she had been rude, and she was certain that he knew it too.

"Come on then," he said suddenly, lifting Willie out of his cage. "It's time you tested your new foot out in the wide world."

They carried the bird inland over the sand behind the shack until they came to the open flats beyond Snapper Bay. Then they stopped, and both of them looked at Willie for the last time. His dark eyes were flashing and blinking. Tessa felt very sad, as if she was about to say farewell forever to a special friend.

"Good-by, Willie," she whispered. "Look after yourself."

"Off you go," said Axel. "You'll be all right now."

He put Willie down on the firm clay near the edge of the mud flats. Willie stood for a second or two as if he was amazed at the sight of everything around him. Then he ran forward for a few steps and rose easily into the air. They both stood watching, holding their hands up to shade their eyes.

"Just look at him fly," Tessa said, "so fast and free."

"Beautiful," said Axel, watching intently. "He's a beautiful fellow."

They both remained with their hands to their eyes until the whimbrel curved downward at last toward the skyline by the marshes and they lost sight of him. Though the world was full of birds, it was suddenly empty.

"Back home, Tessa," said Axel gently. He saw her eyes misting over and her lip trembling. "No need to be sad for Willie," he said quietly. "He's happy back with the other whimbrels — back with all his friends. It wouldn't be right to keep him in a cage, especially when they all fly to the other side of the world. Think how lonely he would be then. You wouldn't like that."

She shook her head. "No, I wouldn't like that."

"And think what a hero he'll be. He'll be able to talk about his wooden leg for the rest of his life."

"His plastic leg."

"Just like Mrs. Elliot with her operation."

Tessa smiled. "He will be sort of special, won't he?"

"Super special," said Axel. "There won't be another whimbrel like him in the whole world."

Author

A native Australian, Colin Thiele has been a teacher, a school principal, and a lecturer, as well as a well-known author. Besides children's books, his writings include poetry, short stories, articles, educational books, and radio plays. His work has won many awards and has been translated into several languages. "The Whimbrel" is from his children's book *The Hammerhead Light*.

105

Comprehension Questions

1. How did Tessa and Axel each help the whimbrel?
2. What made Tessa think of Axel as one of the Wise People of the World?
3. What was Tessa referring to when she said, on page 101, "It must be four inches long"? Why did Axel respond, "Four! More like sixteen; nice streamlined bird, the whimbrel"?
4. Why did Axel decide to set the bird free rather than keep it as a pet?

Vocabulary

The whimbrel gets its name from the sound it makes, so it's called an onomatopoeic (ŏn′ə măt′ə **pē′**ək) word. An onomatopoeic word sounds like the thing that it names or describes. Think of the sound made by each of the following things, and write an onomatopoeic word for it. The first one is done for you.

owl (hooter)   **train**
motorboat   **snake**
telephone   **frog**

Use each onomatopoeic word in a sentence and ask your classmates to figure out what it is.

Writing a Journal Entry

Pretend that you are Tessa. Write a journal entry describing what happened on the day that you set the whimbrel free.

萬里分南去

春鴈水飛

不知何歳月

得与汝同帰

Migrating Birds by Hekigodō

Cloudlets move on high
With their hurried feet, and birds
Go across the sky.

Dictionary

Locating a Word in a Dictionary

Entry words are the words that are listed in a dictionary. They are listed in alphabetical order. **Guide words** are given at the top of each page. They show the first and last entry words on that page. To find an entry word in the dictionary, look for the guide words that would come before and after the word in alphabetical order. The word you want will be on that page. If the guide words at the top are *valentine* and *value,* the entry word *valuable* would be found on that page. Which of the following sets of guide words could appear on the top of the page that has the entry word *motor*?

Set 1:   **mosaic**   **motion**
Set 2:   **motionless**   **mountain**

In the dictionary, the entry word is printed in boldface, and it is divided into syllables with a black dot between each one. Entry words are listed in alphabetical order. The word *gallon* comes before the word *gallop* because the sixth letter, *n,* in *gallon* comes before the sixth letter, *p,* in *gallop.* Which of these words would come first in a dictionary — *steamer* or *steamboat*?

Most of the time, only base words are listed as entry words. Look for base words, not the past tense of verbs or the plural of nouns. So if you wanted to look up the verb *viewed* and the noun *shepherds,* you would look for the base words *view* and *shepherd.* What word would you look for if you wanted to get the meaning for *carried*?

Getting the Pronunciation of a Word

If you are not sure how to say a word, the **special spelling** in a dictionary will help you. The special spelling comes right after the entry word. Below is a word that you more than likely don't know and its special spelling.

chin·qua·pin(chĭng′kə pĭn′)

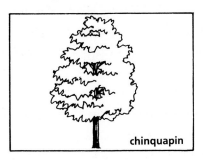

chinquapin

The **pronunciation key** is often found at the bottom of the pages in a dictionary. It gives you the pronunciation of each vowel and certain other letters in the special spelling. This book uses the pronunciation key shown at the bottom of this page.

Look at the first syllable in the special spelling of *chinquapin*. Consonants stand for the same sound they usually stand for, so *ch* stands for the sound it usually stands for. The next letter in the special spelling is *ĭ*. Find the *ĭ* in the pronunciation key. Right after it is the word *pit*. Now softly say the sound of *ch* followed by the sound that *i* stands for in *pit*. Add to that the sound that *ng* stands for. That will give you the first syllable in *chinquapin*.

The second syllable begins with *k* followed by *ə*, which is called a **schwa**. Find the schwa in the pronunciation key. Say the five key words after it softly to yourself. Listen to the sound the symbol stands for. Now say the sound for *k* followed by the schwa sound.

ă pat / ā pay / â care / ä father / ĕ pet / ē be / ĭ pit / ī pie / î fierce / ŏ pot / ō go / ô paw, for / oi oil / o͝o book / o͞o boot / ou out / ŭ cut / û fur / *th* the / th thin / hw **wh**ich / zh vision / ə ago, item, pencil, atom, circus

The consonants in the third syllable stand for sounds you know. Use the pronunciation key to get the sound for ī. Now say that syllable softly to yourself.

The special spelling also shows stressed syllables. The heavy, dark mark (′) after the first syllable is a **primary stress mark**. It shows that the first syllable is said with more force than the others. The mark (′) after the last syllable is not as heavy. It is a **secondary stress mark**. It shows that the last syllable is to be said with some stress, but not as much as the first syllable.

Say the word softly to yourself. Be sure to put the correct stress on each syllable.

Getting the Correct Meaning

You can, of course, also get the meaning of a word in a dictionary. The meaning is given after the special spelling. Sometimes a sentence that uses the word is also given. If there is only one meaning given, read it carefully. Then go back to the sentence in which you first saw the new word. Think of that meaning of the word as you read the sentence again.

Many entry words have more than one meaning. Read the following story about Mary's dog. You will use the boldface words to learn how to select the correct meaning when more than one meaning is given for a word.

Mary's dog, Toby, was chasing a rabbit through the fields. When the rabbit ran into a **depression**, Toby could no longer see it. Toby **rejected** the idea of going home and chased after it. When he ran over the hill, though, his **game** was gone. Toby decided that he really wasn't meant to be a hunting dog.

Here is the way that the first boldface word could appear in a dictionary. Notice that each meaning is numbered.

de·pres·sion (dĭ **prĕsh′**ən) *n.*
   1. Sadness, gloom: *He went into a depression when his team lost.*
   2. A low place or hollow: *She fell when her bicycle hit a depression in the road.* **3.** A time when business is slow and people are out of work.

When you come to a word that has more than one meaning, check to see if every meaning is the same part of speech. Most of the time, the part of speech is given right after the special spelling. The letter *n.* right after the special spelling for *depression* means that the entry word is a noun. Other abbreviations used are *v.* for verb, *adj.* for adjective, and *adv.* for adverb. When every meaning is the same part of speech, read them all. Then go back to the sentence in which you first saw the new word. Read the sentence again, and select the meaning that makes the most sense.

In the story about Toby, the word *depression* is used as a noun. Every meaning is for the word as a noun. When you try all of those meanings in the story, you will find that the second meaning is the one that makes the most sense.

A word may have different pronunciations too. Here is the way that the base word for the second boldface word could appear in a dictionary:

re·ject (rĭ **jĕkt′**) *v.* To refuse to allow or approve: *Mother rejected my plan to skip school.* — *n.* (**rē′**jĕkt′) Something or someone that is rejected: *The coat was a reject because it was too small.*

The special spelling (rĭ **jĕkt′**) and its meaning are correct when the word is used as a verb. The special spelling (**rē′**jĕkt′) and its meaning are correct when the word is used as a noun.

In the story about Toby, *rejected* is a verb; so you would select the pronunciation and meaning for the word *reject* when it is used as a verb. If you were not sure that it was used as a verb, you would use the sense of the story to select the correct meaning. So you would select the first meaning because it makes the most sense. You would then use the pronunciation that goes with that meaning.

Here is the way that the third boldface word could appear in a dictionary:

game¹ (gām) *n.* **1.** A sport or contest with certain rules. **2.** Wild animals, birds, or fish that are hunted for sport or food.
game² (gām) *adj.* Disabled: *The dog had trouble walking on its game foot.*

game

There is more than one entry for this word. Each entry has a small number after it. Notice, too, that for each entry, the word has a different part of speech. Which entry tells you the meaning of *game* as it is used in the story? In the story about Toby, *game* is used as a noun; so you would read the definitions given in the first entry. The second meaning in that entry makes the most sense in the story. So you would pick meaning number two under the entry for *game* when it is used as a noun.

If you were not sure if *game* was used as a noun or an adjective, you would have to read both entries for *game.* You would then decide which meaning made the most sense.

Using a Dictionary

Answer the following questions. You will need to use the Glossary in the back of this book to answer some questions.

1. Would **refuse** be on a page with the guide words **refrain** and **region**?
2. Would the entry word **stargaze** come before or after **start**?
3. What is the key word for the vowel sound in the special spelling (lo͞os)?
4. Which syllable has secondary stress in (tŏl′ə rāt′)?
5. In the following sentence, which syllable has the primary stress in **progress**?

   We couldn't **progress** because the car was stuck in the snow.

6. In the following sentence, what is the key word for the vowel sound in **mow**?

   After we cut the hay, we put it in the **mow**.

Skill Summary

- Entry words in a dictionary are usually base words and are listed in alphabetical order.
- Open the dictionary near the first letter of the word you want. Use the guide words to help you find the right page.
- The special spelling after the entry word, together with the pronunciation key, shows you how to say a word. Stress marks show which syllables should be said with more force.
- When several meanings are given for a word or when the same word is listed as an entry word more than once, use the part of speech to help select the correct meaning. Always pick the meaning that makes sense in the sentence in which you first saw the new word.

Making a Friend

by Myra Cohn Livingston

He wouldn't come at first.
But when
I stood quite still a long time,
Then

His tail began to move.
His eyes
Looked into mine, and in
Surprise

He sort of sniffed and showed
His tongue.
Then, suddenly, he moved and
Sprung

To where I stood. He smelled
My feet
And came up close so we could
Meet.

So then, I gently stroked
His head.
"Good boy — I'll be your friend,"
I said.

He licked me then, and that
Was good,
Because it meant
He understood.

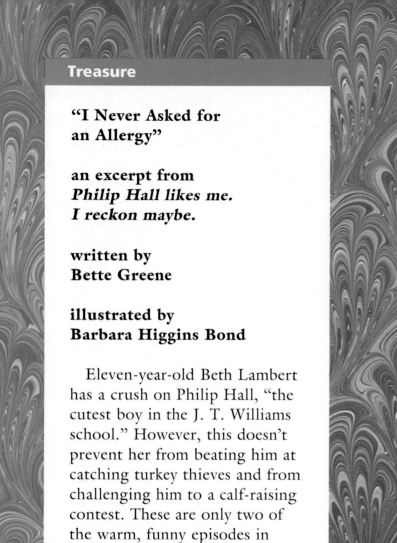

**"I Never Asked for
an Allergy"**

an excerpt from
*Philip Hall likes me.
I reckon maybe.*

**written by
Bette Greene**

**illustrated by
Barbara Higgins Bond**

Eleven-year-old Beth Lambert
has a crush on Philip Hall, "the
cutest boy in the J. T. Williams
school." However, this doesn't
prevent her from beating him at
catching turkey thieves and from
challenging him to a calf-raising
contest. These are only two of
the warm, funny episodes in
*Philip Hall likes me. I reckon
maybe.*, which traces a year in the
life of this Arkansas farm girl.
During this year, Beth learns to
accept things in life that she cannot change — like an unasked-
for allergy — and she learns that
Philip's friendship does not depend on her letting him win.

*Philip Hall likes me. I reckon
maybe.* was chosen as a Newbery
Honor Book in 1975.

Philip Hall likes me.
I reckon maybe.

by Bette Greene
illustrated by Barbara Higgins Bond

I Never Asked for an Allergy

Mr. Barnes stopped the school bus along the side of the highway just at that spot where the dirt road leading to our farm meets the blacktop. First Philip Hall got off. Then I jumped off in front of the faded black-and-white sign at the intersection, which read:

> 1 MILE TO LAMBERT FARM
> GOOD TURKEYS   GOOD PIGS

As I took a flying leap across the frozen drainage ditch that separated the road from the field, I heard Philip calling me.

"Hey, Beth!" He was still standing on the blacktop just where the bus left him. "You shouldn't be going through the field. You might step into an ice puddle."

Of all days to have to stop and start explaining things to Philip Hall. But at any other time I'd be thinking that he wouldn't be fretting about my feet if he didn't really like me. Now would he? "Frosty feet are nothing," I told him, "when you have a spanking new puppy waiting to meet you."

"What if Mr. Grant wouldn't swap a collie dog for one of your pa's turkeys?" asked Philip, grinning as though he hoped it was so.

"That's all you know! When I left the house this morning, my pa was picking out six of our fattest turkeys for swapping." I turned and began running across the field.

"Well, one collie dog is worth more than six of your old turkeys," called Philip.

I kept on running, pretending not to hear. And, anyway, everybody loves to eat turkey, don't they?

When I reached the rise in the field, I could see our house, a nice pale green. As I came closer, I could see the chocolate brownness of my mama against the paleness of the porch. She was hanging work-worn overalls across the porch clothesline. I tiptoed up behind her and threw my arms around her.

"Ohhh!" She jumped. "What do you mean scaring me clear out of my wits, girl?"

"Where is he?" I asked. "Where's the collie?"

Then she put on her I'm-not-fixing-to-listen-to-any-nonsense face and said, "I don't know anything about a collie."

"Did Pa make the swap? Did he?"

"Get out of here, girl. Go on into the kitchen."

"Tell me if Pa got the collie," I pleaded. "Now did he?"

Her mouth was still set into that no-nonsense way of hers, but it was different with her eyes. Her eyes were filled up with pure pleasure. "I told you," she said, "to get on into the kitchen, didn't I?"

Suddenly I understood. I threw open the screen door and, without waiting to close it gently behind me, ran in a straight line through the living room and into the kitchen.

Then I saw him. There in a cardboard carton next to the cookstove was a reddish-brown puppy with a circle of white fluffy hair ringing his neck and spilling down to his chest. I dropped to my knees and showed my open palms. "Hi, puppy. Beautiful little collie puppy."

"He's beautiful, sure enough," said Ma from behind.

The collie just looked at me for a few moments. Then he got to his feet and trotted over.

"And you're friendly too," I said, patting his back. "Hey, that would be a good name for you."

"Friendly," said Ma, smacking her lips like she was word tasting. "That's a right good name."

120

I gave Friendly a hug and a kiss. "I will now name you — *ah-choo!*" I tried again. "I will now name — *AHHHH-hhhhh-choo!!*"

Ma shook her head the way she does when she catches me at mischief. "You have a cold, now, don't you?"

"*AHHHHhhhhh-ha-ha-ha-choo!* I now name you Friendly," I said at last.

By bedtime I was sneezing constantly, and water kept pouring from my sore, itchy eyes. But, thank goodness, all my sneezing didn't seem to bother Friendly, who slept peacefully in his cardboard carton at the foot of my bed.

I could hear my folks in the kitchen talking about what they were always talking about these days — names for our soon-to-be-born baby. When they finally tired of that topic, Ma said, "Beth has me worried. All those wheezing sounds coming from her chest."

"I saw Doc Brenner in town this afternoon," said Pa. "He asked me to kill and clean one of our twenty-pound birds. Said he'd stop by this evening to pick it up."

"When he comes by," said Ma, "ask him to kindly take a look at our Beth."

I climbed out of bed to take off my old nightgown and put on the one that Grandma had given me last year. Friendly started to bark.

"Don't you be frightened, little Friendly. It's only me, only Beth."

While I patted my new pet, I told him how glad I was that he had come to live with us. "You're going to like it here, you'll see. I'm going to bring all my friends to meet

you. Philip Hall, Susan, Bon — *ahh-choo-whoo! Ahh-choo!* Bonnie, Ginny, Esther. You're going to like all my friends, Friendly, but you're going to like me best of all . . . I reckon maybe."

Ma called out, "Are you out of bed, Beth?"

I jumped back into bed before answering. "No, ma'am, I'm right here. Right here in bed."

I kept my eyes open, waiting for the doctor to come, but after a while my eyelids came together. Sleep stood by waiting for me to fall . . . fall asleep . . . sleep . . . sleep.

"Let me take a look at my old friend, Beth," said a big voice.

My cheeks were being patted. "Doctor's here, Beth honey," Ma was saying.

I pulled myself up and looked into the face of Dr. Brenner, who said, "This won't hurt," as he placed a freezing stethoscope on my chest.

I jumped. "It's cold."

He rubbed the stethoscope warm with his hands. "Just breathe naturally," he said as he put the warmed tube back on my chest. He listened quietly without saying a word. Then he took the stethoscope from his ears. "I heard some wheezing sounds coming from your chest. Tell me, how do your eyes feel?"

"They feel like I want to grab them out of their sockets and give them a good scratching. They're so . . . so itchy."

"Uh-hun," answered Dr. Brenner, as though he knew all about itchy eyes. "Beth, can you remember when all this sneezing and wheezing began?"

Across the room, my sister turned over in her bed and let out a groan without once opening her eyes. It was as if Anne was making a complaint that her sleep was being disturbed by inconsiderate folks.

"Yes, sir," I told the doctor. "It all started when I met Friendly."

Friendly must have heard his name called 'cause he jumped out of his carton and jogged floppily on over.

"Hi, little Friendly, little dog." I picked him up and gave him a hug and a kiss. *"AHHHHhh — choo! Ah — choo!"*

"Beth," said Dr. Brenner, running his fingers through his silver hair. "I'm sorry to do this, but I'm going to have to tell you something — something you're not going to like hearing. I believe you have an allergy to Friendly."

"Oh, no sir. I don't!" I cried. "I don't have one, honest. I never asked for an allergy. Why, I don't even know what that means."

Dr. Brenner took my hand. "It simply means that Friendly's dog hair is making you sick. And, furthermore, it means that he must be returned to wherever he came from."

"But Friendly is *my* dog. He belongs to me. And he's never *never* going to go back to that kennel!" I felt tears filling up my eyes. "I love Friendly; Friendly loves me."

"I know you love one another," agreed Dr. Brenner, "but all this sneezing, wheezing, and red eyes is your body's way of telling you something."

I shook my head no.

Doc Brenner nodded his head yes. "Bodies don't need to say fancy words like allergic rhinitis — or any words at all, Beth. When your throat is dry, you don't wait to hear the word *water* before taking a drink. And do you really need the school's lunch bell to ring before you know when it's time to eat? Well, now your body is saying something just as important. Listen to it!" he said, cupping his hand around his ear. But the only sound in the room was the hissing noise coming from my own chest.

When the morning sun came flooding through my bedroom window, my eyes opened and I remembered about the allergy. Was it real or only a dream?

"Friendly," I called. "Come here, little Friendly."

Friendly didn't come, though, and I didn't hear him either. I jumped to the foot of my bed. The cardboard box was empty. They've taken him back to Mr. Grant's kennel!

I was just about to shout out for Friendly when outside the kitchen window I heard Luther's and Anne's voices: "Get that ball, Friendly. Friendly, you going to get that ball?"

Ma laughed. "That dog won't do anything he hasn't a mind to do."

I went out the kitchen door still wearing my new nightgown and sat down on the back steps next to her. She put her arm around me and gave me a quick squeeze. "How you feeling, honey babe?"

I thought about her question. My chest felt as though it was still filled up with old swamp water, while my head carried around last night's headache. Finally, I gave my answer, "I'm okay, Mama. I reckon."

"After you come home from school, I want you to take a little nap. Never mind the chores; just put your head down on the pillow and nap. 'Cause you spent half the night crying into your pillow."

"About what the doctor said . . . about taking Friendly back to the kennel. We're not going to listen to that, are we?"

She looked past me, out to where Luther and Anne were playing with Friendly. "Life isn't always the way we want it to be. Life is the way it is. Nothing we can do."

"You *can't* take him back!" I shouted. "Besides, Mr. Grant's probably eaten up all the turkeys."

"If he did, he did," answered Ma.

"You don't understand," I said, bringing my voice back down to size. "I *need* Friendly! Luther was three and Anne was two when I was born, so they had me; but I never had anything little and soft to ——"

"And I told you," she said, "that life is the way it is. There's nothing we can do. But if you miss that school bus, there is something I can do. So *get!*"

127

At school I felt better and worse. Better because I didn't sneeze or wheeze and even my eyes stopped itching and watering. And worse because tonight, after supper, Friendly was going back to Mr. Grant's kennel.

If only I had some magic. One time I remembered my teacher, Miss Johnson, pointing to shelves of books and saying that they held many secrets. Could one of her books hold the secret of making the allergy go and the dog stay?

At recess, she stood on a three-step ladder to bring down a heavy book from the top shelf.

"This book may have the secret we're looking for," she said, pointing to a page. "Right here," she whispered, the way people do when they're telling secrets. "It says that people who have an allergy to long-haired dogs, like the collie, might not have an allergy to a short-haired dog, like the Chihuahua."

At the kennel, I held Friendly close to me while Pa explained about the allergy to Mr. Grant.

"We don't usually sell Chihuahuas," said the kennel owner, "but we happen to have one that I got in trade from a customer in Walnut Ridge. So you sure are welcome to swap," he said, reaching out for Friendly.

"Wait!" I said. "A person has got to say good-by." I looked into Friendly's eyes and wondered how I could make him understand. "I never wanted to get rid of you, Friendly. I only wanted to get rid of the aller — *Her —* *her — choo!* — of the allergy."

He licked my ear almost as if to tell me not to worry because any dog as friendly as Friendly would get along just fine.

Again Mr. Grant reached out, only this time I gave him my Friendly. As he took Friendly away, I heard him say, "Rest of the collies are going to be mighty happy to see you again."

When he returned, Friendly wasn't with him. "An allergy sure is a bothersome thing," said Mr. Grant. "Reason I know that is because I've had an allergy ever since I was about your age."

It was so hard to believe. "You've got an allergy to collies too?" I asked.

"Nope." Mr. Grant pointed to the bend in his sun-tanned arm. "Tomatoes — that's what gets my allergy going. One tomato and my arm breaks out like a strawberry patch."

"Tomatoes don't bother me a bit," I said proudly.

"Reckon that's what an allergy is," said Mr. Grant. "What doesn't bother some folks, bothers other folks a whole lot."

When we stopped in front of the Chihuahua's run, a tiny fellow came rushing to the gate, barking. "That's the dog for me," I said.

On the drive back home I held the Chihuahua in my lap while my folks went back to trying to pick out a baby name. When Pa turned off the highway onto the dirt road leading to our farm, the puppy jumped off my lap. He

stood on his toes, pressing his nose against the truck's window. I hollered, "Looky there! Look at Tippietoes!"

"Ohhhh," said Ma, turning her head. "Now isn't that something? And what a fine name for him too."

I put my hands against the little dog's cheeks and gave him a kiss between the eyes. "I now name you — *ah* — I now name you — *ah-ah-ah-choo!*"

"Oh no!" said Ma and Pa at exactly the same time.

But finally I was able to say, and say proudly, "I now name you Tippietoes."

By the time I crawled into bed, my eyes were red and itchy. My nose was sneezy, and my chest was wheezy. Ma stood at my doorway. "Tippietoes is going to sleep next to the cookstove tonight, but tomorrow evening we're going to take him back."

I shook my head no. "Mama, don't say that. I don't care about a little allergy; cross my heart I don't. All I care about is my little dog — my own little Tippietoes."

"Girl, you're talking nothing but a heap of foolishness. I'm not about to let you walk around sick. Not as long as I'm your mama. Now you get yourself to sleep."

At first recess, I told Miss Johnson about having an allergy not just to long-haired dogs but to short-haired ones too.

"Maybe I can find still another secret in that book," she said, bringing down the big book again. She fingered through a lot of pages before she finally began to read aloud: "'People who have an allergy to both long-haired and short-haired dogs might not have an allergy to poodles, as they never shed hair.'"

Pa explained to Mr. Grant what I had learned from the book. "So we'll be much obliged if you'll kindly swap Tippietoes here for one of your poodles."

"Fine with me," said Mr. Grant, reaching for Tippietoes.

"Wait!" I said, holding onto the little one for another moment. "A person still has to say good-by." I patted his chin. He licked my fingers. "Good-by, little boy, little Tippietoes. I'm sorry you couldn't be my dog."

I closed my eyes as I gave him over to Mr. Grant, who took him away. When he came back he said, "Come along folks. Let me introduce you to my poodles."

We followed him until he stopped at the gate of a chainlink fence. "Poodles may be just the right dog for a girl with an allergy," he said, pointing to two white dogs that looked more like fluffy powder puffs than real dogs. "The book is right. They never shed a single hair."

He unhooked the gate, and I walked in saying, "This time I'm going to be lucky. This time I *hope* I'm going to be lucky."

"Hope so," said Ma and Pa at exactly the same moment.

Both poodles walked over to say hello. They were quite polite. I bent down, and one of the puppies came closer. "Is it you?" I asked him.

He took one step closer, resting his fluffy head in my hand. I whispered, "I'm going to take real good care of you."

Inside the crowded cab of the pickup truck, I held the poodle puppy on my lap as Pa turned on the headlights and started for home. My patting must have relaxed the little dog 'cause he closed his eyes and went to sleep.

After a while Ma said, "I think we ought to name the baby after my great-aunt Alberta."

Pa's nose crinkled. "What do you want to name our baby after her for?"

Ma's nose climbed. "Isn't she my grandma's sister? The oldest living member of my family?"

"Have you all noticed," I asked, hoping that my interruption would stop an argument from starting, "that I haven't sneezed even one time?"

Ma smiled. "Isn't it the truth."

"And Puffy will never have to go back to Mr. Grant's," I said.

"Puffy?" asked Pa, surprised.

"Don't you see," I asked, "how he's all puffy like cotton candy?"

Ma turned to look at Pa. "Beth has thought up three good names for three dogs while we're still fussing over one name for one baby."

Puffy opened his eyes and looked around. "You're here, Puffy," I said, putting my face into his white fluffiness. "And you're always going to be . . . my — *choo!* My — *ahhhhhhh — ey!*"

"Don't go telling me I heard what I think I heard," said Ma, fixing her eyes on the ceiling of the truck.

"It's not what you think," I said quickly. "I really — *ahhh-choo! Ah-choo-who!* I really think I'm catching Billy Boy Williams's cold. He had one at school today. Sneezed all over the place — choo, choo, choo, like that! Spreading his germs about."

Pa drove the truck over to the side of the road and turned off the engine. "Beth, I am sorry to disappoint you. I know how much you wanted a pup, but there's nothing I can do."

"If you take him back," I warned, "I'm never going to live at home again. For the rest of my life I'm going to live in the kennel with Puffy."

My mama patted my hand. "In this life you have to be happy about the good things and brave about the bad ones."

"I don't want to be brave," I shouted. "All I want is my little dog."

Pa started up the truck, made a U-turn on the highway, and headed back toward the kennel. "There's nothing in this wide world we can do," he said, shaking his head.

The next morning I asked Miss Johnson to bring down the book again, but after a while we stopped reading. It didn't have any more secrets to tell. I walked away because I didn't have a single word for a single solitary soul. But later in the afternoon I told her, "I guess it's nobody's fault. I reckon I'm learning to be brave about things I don't like."

"I want you to know," said Miss Johnson, taking off her glasses, "that I think you're learning very well."

When the school bus stopped in front of our sign, I jumped off and with a running leap crossed the ditch.

"How come you're shortcutting through the field again?" called Philip Hall. "There's no dog waiting for you today."

"Guess I know that," I said, wondering how I could have forgotten. Yet for some reason I really was in a hurry to get home.

When I reached the rise, I could see the chocolate-brown outline of my mother. But it didn't look like her, not exactly. After I passed the vegetable garden, I could see that it wasn't her. It was . . . my grandmother.

I started running my fast run. "Grandma, Grandma! Hello!"

"Howdy there, Beth babe," she called back.

I ran into her arms as she closed them around me. "How come you're here? All the way from Walnut Ridge?"

Grandma smiled. "I came to see my new grandbaby. Born this very morning, a few minutes after nine."

"Where are they?" I asked.

"Shhhh," she said, pointing to the inside of the house. "They are both real fine, but they're resting just now."

I asked, "Is it a . . . is it a brother?"

"A brother for you; a grandson for me," she said, hugging me some more.

I danced a circle around her. "My own little brother. He's going to be fun to take care of and fun to play with. Sometimes boys are almost as much fun to play with as girls. I've noticed that."

"Reckon I've noticed that too," said Grandma, joining my dance.

"What's my brother's name?"

Grandma stopped dancing. "Your folks didn't come to a decision on that," she said.

"Don't fret about that," I told her. "I happen to be good at names."

Then I heard Pa calling from inside the house, "Beth, come on in and meet your brother."

I closed the screen door quietly behind me the way I always remember to do when there is a visitor in the house. Pa stood at the door of his and Ma's bedroom and waved me on. "I want you to see something real pretty," he said.

Ma was sitting up in bed, propped up by two pillows. She was wearing her "sick" nightgown — the pink one with the lace running around the neck and collar. When I used to remind her that she ought to get some wear out of it because she's never been sick a day in her life, Ma always said, "We'll see."

As I came closer, I saw something in her arms that I had never seen there before. A baby.

Ma said, "Fold your arms."

"Like this?" I asked.

"Just like that," she said, placing my soft little brother in my arms.

"Ohhhhh," I said, touching my lips to his warm head. "You are a beautiful baby brother. My baby brother Benjamin."

"Benjamin?" asked Ma. "Benjamin? *Benjamin!* — Oh, my, yes. That's it. That's the name!"

Pa smiled. "Benjamin is a good strong name for a boy."

"Finally," said Grandma, coming into the room. "A name for the baby."

I put my face next to Baby Benjamin's and breathed in deep. I didn't sneeze. "You're always going to be our Baby Benjamin," I whispered in his ear. "And anyway, Mr. Grant wouldn't know what to do with a real baby."

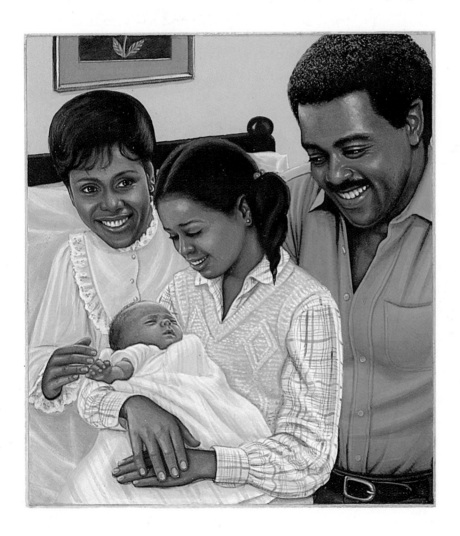

Author

Bette Greene grew up in a small Arkansas town and in Memphis, Tennessee. She studied in Paris for a year, then attended Columbia University in New York. Her first book, for junior and senior high schoolers, grew out of her childhood experiences in Arkansas. It won several awards.

Her second book, *Philip Hall likes me. I reckon maybe.*, from which "I Never Asked for an Allergy" was taken, was also set in rural Arkansas. Mrs. Greene says, "Without the memory of childhood sights and feelings and events, I'd be a writer with nothing to say." That book, too, won several awards. A sequel is *Get on out of here, Philip Hall.* Mrs. Greene has also written short stories and newspaper and magazine articles.

Illustrator

Born and raised in Arkansas, Barbara Higgins Bond entered the advertising industry after receiving a degree in design from the Memphis Academy of Arts. When her son was born, she gave up her advertising career to become a freelance artist. Her sensitive, realistic illustrations have appeared in many books, magazines, calendars, and advertisements. As one of America's foremost illustrators, Barbara Higgins Bond often lectures at universities. Her work has also been exhibited at New York's Museum of Modern Art.

Comprehension Questions

1. Why did Beth's mother tell her that life isn't always the way we want it to be?
2. What reason did Beth give for wanting a puppy so much?
3. Why did Beth get a Chihuahua when she found she was allergic to the collie? Why did she get a poodle when she found she was allergic to the Chihuahua?
4. What will help ease Beth's disappointment at not being able to have a dog?

Vocabulary

The meaning of a hyphenated compound word is a combination of the meanings of the words that form it. For example, Beth's baby brother was a **soon-to-be-born** baby. Below are definitions for other hyphenated compounds in "I Never Asked for an Allergy." Figure out each word that is being defined.

- a ladder that has three steps
- overalls worn out from working in them
- a serious expression
- a turn that makes you go back the other way

Making a Dictionary

Beth's parents got her several different breeds of dogs before realizing that Beth was probably allergic to all kinds of dogs. What other kinds of dogs are there? Make a dictionary of different breeds of dogs. Include those that Beth had briefly as pets, as well as two others.

Magazine Wrap-up

Literary Skill: Conflict

You have learned that the plot is the author's plan for a story. Often, the plot involves a problem, or **conflict**, that one or more of the characters face. The conflict keeps readers interested in the story. They want to find out how the conflict is resolved.

In "Emergency Please" Jeff's problem was that Fletcher became injured while Jeff was caring for him. How was Jeff's conflict finally resolved?

For each of the following stories, tell what character or characters had a conflict and what the conflict was: "Rustytoes," "The Whimbrel," "I Never Asked for an Allergy."

Vocabulary: Suffixes

Choose a suffix from the box to complete each boldface base word in the sentences below. Write the word on your paper. You may use a suffix more than once.

ist	ian
ous	or
ish	

1. The farmers with the most money helped their less **prosper**____ neighbors.
2. You can tell that these pictures were drawn by a talented **art**____ .
3. The giant shook the valley with his **thunder**____ roar.
4. Every **music**____ in the band practiced hard for the recording session.
5. The person who matches the film and the sound track to complete an animated cartoon is called the **edit**____ .
6. The farmers thought their new neighbor was too **outland**____ to fit into the village.

Language Skill: Reporting

Pretend that you are a newspaper reporter. Write a news story to go with one of the following headlines based on stories from Magazine One.

- Quick-Thinking Baby Sitter Aids Injured Tot
- Local Farmers Help Ailing Giant
- Australian Beachcomber Invents Foot for Injured Bird

Books to Enjoy

The Winter Worm Business
by Patricia Reilly Giff

Leroy finds a rival for his winter worm business when his look-alike cousin Michael moves into town.

A Girl Called Bob and a Horse Called Yoki
by Barbara Campbell

A girl has a secret plan to save the life of an old delivery horse.

Where's Buddy?
by Ron Roy

Realizing that his diabetic brother is lost without his medication, Mike begins a desperate search for the boy.

The Best Bad Thing
by Yoshiko Uchida

When she spends part of her summer vacation helping her mother's widowed friend, Rinko learns that bad things can turn out to be good.

142

Explorations
Magazine Two

Contents

GRAMP

by Joan Tate

The move from a house to an apartment had left
Gramp without a place for his workbench — and without anything to do. Why was this a problem for Simon
as well as for Gramp? What did Simon do about it?

Simon had lived with his parents and Gramp in an old house with a yard that included a garden and Gramp's workshop shed. There Gramp had taught Simon to use tools, and together they had built a guinea pig hutch. When the row of houses where they lived was torn down, the tenants were moved to a high-rise building where there was no room for Gramp's workbench.

That summer when Simon was ten was a time full of new things. Gradually, the apartment became home. Gramp and Mum put everything right. Soon Simon was quite used to the differences, actually liking his room in the sky. He enjoyed going up and down in an elevator or even sometimes running the whole way down the stairs, hundreds of steps, to arrive breathless and panting at the bottom, dizzy with it all.

It was not the same with Gramp though. At first it was all right, as there was a lot to do to help Mum fix up the apartment. When the apartment was finished, though, it was easy to clean and look after — much easier than the house. Mum got a part-time job, mornings only, and Gramp was alone a lot. He sat in his room or in the living room, not even watching television but just sitting there, staring out the window or staring at nothing.

Sometimes he sat on his bed, staring at his feet, and Simon would go in to talk to him, to tell him about his guinea pigs.

"They're big now, Gramp," he said one day. "Why don't you come down and look?"

Gramp looked up at him.

"That's good, boy," he said. "That's good."

"Come down and look," said Simon again.

Gramp shook his head.

"Too far down there," he said.

"There's the elevator. It'd only take five minutes."

But Gramp shook his head.

"What's the matter with you, Gramp?" Simon asked.

"Nothing's the matter," he said. "Nothing. That's it."

"You mean you've nothing to do?"

"That's it," said Gramp, looking at his hands. "Nothing."

"Why don't you put a bench up here?" said Simon. Gramp looked around.

"In here?" he said. "In this room? There's not room."

"You could have a small one," said Simon. "Just so that you could fasten the vise on, anyhow."

"The mess, boy," Gramp said. "The mess. You can't do that sort of thing indoors, in an apartment like this."

"We could keep it clean," persisted Simon.

"You don't know what you're talking about," said Gramp curtly, and then he just turned his head away, refusing to talk anymore, not looking at Simon.

"Gramp!"

It was no good. Gramp had been talking in a way he had never talked before. Then he gradually got more and more silent and would not speak to any of them, sometimes for days on end. Even Dad could not get a word out of him if he was feeling in that mood. Gramp began to sit in a chair at the window all day long, sitting there with a small hammer in his hands, turning it over and over, rubbing it, and polishing the wood over and over again, the hammer that he never used anymore. Simon could not bear seeing him sitting there, but he did not know what to do.

Mum just said that he was getting old, and she told Simon not to bother him.

"He's always been old," protested Simon. "And he never minded me bothering him before."

"Older, then," said Mum. "You get like that when you're old."

"Like what?"

"Like Grandpa."

"But he wasn't like that before."

"Before what?"

"Before we came here."

"What d'you mean, before we came here?" said Mum. "He's better off here than where we were before. The room's lighter and cleaner and not so damp. It's warmer too."

Simon fell silent. She didn't understand. Then he looked at his mother, standing by the table in the kitchen, mixing something in a big bowl. He watched her turning the mixture over and beating at it with a spoon, then slicing through it with a knife. She moved quickly and took things out of the kitchen drawer, shut the drawer, darted across the kitchen, fetched a baking pan, turned the oven on, came back.

"What are you standing there staring at?" she said. "Go on down and out into the fresh air."

"Gramp would be all right if he had a bench. Like you have your kitchen," said Simon, holding his breath, knowing his mother would be cross.

"Oh, you and Grandpa and that bench!" she said. "Where can you find a workbench in a place like this?"

"We could try."

Simon did not know why he went on about it, because he knew his mother was right. But he kept thinking of their old shed, of him and Gramp talking and working, sometimes saying nothing, and now it had all gone. His mother leaned across the table and knocked a small bowl off the edge by mistake. It fell to the tiled floor and broke.

"Now look what you've made me do," she said. "That was your fault, standing there carrying on about Grandpa and his bench and all that. Getting in my way and making me drop things. Get along now. If it's that important to you, why don't you go out and find him a bench yourself?"

"All right!" said Simon. "I will! I'll find him one. No one cares about him any longer. Only me."

He turned and dashed out of the kitchen straight through the hall, wrenched open the door, and slammed it hard behind him. He felt hot and angry, and he couldn't wait for the elevator. He began stamping down the stairs, crashing his feet on each step, until they were both sore.

"I'll find him one somewhere," he said to himself. "I will. I'll find him one. I'll get one somewhere, so he can use his tools again, and we can talk again."

He stumped down the road, not quite sure where he was going to start looking, his hot face slowly cooling. "Where can I look?" he asked himself. "Where do you find things like that? Where do people do their odd jobs when they live in apartments? Perhaps they don't have odd jobs to do."

The other blocks of apartments on the opposite side of the road were going up fast. The one opposite Simon's was complete on the outside, and the crane had gone from the top of it. There were painters and decorators inside it now. The next two blocks were about halfway up, and the next two just beginning to grow out of the ground. Simon saw them every day from his window and on his way to school, and each day they were a little higher. Soon they would all be full of people.

He stopped and looked through the gap in the fencing. The site was dry and dusty, and the doors of all the builders' sheds were open in the sunlight. There were workers standing about everywhere, as it was payday and they were just getting off work.

"The sheds?" he thought.

They were fine sheds, wooden and sturdy, much larger than the shed they had had at home. In fact, some of them were almost as large as a small house. "Surely one of them would have enough room inside for a bench for Gramp?" Simon thought. "Surely he wouldn't be in the way there? He might even be useful, mending and making things for the builders and the engineers."

Simon moved inside the fence. He knew you weren't supposed to go in, but no one seemed to notice him. He waited until the workers had gone away, and then he moved over toward one of the sheds.

"Hey, you!" a voice cried out. "What are you up to over there?"

Simon turned around. A man was standing in the doorway of a smaller shed near the gateway.

"Get out of there!" the man shouted. "You've no business here. Beat it!"

"I was just looking," Simon said, as he came nearer the man.

"Well, you just go off and do your looking somewhere else. You're trespassing, you know. I could put the police onto you."

"I suppose it wouldn't be possible for my grandpa to have a bench anywhere here?" Simon said boldly, looking straight at the man.

"A what, did you say?"

"A bench, a workbench, where he could have his tools. Where he could come every day and do a bit of work at the bench."

"What? Here? On a building site?"

The man looked puzzled. Now that he was closer to him, Simon could see that the man was rather like Dad, a little older, perhaps, but not much.

"My grandpa," he went on. "We've come to live in the apartments there." He pointed back the way he had come. "And Grandpa hasn't got a shed for his tools and a bench. And he's . . . he's . . ."

For some reason he couldn't go on. He couldn't understand why tears had come into his eyes, and he hurriedly wiped them away with his sleeve. Perhaps it was because the man in front of him wasn't looking angry anymore, and because he looked rather like Dad. All he could think of was Gramp sitting there in a chair, rubbing his hands up and down the handle of a small hammer, the one he used for tacks and little brass nails.

"I'm looking for a place for him — somewhere near. Where he can put his bench. A new bench. He's got all his tools and nowhere to use them."

"Well," said the man, scratching his head, "I've heard some pretty funny things here, but you're the first to come and ask for a place for a bench."

"It wouldn't take up much space," said Simon. "And he wouldn't be a lot of trouble. He's awfully neat. He just wants somewhere to come every day for a little while. He would be useful too. He's very good with tools. He's teaching me. Or he was."

The man shook his head.

"I know just what you mean, son," he said, "but I can't help you. This is a building site, and it would cost me my job to let your granddad come on the site even, much less use a bench. You can see for yourself that these sheds are all used. The engineers have that one, this one is an office, and the others are all full of supplies. We can't have old gents coming along here to do their carpentry, now, can we?"

"I suppose not."

Simon sounded so miserable that the man put his hand on his shoulder and shook him gently.

"I know what you mean," he said. "The old man doesn't like the apartments, I suppose. They never do, the old ones. I know, but I can't do anything about it. I've got my own worries; and anyhow, all these sheds will be gone soon. You scoot along home now."

He gave Simon a push toward the gap in the fencing.

Simon went home. There was nothing else he could do. When he got there, he closed his eyes and waited for the punishment he expected. However, his mother said nothing but "Tell Grandpa his tea is ready, will you?"

Gramp was sitting in his room, the hammer in his hand.

"Tea is ready, Gramp," Simon said.

The old man didn't even turn his head.

That night Simon dreamed he had found a bench for Gramp, down at the end of the road, in one of the factories there. The dream was so clear that when he woke he could hardly believe that it wasn't true.

Simon tried the factory the next morning. He felt he knew just where Gramp could go and just what they would say. It had all been so real the night before. He walked straight down the road to the far end and then turned in at the factory gate. For the first time, he hesitated, suddenly not so hopeful. The factory looked large and not what Gramp would like at all, but he would have to try. He couldn't go back without even trying.

The gatehouse had two men in it, one of them in a peaked cap. Simon went up to the open window.

"Well, young fellow, what can I do for you this fine morning? Looking for a job, are you?"

It was the man in the cap speaking, and Simon saw him wink across the room.

Simon drew a deep breath. It was not easy to explain. He thought he would try the other way around this time.

"I've come to live in the new apartments," he said.

"Oh, yes, and how do you like that, eh?"

"Oh, it's all right, but it's not that."

"What's not that?"

"It's not that I've come about. It's my grandfather."

"Oh, indeed. And what can I do for your grandfather, may I ask?"

"At our old place, where we used to live on the other side of town, we had a garden and a shed. It was Gramp's shed, really. He used it all the time and had his bench and tools in it. He made all sorts of things and mended things for Mum."

"Here, come and listen to this, Jim. Here's someone with some rigamarole about his granddad."

The other man came over to the open window too, and they both leaned out and looked down at Simon.

"Well, go on, then. Does your granddad want a job, or something?"

"Oh, no," said Simon. "Nothing like that. He just wants somewhere where he could put his bench and tools."

"Is that all?" said the second man. "So you came along here, did you? Aren't you a smart young fellow?"

Simon's hopes began to rise. Perhaps they would find a small space somewhere. Perhaps they understood. Perhaps they even had an old bench that Gramp could use just like that. He went on.

"He wouldn't be a nuisance. He would just come every day for a while to use the bench. He wouldn't be in the way. It's just that he hasn't anything to do when he hasn't got a bench. You can't have workbenches in those apartments."

"You can't indeed," said the man in the peaked cap. "You're dead right there."

"There isn't room, you see."

"Yes, indeed I see," said the man. "And so you came along here to see if we had a bench to spare for your poor old granddad? Is that it?"

"Yes, please."

The man in the cap frowned. "Now, look here, boy," he said. "This is a factory, and a couple of thousand people work here for their living, see? Just think what'd happen if every granddad for miles around came around here asking for a bench. Now, go on, scram!"

Simon had already turned around to go. He felt hot and uncomfortable. He walked slowly back toward the apartments. He did not want to go in. He didn't want Gramp and Mum and Dad to see that he hadn't been able to do anything, either. He thought about going into town to the park, but then he couldn't be bothered. It was too far to walk, and he had no money with him for the fare. He wandered about and then finally pushed his way through the big glass doors into the hall of the building. Neither of the elevators was down, so he stood there waiting. There was no one there at all.

Just as he heard the elevator coming down, a man came in through the main doors and headed for the stairs that led down to the basement, where there was a notice saying

KEEP OUT

Simon knew who the man was. It was Mr. Gideon, who lived on the ground floor around the other side. Mr. Gideon was the caretaker. He sometimes kept some greens for Simon's guinea pigs.

"'Lo, Simon," he said.

"'Lo," said Simon.

"Well, that's a long face to pull on this fine morning. Anything wrong with those guinea pigs of yours?"

"No," said Simon.

"If you wait there a minute, I've got some greens for them," said Mr. Gideon. "Hang on a moment and I'll be back."

He started off down the basement steps. Then he stopped and came back again.

"Like to have a look around?" he said.

"What? Me?" said Simon, in surprise, because he knew Mr. Gideon didn't allow anyone down there, especially boys.

"Yes. Come on, then," said Mr. Gideon. "I'll show you."

Simon followed him down the stone steps. At the bottom there was a heavy metal door that Mr. Gideon opened with a key, and suddenly they were in a different world altogether. This was where the heating of the whole building came from, and Mr. Gideon was in charge of it all.

Mr. Gideon took Simon around and showed him how the heating system worked. Of course it was not all turned on now, as it was summer, but the smaller boiler for water heating was working. Pipes snaked all around, some of them as thick as drainpipes. Others were smaller, disappearing up through the ceiling to the apartments above.

"Looks like a factory, doesn't it?" Mr. Gideon said as Simon bent his head all the way back to look up at the pipes high up on the ceiling.

Simon stared.

Mr. Gideon took a large broom down from a double hook on the wall and began sweeping around the bases of the boilers.

Simon was so quiet that Mr. Gideon noticed.

"What's up with you today? Have you lost your tongue, or something?"

But Simon was still staring. Right in the far corner of the boiler room, up against the wall, quite empty and unused, there was an ordinary wooden workbench.

"What are you staring at?"

Simon slowly lifted one hand and pointed at the bench.

"That bench. Is it yours?"

"Oh, that," said Mr. Gideon. "That's been here all the time. Only use it now and again. It's for repairs, smaller ones. But since everything is new here, I've had nothing much to repair so far."

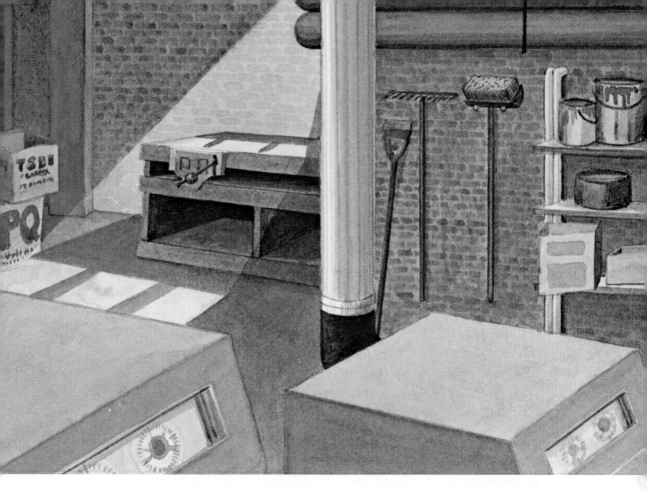

"Do you know my granddad?" said Simon.

"Didn't even know you had one. Here, do you mean? Here in the apartments?"

"Yes," said Simon.

"Well, of course, I wouldn't know which he was, would I? I can't tell one granddad from another, can I? And they're mostly younger here."

"He doesn't like it, and he doesn't go out much now, either. He's lost his workbench and has nothing to do."

"That's bad."

"I've been out today and yesterday," said Simon, "looking for a place for him to have a bench. He used to have one in the garden shed. Now he's got his tools up in the storeroom and nowhere to put them. He couldn't . . . he couldn't . . . ?"

Mr. Gideon turned around and looked at the bench on the other side of the boiler room.

"So that's what it's all about, is it? Thought you were in a bit of a state about something," he said. "Well, no one uses it except me, and I haven't got any tools down here yet. It's an idea. I don't see why not. Bring him down some day, and we'll see what we can do. He'd have to fit in with my times, mind you, because I lock up when I go out of here. Got to keep you young mischiefs out of the place, haven't I?"

"You mean he could? Can I go and get him down now?"

"If you like. No time like the present. I've got about another half hour down here. After that, I'll have gone."

Simon ran as he had never run before. He ran up the basement steps and around to the elevators. As usual, both were up somewhere. He couldn't wait. He began running up the stairs but soon found he was puffing and panting, and his legs felt weak and feeble. He slowed down and struggled on up the stairs, his chest heaving and his face scarlet. But he got there in the end and in his excitement could hardly get his key into the lock.

No one was home except Gramp.

Simon rushed into Gramp's room, trying to calm down a little.

"You've been running up the stairs, or something," said Gramp, looking up as Simon appeared so suddenly.

Simon nodded.

"What's all the hurry today?"

"I . . . I . . . I . . ."

"Come on, then, out with it. What's the excitement?"

"I've found a bench for you."

"What did you say?"

"I've found a bench and a place for your tools. I think."

"What d'you mean, a bench? And what d'you mean, you think?"

"Well, you may not like it."

"A bench?"

"Yes."

"A workbench?"

"Yes."

"Where?"

"Come with me. I'll show you."

"Are you pulling my leg?"

"Gramp!"

"Oh, all right, then. What, now?"

"Yes."

"Where?"

"Only downstairs."

"Downstairs?"

"Yes."

"Well, I suppose I'd better come and see what tricks you've been up to."

It took a long time, a very long time, to get Gramp down to the basement, and Simon was afraid Mr. Gideon would have gone. Gramp had got out of the habit of going anywhere. But they did get there. Mr. Gideon was still there. They talked. They looked at the workbench. They talked again.

"I could make a rack to go on the wall there," said Gramp.

"Yes," said Simon.

"Perhaps I could do a job or two for you, Mr. Gideon?" said Gramp.

"Perhaps you could," said Mr. Gideon. "There're odd things that need doing all the time."

"I could get my tools down from the roof storeroom, couldn't I?" said Gramp.

"I could help you sharpen them," said Simon.

"You'll not touch a single one until I say so," said Gramp.

They looked at each other. They grinned. That was more like Gramp.

So it was arranged.

It took a long time. Gramp's tools had to be unpacked, and that meant waiting for Dad to get back. Then Gramp had to make a rack for them, and that took a lot of mornings down there in the basement. Then he had to clean and sharpen all his tools and put them in the new rack. Then it was ready.

Each day Gramp seemed a little younger, a little quicker. Each day he moved a little more quickly. Each day he went down to the basement in the same building, and each day he got his tools down and made something, mended something, or put something in order.

Each day he told them what he had done.

"I found Gramp a shed in the end, didn't I, Mum?" said Simon, one night, long afterward.

"You certainly did," she said.

"You certainly did," said Dad. "Some shed too."

"You certainly did," said Gramp. "Biggest shed in the whole wide world, I'd say."

His old blue eyes were bright.

Author

Joan Tate, who was educated in England and in Sweden, is a British translator and the author of more than a hundred books for children and young adults. She says, "I write all the time and read when I'm not writing." The author and her family live in England, where *Gramp* was first published as a separate book. In the United States it appeared as *Luke's Garden and Gramp* and was chosen a Notable Children's Trade Book in the Field of Social Studies.

Comprehension Questions

1. What was Gramp's problem? Why was it a problem for Simon too?
2. What did Simon decide to do to solve the problem?
3. Did Simon accept his mother's explanation of Gramp's behavior? Why or why not?
4. To what places did Simon go to look for a bench?
5. What did Gramp mean when he said that Simon had found him the "biggest shed in the whole wide world"?

Vocabulary

Below are some words that are names for woodworking tools and some that are not. List the words that *are* woodworking tools. Use the dictionary to look up any word you are not sure of. (Caution: Some of these words may have more than one meaning.) After each word you list, tell what that tool is used for. Again, use the dictionary if you need help.

plane	round	chisel	pile driver
saw	vise	fire drill	pliers
beater	screwdriver	file	chives

Writing a Letter

Pretend you are Gramp. Write a thank-you letter to Simon. Explain to him *why* you appreciate the "shed" he found for you.

The Crow and the Pitcher

a fable by Aesop

A thirsty crow found a pitcher with some water in it. The water was at the bottom of the pitcher, though, and try as she might, she could not reach it with her beak. At last she hit upon a clever plan. She began dropping pebbles into the pitcher, and with each pebble, the water rose a little higher. Finally the water reached the brim of the pitcher, and the wise bird was able to drink all she wanted.

Where there is a will there is a way.

Challenging the Sea

The sea can be as dangerous as it is beautiful. Yet, for centuries, people have made their living at sea — as sailors, fishers, traders, and explorers.

Sea-Fever

by John Masefield

I must go down to the seas again, to the lonely sea and the sky,
And all I ask is a tall ship and a star to steer her by,
And the wheel's kick and the wind's song and the white sail's shaking,
And a grey mist on the sea's face and a grey dawn breaking.

I must go down to the seas again, for the call of the running tide
Is a wild call and a clear call that may not be denied;
And all I ask is a windy day and the white clouds flying,
And the flung spray and the blown spume and the sea gulls crying.

Special Words

Many jobs and hobbies have special words that describe activities, tools, or equipment. These words are almost like a secret language, spoken and understood only by certain people. Look at the dictionary at the bottom of the page. What kind of people might know the words in that dictionary?

The words in the dictionary would be known by people who work aboard a ship or who enjoy sailing as a sport.

See if you can speak the language of the sea. Read the story on the next page. Then number your paper from 1 to 7. Match the boldface words in the story to the numbered parts in the picture.

Something Extra

Use the words in the sea dictionary to write a make-believe ship's log entry, such as the one the cabin boy wrote.

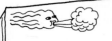

anchor A heavy object attached to a ship by a cable, cast overboard to keep a ship in place.

ballast Material placed below the deck of a ship to make it stable or steady.

bow The front of a ship or a boat.

cabin boy A boy who works as a servant on a ship.

galley The kitchen on a ship.

lifeboat A boat carried aboard a ship, used if the ship has to be abandoned.

mainmast The most important mast on a ship.

mainstay A strong rope that supports the mainmast.

mast A pole that holds up the sail on a ship.

port The left-hand side of a ship as you face forward; opposite of **starboard.**

"Ship's Log, July 9," wrote the cabin boy.

"Today a big storm came up. I was sure it would snap our **mainmast** in two. Luckily, the strong **mainstay** held tight. We were tossed all around on the rough sea, unable to hold the ship steady. We even had Cooky go below to the **galley** and prepare rice pudding to use for **ballast**. That's how desperate we were! Puff, our ship's cat, hid in the **lifeboat**. She wanted to be the first to abandon ship!

"Finally the storm passed over. The first mate and I were just lowering the **anchor** when I spotted a sea serpent off the port side! It must have smelled the rice pudding below deck! Fortunately it turned out that the fierce-looking monster was really a coward. It was frightened away by the figurehead on our **bow**."

The cabin boy jumped when the captain walked up and said, "Here you are! Dreaming again, I see!"

Shackleton's Epic Voyage

by Michael Brown

Captain Ernest Shackleton's ship had sunk beneath the Antarctic ice. How could he find help in time to save the lives of his crew?

"Stand by to abandon ship!"

The command rang out over the Antarctic seas, and it meant the end of all Ernest Shackleton's plans. He was the leader of an expedition that had set out to cross the unknown continent of Antarctica. It was a journey no one before him had ever attempted.

For months his ship, the *Endurance,* had been trapped in ice. It drifted helplessly in the Weddell Sea, over four hundred miles east of the Antarctic mainland and twelve hundred miles south of the southernmost tip of South America. The pressure on the hull of the *Endurance* was extreme, and the ship's timbers groaned under the strain.

Now Shackleton's first goal was to lead his men to safety. They would try to cross the polar sea on foot and head for the nearest tiny island, 250 miles to the west.

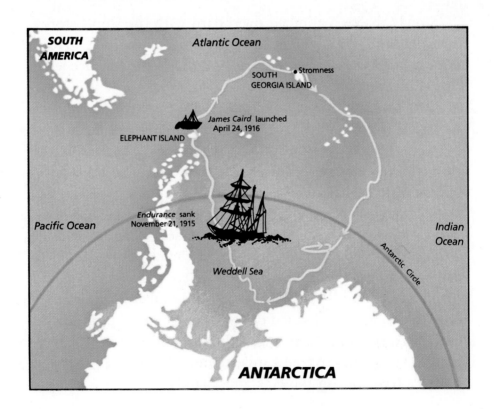

Slowly the men climbed overboard with the ship's stores. Shackleton, a gaunt, bearded figure, gave the order, "Hoist out the boats!" There were three, and they would be needed if the ice thawed.

Two days later, on October 30, 1915, the *Endurance* broke up and sank beneath the ice. In the bitter cold, the chances of survival seemed small; but spurred on by Shackleton the twenty-seven men set off, dragging their stores and the ship's boats on sledges across the uneven ice.

For five months the crew of the *Endurance* pushed their way slowly northwest across the frozen seas. Sometimes they dragged the sledges painfully behind them. Sometimes they drifted on large ice floes that slowly split into smaller and smaller pieces until they had to be abandoned. At times they took to the boats and sailed or rowed through melting ice. At last, in April 1916, they reached Elephant Island — a tiny, barren, rocky outcrop 540 miles from the nearest inhabited land, Port Stanley in the Falkland Islands.

By now the situation was grim. Food and other supplies were low. Still worse, five months of constant cold and hardship had weakened all of the men. They were in poor condition to face the coming winter.

Seeing this, Shackleton knew that he and his crew could not last much longer. He decided on a desperate attempt to find help before winter set in. He turned to the men. "We will make our camp here. Six of us will take the *James Caird* and try to reach Stromness. It's our only chance." Stromness was a whaling base on the island of South Georgia, eight hundred miles northeast of Elephant Island. To reach it they would have to cross some of the stormiest seas in the world.

The *James Caird* was the biggest of the ship's boats. Even so, it looked pitifully small to face the great gray seas of the southern ocean. Shackleton had the keel strengthened and added makeshift decking to give more shelter.

By April 24 all was ready, and the *James Caird* was launched from the beach. Some of the crew were soaked to the

skin as they worked. This could be deadly in the bitter cold and wind, so they changed clothes with those who were to stay behind. Shackleton shook hands with the men he was leaving, and then, amidst cheers, the *James Caird* set sail.

The little knot of men left behind was dwarfed by the high peaks of Elephant Island and was soon lost from sight.

The *James Caird* was alone on the vast heaving seas. With one arm gripping the mast, Shackleton guided the boat through the ice floes that threatened to hole the sides. At last they were in clear water, and with a fair wind they set their course for South Georgia.

Now began a fierce ordeal for the crew of the *James Caird*. The boat was small and crowded. It was almost impossible for the men to find space among the stores and the rocks carried for ballast. All cooking had to be done over a single stove that needed three men to handle it. One held a lamp; the other two lifted the cooking pot off whenever the violent pitching of the boat threatened to upset it. A fine spray of water constantly soaked its way through the flimsy decking.

There were storms and seas so big that the boat sometimes seemed surrounded by mountains of water. The waves towering above cut off the wind, so that the sails flapped uselessly.

Four days passed. A gale sprang up that threatened to swamp the *James Caird* and hurl its crew into the icy seas. "Lower the sails," shouted Shackleton, above the roar of the wind. "We'll heave to under bare poles and lie to the sea anchor." The sea anchor was a triangular canvas bag at the end of a long line, which held the bow of the boat into the wind. If the seas hit them sideways on, they would capsize.

No man aboard had faced such waves before. Sometimes they could see a great tunnel formed as the crest of a towering wave hung toppling over its base, then broke. Time after time it seemed they would be overwhelmed, but they survived.

The spray shot at them like burning arrows. It froze thick on the decks and the bare masts and would soon make the boat top-heavy. Shackleton saw the danger. "We must get the ice off, or we'll capsize," he warned.

Some of the men struggled onto the heaving deck and chipped ice away with axes to free the boat of the deadly weight. Others hurled things overboard — spare oars and sleeping bags — anything they could do without that would lighten the load.

At last on the morning of the seventh day, the wind dropped. The sea calmed, the skies cleared, and for the first time the sun shone. Thankfully, the men dragged out sleeping bags and sodden clothes and hung them in the rigging to dry. Cape pigeons flew overhead, and porpoises played in the sea alongside. Shackleton and his men lay on deck soaking up the warmth. Hope surged in them; life was not so miserable after all.

For three days they sailed steadily on, and then a gale hit them like a blast from a great gun. Sun, pigeons, and porpoises disappeared. Snow squalls and huge waves hid everything from sight. At midnight, Shackleton was at the helm when he thought he saw a break in the sky. "Is the weather clearing?" he wondered. Then, to his horror, he realized that he was looking at the foam-capped top of the most gigantic wave he had ever seen!

"Hold on! It's got us!" he shouted from the helm. The breaking wave seized the boat and flung it forward, out of control, with the sea surging and foaming around it. Water poured in. "Bail for your lives!" cried Shackleton.

The men bailed frantically. At last they had flung enough water over the side to be safe, but conditions aboard were now much worse. Everything was drenched; there was not a dry place in the boat. For three hours they struggled to light the

stove and boil up some milk to warm themselves against the biting cold.

The next day the weather was better, but now there was a new danger. The water supply was running out. Unless the *James Caird* reached South Georgia soon, its crew would die of thirst.

Shackleton and his men were weary and downhearted. Tortured by thirst, they sailed listlessly on, believing that the end was near, yet hoping to sight land. Then on the morning of the fourteenth day, they saw two shags perched on a mass of seaweed. These birds never flew far from shore. Surely land was near.

At noon, through a break in the clouds, Shackleton glimpsed the dark cliffs of South Georgia. It was a glad moment.

He steered the boat inshore, looking for a landing place, but everywhere rocky reefs or sheer cliffs barred the way. Night was closing in, and there was no hope of getting ashore until the next morning. It was a bitter disappointment to spend another night at sea.

That same night another storm blew up. As hours passed, it swelled in strength until the wind was hurricane force. Nothing could be seen through the driving spray. The *James Caird,* tough as it was, strained to the utmost, so that its seams cracked open and water poured in. To add to this nightmare, the wind swung round and drove the boat slowly backwards, towards the dangerous coast they had seen the day before.

When all seemed lost, the wind dropped and shifted to blow them offshore. They were saved from the reefs! However, there was still the torment of thirst. Shackleton knew they must land soon and find water.

After one more night at sea, the boat neared the shore again. They could see a wide bay. The wind was rising, and Shackleton decided he must run for that bay and take his chance. But as the *James Caird* neared the entrance, the crew saw that the way was blocked once more by a line of rocks like broken teeth. The sea thundered over them, sending up fountains of white spume.

The men braced themselves. They were sure that the *James Caird* would be dashed against the rocks.

Suddenly Shackleton shouted to the helmsman. He had seen a narrow gap. The next wave carried them forward and through this opening, so narrow that they could almost touch the rocks on either side. Then, at last, they were safe in calm

water. In the gathering darkness they beached the boat, and Shackleton leaped ashore. At his feet ran a stream of fresh water, and in a minute he and his crew were on their knees slaking their thirst. The worst was over.

Now Shackleton and his men began to explore the cove where they had landed. They found a small cave in which they lit a fire, and for the first time in two weeks, they spent a night ashore. However, a long and dangerous journey was still ahead.

The whaling station at Stromness lay beyond high mountains, which had never yet been crossed. Shackleton set off with the two strongest members of his party, leaving the others with enough food for a few days.

The mountains rose four thousand feet, and the three men were often forced to turn back. They had no tent and kept going through the night, resting now and then, but not for long. They were exhausted but knew that if they stopped they would freeze to death.

Early the next morning they heard a strange sound. It was shrill and high pitched, eerie, spine tingling.

It did not, however, signal their death. It was only a steam whistle calling the people of the Stromness whaling station to work.

Shackleton and his men topped a final ridge. Below them were huts and distant figures.

In astonished silence, the workers watched as Shackleton and his men staggered towards them, like creatures from some earlier savage time. Two little boys took one look and ran, terrified by the sight of the ravaged, bearded faces and tattered clothes.

The epic journey was over. Rescue of the entire crew was now certain. By his courage, Captain Shackleton had led his men through the perils of ice, thirst, wind, and storm. They had challenged the sea and won.

Author

Ever since his childhood, which he spent near the ocean in England, Michael Brown has loved the sea and sailing. The basis for his book *Shackleton's Epic Voyage,* which you have just read, was Ernest Shackleton's own short account of his adventure. Mr. Brown retold it and expanded it into a book.

Comprehension Questions

1. How did Shackleton save the lives of his crew?
2. Describe some of the hardships faced by the crew of the *James Caird*.
3. What kind of leader was Shackleton? Give examples from the story to support your answer.
4. Why were the little boys frightened at the sight of Shackleton and his crew?

Vocabulary

Read the following sentences:
"They saw two **shags** perched on a mass of seaweed. These birds never flew far from shore."
What are *shags*? How do you know?
Often you can get the meaning of an unfamiliar word from clues right in the story. Find each of the following words in "Shackleton's Epic Voyage." For each word, write down the clues to its meaning that are given in the story. Then write a sentence of your own for the word.

expedition (page 171)   **sea anchor** (page 175)
bare poles (page 175)   **strain** (page 171)

Writing a News Story

Pretend you are a TV news reporter assigned to cover Shackleton's "epic voyage." Write a brief TV news story.

In Winter

by Robert Wallace

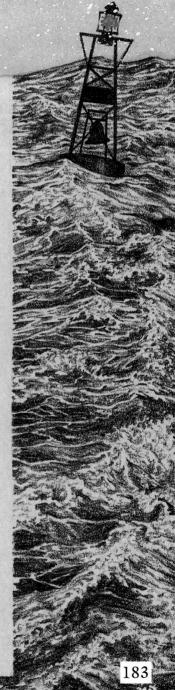

It is hard, inland,
    in winter,
when the fields are motionless in snow,

to remember waves, to remember
    the wide, sloshing
immensity

of the Atlantic, continuous,
    green in the cold, taking snow
or rain into itself,

to realize the endurance
    of the tilting bell buoy
(hour by hour, years

through) that clangs, clangs,
    leaning
with the rocking waters, miles

from land; even in storm and
    night-howling
snow, wet, red, flashing

to mark the channel. Some
    things
are, even if no one comes.

Antarctica

Surrounding the South Pole is the continent of Antarctica, the coldest place on Earth. Even in summer, which occurs in December, January, and February, the average temperature is below freezing. However, in summer there are long periods of daylight. The photo above, left, was taken in December at 10:00 P.M.

Antarctica is covered with a solid ice cap that in some places is a mile thick. Huge sheets of ice called glaciers (above, right, top) creep slowly down the mountains to the sea. When chunks of ice break off from glaciers, they form icebergs, such as the one shown drifting in Hope Bay (above, right, bottom).

The Transantarctic Mountains (left) divide the continent in two. Some of these mountains rise over fourteen thousand feet; some are completely buried in the ice cap. There is almost no life in the interior of the continent. In the surrounding waters and along the coasts, however, are fish, birds, whales, and six kinds of seals.

The leopard seal (above, top) has strong jaws and sharp teeth. It sometimes preys on penguins and other seals. A more peaceful creature is the Weddell seal (above, bottom, left). The most common Antarctic seal is the crabeater (above, bottom, right). It does not eat crabs at all, but small sea animals called krill.

The birds that make Antarctica their home depend on the sea for food. Even those that fly, such as the blue-eyed shags (above, top) and the southern giant fulmar (above, bottom), rarely venture far inland.

The most familiar Antarctic birds are penguins, which don't fly at all. A colony of king penguins (center) on South Georgia Island give a friendly greeting to a visitor. Although only ten days old, these chinstrap penguin chicks (far right, top) are eager for food. A thick layer of fat protects penguins' bodies from the harsh Antarctic climate. These gentoo penguins (far right, bottom) are weathering a fierce storm quite comfortably.

189

Ernest Shackleton and other explorers of his day sought to cross the Antarctic continent and to reach the South Pole. The Antarctic explorers of today are scientists. They staff about forty research bases, such as the Amundsen-Scott South Pole Station (above) located at the geographic South Pole. The twelve flags represent twelve nations, including the United States, that have signed a treaty to protect Antarctica.

Supplies are brought to the coast of Antarctica in ships called icebreakers. From there they are brought by plane to the research stations. Ski-equipped planes, like the one in the picture above, stop only long enough for

supplies to be quickly unloaded. Pilots do not turn off the engines, since they might not start again in the cold air and thin atmosphere.

Antarctica is a good place for scientists to study, because it is "unspoiled" by the effects of civilization. Until fairly recent times, no people had ever lived there. Scientific research is carried on above and below the surface of Antarctica, as well as on it. Above, right, top: a weather balloon is launched at the South Pole Station. Above, right, bottom: a diver is lowered through the ice of McMurdo Sound to collect samples of tiny plants that live on the underside of the ice.

Stormalong Goes to Sea

by Anne Malcolmson and Dell J. McCormick

Thirteen-year-old Alfred Bulltop Stormalong wanted more than anything else to be the cabin boy aboard the *Silver Maid*. How could he convince the captain to give him the job?

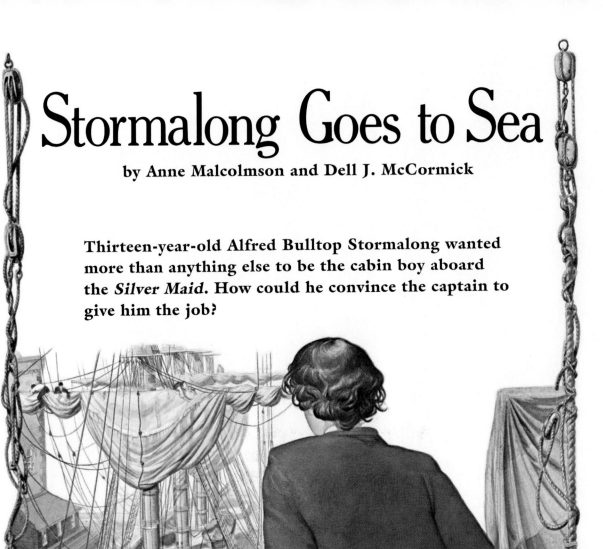

Captain Snard looked up at the flag that told the whole of Boston Harbor that his ship, the *Silver Maid,* was ready to leave for China. The hold was filled with hides, beaver skins, and good English coal. But everything was going wrong! The cabin boy was at home, sick with measles. The rigging lines were hopelessly tangled. The anchor was stuck. Captain Snard paced the deck, fidgeting and looking at his watch.

His men tiptoed about their duties and whispered among themselves. They knew enough not to cross the captain when he was in a temper. But they, too, knew that it was time to leave. The tide was running out. Still, the mate had not returned from town with a new cabin boy. The lads in the rigging were getting nowhere. And, try as they might, the hands straining at the capstan could not budge the anchor chain.

Suddenly from the dock the mate's voice was heard as he ran to the ship. "Captain! Captain Snard!"

The captain leaned over the rail. "Have you got a cabin boy?" he shouted.

"No!" hollered the mate. "There's not an experienced cabin boy to be had in Boston, sir."

"Then come aboard," roared the captain. "From here to Canton, *you'll* be my cabin boy!"

Neither the mate nor the captain had noticed a group of schoolboys sitting on the piles of the wharf beside the ship. Every Sunday the lads gathered on the docks to watch the ships sail and to dream of the time when they, too, would be sailing. Among them was a youngster who had heard the mate's call and the captain's answer. This was his long-awaited chance! He had always wanted to go to sea. The *Silver Maid* needed a cabin boy! With a light leap the boy cleared the wharf and landed on the starboard deck, right under the captain's nose.

The vessel gave a lurch. Its topmast crosstrees brushed the roof of the warehouse on the pier. The *Silver Maid* listed dangerously to starboard.

"What is the meaning of this?" bellowed the captain, who had had enough to irritate him already.

"Excuse me, sir," said the schoolboy. "I hear you need a cabin boy."

The captain clung to the wheel to keep from slipping into the arms of the youngster who had jumped aboard. The youngster was large for his age. He stood about thirty feet tall and looked as if he weighed several tons. No wonder the *Silver Maid* was listing!

"If you don't shift your weight more to the port side, I'll need a salvage crew more than a cabin boy!" roared Captain Snard.

Stormy, the little fellow who was causing the trouble, blushed with embarrassment. "I'm sorry, sir," he stammered, and carefully placed one foot beside the port rail. The ship creaked and righted itself.

"Well!" said the captain, wiping his brow and looking up at the lad. "What makes you think you can be a cabin boy?"

Tears came to the young boy's eyes. "The sea is in my blood, sir," he said simply. "All my life I've wanted to join the China trade."

"And how long is that?" The captain meant to snap out his question, but the words came weakly.

"Thirteen years, sir," answered the little fellow politely.

"You're large for thirteen years," said the captain, relaxing a bit. "Have you had any experience?"

"Oh, some, sir," Stormy replied, and began to tell his story. The words tumbled out of his mouth as he spoke.

Alfred Bulltop Stormalong, aged thirteen, was born in Kennebunkport, Maine, of a long line of seafarers. His mother's great-great-great-great-great-great-great-great-great-

great-great-grandfather was the naval architect who designed Noah's Ark. One of his ancestors, Leif Ericson, the Viking, is said to have discovered America long before Columbus. And, incidentally, Columbus was related to the family through a cousin on his mother's side. Stormy's own father had been the first Yankee skipper.

Stormy really did have the sea in his blood. His veins and arteries were filled with salt water, which shone out in the bright sea blue of his eyes. He had cut his teeth on whalebone, and in the days when he was too young to walk, he had been cradled in a dory. On one occasion he gave his mother fits when he tied his diaper to his teething rattle, used it for a trysail, and headed out to sea while she was preparing his evening bottle. At the age of five he could handle any sailing vessel in Kennebunkport.

It was not until he started school, however, that he truly learned to love the sea. Because of a shortage of primers, the teacher taught him to read from Bowditch's *Practical Navigator*. That set the course for his whole life. Kennebunkport was a small town, and there were very few boys of his own age to play with. Stormy soon fell into the habit of swimming down to Gloucester or Provincetown, or sometimes Nantucket, after school to play. His mother knew he was perfectly safe and could handle himself in any sort of squall. Her only objection was that the long swim gave him an even larger appetite.

She did become angry, however, the fourth time he tried to stow away on a whaler at the age of eleven. Fortunately, from her point of view, Stormy was so large for his age (he had already reached a height of twenty-one feet) that he could not hide himself successfully in a lifeboat. He was discovered before the whaler put to sea. As she told her friends later, she was cross because she worried that her son might be mistaken for a whale and cut up for oil.

When the family moved to Boston, his mother knew that Stormy's days at home were numbered. She gave him her blessing, along with a note explaining that her son, Alfred Bulltop Stormalong, had her permission to join the crew of any vessel that would give him a berth.

Before Stormy had finished his tale, the captain had taken the boy to his heart. He knew, however, that he could not take on a new hand for whimsical reasons. The crew had gathered in a circle to hear the amazing tale of the young stranger. Therefore, Captain Snard felt forced to test the boy.

"Your background is fitting for a life on the sea, my lad," he said. "But I'll have to test your seamanship."

Stormy's eyes shone at the chance to prove himself. The captain stroked his chin for a moment. Then he held up a length of line for the little giant. "Show me what you can do with a piece of rope," he said.

Stormy took the line between his fingertips. He rubbed his thumb and ring finger together. Without further ado he held out his handiwork for the captain to see. In the ten-foot length of rope, Stormy had tied three perfect knots.

"This is all very fine," agreed the captain, trying not to show how pleased he was with the boy. "However, you look to me as though you might be pretty clumsy. Do you think you can climb the rigging?"

"Aye, aye, sir!" Stormy was out of his jacket and halfway up the mainmast before the captain could close his mouth. Up, up, up he went, hand over hand, until he was perched dangerously on the topmast crosstrees. His curly black hair, blown by the wind, fluttered out like a shiny dark flag. "Captain. Oh, captain, sir," he called down from his perch in the sky. "It looks to me as though the lines are tangled. If it's all right with you, sir, I'll straighten them out."

Captain Snard shouted, "Be smart about it, son! And see that you don't make things worse!"

"Aye, aye, sir!" came the reply. From the deck the captain and his crew could see the little fellow reaching out to right and left, deftly unwinding the ropes that formed a spider web around him. One by one the lines fell into their proper places. Flushed with excitement, Stormy forgot himself. One last tangle remained. Without thinking, he hitched himself along the yard in order to get a better hold on the line. Oooooops! Slowly, as his weight shifted, the *Silver Maid* heeled over to port. The members of the crew skidded down the deck to the port rail. The captain grabbed the binnacle to keep from falling.

"Ahoy there! None of your tricks! Come down before you ruin the ship," shouted the captain.

Stormy caught himself just in time. He scrambled back to the mainmast. The ship righted itself. "Phew!" said Stormy to himself. "That was a close one!" Then he grabbed a mainstay and slid to the deck like a firefighter down a brass pole.

Unfortunately, just as he started down, Porky, the cook, came out of the galley carrying a kettle of hot shark soup to cool on deck. As luck would have it, Porky and his chowder reached the exact spot at which Stormy landed at exactly the same moment. Cook, kettle, and Stormy disappeared behind a great splash of soup. The hot, greasy liquid splattered the ship in all directions and ran over the decks and down the hatches. The crew, who had spent the morning polishing the deck and the brasses, roared in dismay. Porky was speechless with surprise and anger. Only Captain Snard, who was protected from the splash by the large wooden circle of the wheel, thought it was funny.

"That was a hot one!" he said. Then, seeing the wittiness of his own pun, he slapped his knee and felt very pleased with himself.

Stormy, of course, expected to be ordered off the ship. The captain, however, looked at him with indulgent affection as

the lad apologized. "What we need aboard this ship," he thought to himself, "is a little liveliness."

The captain would have hired Stormy then and there. The crew, however, were still angry about the soup. One further test was necessary to make them accept a new hand. Sailors need knowledge and agility, but they also need strength. It was obvious, looking at the boy, that he had strength; but it was difficult to know what kind of test would satisfy the crew. The only thing the captain could think of was the stuck anchor. He had no hope that Stormalong could raise it, but the lad might be able to budge the chain. That at least was worth trying.

"Man the winches, lad," the captain cried to Stormy.

"Aye, aye, sir!" Stormy answered to the captain's order. The captain watched as the boy pushed and strained against the capstan bar. Slowly, slowly, the heavy iron chain moved a little. There was a rumble as the anchor budged in its bed. Inch by inch, the chain clanked up around the capstan. Little by little, the stone that held the anchor gave way. Without warning, the resistance disappeared. Stormy, with one hand, turned the capstan. The anchor chain coiled up as though it had been woven of daisies.

A cheer went up from the crew. The men ran to the foredeck to watch the little giant wind the capstan. Without thinking, they burst into an old chantey:

A Yankee ship comes down the river,
Blow, boys, blow!
A Yankee ship and a Yankee skipper,
Blow, my bully boys, blow!
And how do you know it's a Yankee clipper?
Blow, boys, blow!
Because the mast and yards shine like silver,
Blow, my bully boys, blow!

The *Silver Maid* strained and snapped its painters as the anchor lifted. Suddenly it was drifting out to sea with the tide.

"Unfurl the main course!" shouted the bosun.

"Haul down the flag," shouted the captain. "We're off to Canton!" The men cheered as they raced to their posts. The *Silver Maid* put out to sea.

It was too late now for the captain to dismiss the new cabin boy. He ordered the mate to bring out the ship's ledger and told Stormy to write down his name. Stormy, boy that he was, felt very grown-up. He had got the job he wanted and was finally a member of a ship's crew. So he wrote himself down in the most grown-up way he could think of: Stormalong, A.B.!

Captain Snard took one look at the signature. "Stormalong, A.B.," he said. "There's an able-bodied seaman for you."

That is how Stormy got his first berth in the China trade. Ever since that day, sailors in the merchant marine have written themselves down as able-bodied seaman with the initials *A.B.*

Authors

Anne Malcolmson and Dell J. McCormick together wrote the book *Mister Stormalong,* from which this story was taken. Anne Malcolmson was a teacher for many years. She says that she wrote most of her books so that she would have stories to read to her classes. Dell McCormick once worked in a sawmill in Idaho, where he heard the tall tales he wrote down as stories.

Comprehension Questions

1. What did Stormalong do to convince Captain Snard to give him the job of cabin boy on the *Silver Maid?*
2. How did Stormalong's size help him get the job?
3. What did the authors mean when they said Stormalong had "the sea in his blood"?
4. Why do sailors write the initials *A.B.* after their names?

Vocabulary

Make up a Concentration game with the terms listed below and their definitions. Write each word on a 3" X 5" card. Then write the definition for each word on another card. Turn the cards face down on a table, in rows. Turn over two cards at a time. If you turn over a word and its definition, you get to keep the cards. If they do not match, put them back, face down. The player who has the most matching cards at the end of the game wins.

rigging	**port side**	**painters**	**binnacle**
starboard	**yard**	**foredeck**	**listed**

Writing a Report

Choose one of the following topics to look up in an encyclopedia. Write a report based on your findings.

Alfred Bulltop Stormalong	clipper ship
China trade in the 1800's	Boston Harbor
Yankee	able-bodied seaman

Reading Strategies

Expository and Narrative Writing

All authors have a reason in mind when they write. They may want mostly to give their readers facts, or they may want mostly to tell stories. You can improve your reading by paying attention to the different ways in which authors write.

Expository writing gives readers facts. The author presents a main idea and gives details to support it. You can find this kind of writing in textbooks, magazines, and newspapers.

In **narrative writing** the author tells a story by presenting characters and telling you about their thoughts, words, and actions. You can find this kind of writing in novels and short stories.

If you pay attention to whether the author is mostly giving facts or mostly telling a story, you will know what kind of writing it is — expository or narrative. Knowing the kind of writing will also let you know the kinds of reading skills that you are going to need to use as you read.

Seeing the Differences in Writing

The kind of writing being used affects both your reason for reading and the way you read. Your most important reason for reading an article is to learn the facts the author is telling you. Your most important reason for reading a story is to enjoy the story and to learn something about life from the things that happen to the people in the story. The way authors give facts is very different from the way they write stories. You need to notice and understand those differences in order to read well.

Read the following two paragraphs about the praying mantis. Is the author mostly telling a story or mostly giving facts? As you read, think about these two questions:

- *What* does the author tell you about the praying mantis?
- *How* does the author tell you about the praying mantis?

The Praying Mantis

The praying mantis is an insect that has many humanlike characteristics. It can stand up. It has an alert look in its large, bulging eyes. It can move its head freely. These are just a few of its humanlike characteristics. Many scientists think that the ancient Greeks gave the insect the name *mantis*, which comes from the Greek word "prophet," because of these characteristics.

The praying mantis eats its food live. Its quick front legs have sharp spines, which are used to catch its prey from leaves, flowers, tree bark, twigs, or the ground. The praying mantis never catches its food in flight.

A Chinese praying mantis.

What does the author tell you about the praying mantis? In "The Praying Mantis," there are no characters, conversations, or events as there are in a story. Instead, you learn something about the praying mantis. In expository writing, the writer gives facts about a subject.

How does the author tell you about the praying mantis? In the first paragraph of "The Praying Mantis," you can pick out the main idea in the first sentence: *The praying mantis has many humanlike characteristics.* The remaining sentences in the paragraph give supporting details about the main idea.

When you read to learn from expository writing, you use a reading skill that you already know: looking for the main idea and picking out the supporting details. Knowing the author's reason for writing and for arranging facts makes it easier for you to understand what you read.

Now read the following three paragraphs taken from a story that you have read, "Stormalong Goes to Sea." Ask yourself if the authors are telling a story or giving facts. As you read these paragraphs, think about these two questions:

- *What* do the authors tell you about Stormalong?
- *How* do the authors tell you about Stormalong?

Stormalong Goes to Sea

Stormy, the little fellow who was causing the trouble, blushed with embarrassment. "I'm sorry, sir," he stammered, and carefully placed one foot beside the port rail. The ship creaked and righted itself.

"Well!" said the captain, wiping his brow and looking up at the lad. "What makes you think you can be a cabin boy?"

Tears came to the young boy's eyes. "The sea is in my blood, sir," he said simply. "All my life I've wanted to join the China trade."

What do the authors tell you about Stormalong? In these three paragraphs, the authors are telling a story. They show Stormalong trying to make the captain of the ship believe that he would be a good cabin boy.

You can tell that this is narrative writing because you find out what happens in the story from what the authors tell you about the characters and from what the characters do, think, and say. From what the authors tell you about Stormalong and from what he says himself, you discover that he wants to be a cabin boy and why.

How do the authors tell you about Stormalong? They have written the story in the order in which things happened. This is how narrative writing is often arranged. When you read narrative writing, you follow the actions, the characters' words, and the characters' thoughts as they happen.

Now go back and read again "The Praying Mantis" and the paragraphs from "Stormalong Goes to Sea." Compare them again. To help you understand the differences between the two kinds of writing, read the following points:

- "The Praying Mantis" gives facts. "Stormalong Goes to Sea" tells a story.
- "The Praying Mantis" does not have characters, conversations, and events. "Stormalong Goes to Sea" does.
- In "The Praying Mantis," the sentences give details about the main idea. In "Stormalong Goes to Sea," the sentences are in the order in which the action happens.

Expository and Narrative Writing Used Together

Sometimes authors give you facts *and* tell a story. When they do this, they use both expository writing and narrative writing. In the three paragraphs from "Conquering the Congo" that follow, see if you can find both kinds of writing.

Conquering the Congo

The Congo River winds like a black snake through Africa. The waters are dark and mysterious. The plant life is so thick and green that it seems to invite the mighty river out of its banks.

There are quiet pools and raging rapids. The animal and human life around the river depend on the river for their lives. However, in this sleeping giant, death lies side by side with life.

I thought of all this as I steered the small raft from side to side in the river. I had to go around many stumps and vines that guarded my way.

In the first two paragraphs of "Conquering the Congo," the author gives you facts about the Congo River. The author uses two paragraphs to describe the river and the land around it. This description sets the scene for the story, which begins in the third paragraph.

The author of "Conquering the Congo" has presented facts and also started to tell a story. When you read this writing, you learn facts about the Congo as well as what the person telling the story thinks and does.

Reading and Comparing Expository and Narrative Passages

Now that you have learned why and how authors write differently, use your reading skills as you read the following two passages. Be ready to talk about these questions:

- Which kind of writing has each author used?
- How are each author's ideas arranged — to give you facts or to tell you a story?

Passage 1

Mark was visiting his aunt Sara and uncle Bill, who lived in a high-rise apartment building in New York City. It was his first visit to New York and the first time he had ever been on the thirty-fifth floor of a house. "Look at that!" he shouted as he looked from the window in his room. "I can see for a million miles! The people look like ants!" This was going to be an exciting adventure for Mark!

Passage 2

The way the land looks today is a result of glaciers. Glaciers are great sheets of ice that moved across the country thousands of years ago.

When glaciers stopped and began to melt, they left huge deposits of soil that had been scraped from places far to the north. The rich soil in the Great Plains and Mississippi Valley most likely came from Canada. The fossils found in these places are from animals that lived hundreds of miles away.

Skill Summary

- Authors have different reasons for writing: to give facts or to tell a story.
- Expository writing mostly gives facts. To read this kind of writing, look for the main idea and supporting details.
- Narrative writing mostly tells a story. To read this kind of writing, read the events and the characters' actions, words, and thoughts in the order in which they happen.
- Sometimes authors use both narrative and expository writing in the same piece.

Pearson, A Harbor Seal Pup

by Susan Meyers

Ordinarily, an orphaned seal pup has very little chance of survival. Why was it different for Pearson?

"Let's Call Him Pearson"

The pup was an orphan. He was found one morning in April, alone and half starved, on a deserted beach in northern California. Like all young harbor seals, he had soft, gray-spotted fur and big, dark eyes. He moved by inching along the sand on his belly, and he made a plaintive *krooh, krooh* sound like the mooing of a hungry calf.

No one knew what had happened to his mother. The woman who found him watched and waited to see if the mother seal would return, but she didn't. Perhaps she was dead. She may have been killed by a shark or a hunter. Without someone to feed and protect him, the pup would die.

So the woman made a phone call. She called the California Marine Mammal Center. That afternoon, the seal's new life began.

The Marine Mammal Center is located on the coast of the Pacific Ocean, just outside the city of San Francisco. It is a combination hospital, orphanage, and shelter for sick and abandoned seals and sea lions. Most of the workers there are volunteers who have a special interest in marine mammals. They give the animals brought to the Center the medical attention they need. They feed and care for them until they are healthy enough to be returned to the sea.

On the afternoon in April when the orphaned pup arrived, nine elephant seals and three harbor seal pups were already at the Center. Holly Garner, the acting curator, greeted the new seal. She stroked his sleek body and let him sniff her hand with his whiskered nose.

The pup was thin, but his eyes were bright and alert. He was no more than two weeks old. In his short life, all he had known were the sea and the sand and the comfort of his mother's body. Now, human hands were holding him, but he showed no fear. He looked around curiously. He listened alertly to the strange sounds and breathed in the strange smells.

"Let's call him Pearson," Holly said. It was a good-luck name — the name of a volunteer who had worked at the Center the summer before and had had great success with harbor seal pups.

Holly hoped that this pup would be a good-luck seal. She

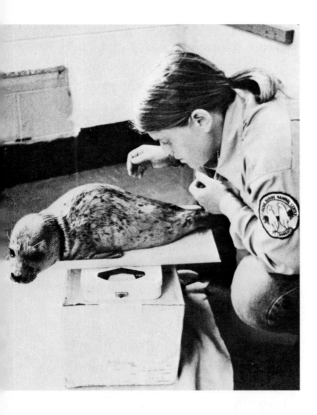

wrote the name on a chart and then began to examine the new patient.

Holly was glad when she put Pearson on a scale and found that he weighed twenty-one pounds and two ounces — less than a pup his age should have weighed but still enough to give him a good start.

His temperature was normal. His eyes were watering. This was a good sign too; for unlike land-living mammals, seals have no internal tear ducts. When they are in good health, tears flow continuously down their cheeks. The area beneath their eyes is always wet.

Holly opened the pup's mouth and saw that his gums were pink and healthy looking. This meant that he was not in shock or bleeding internally. Sharp little canine teeth protruded through the gums. Harbor seals are born with these teeth already in place, for they must be able to catch fish on their own when they are very young.

However, catching fish lay in the future for Pearson. Right now, he used his teeth for another purpose. As Holly took her hand away from his mouth, he reached out and nipped the sleeve of her shirt.

Holly laughed. Pearson had spunk. There was no doubt about that. He was also, as far as she could tell, in good health. She wrote the findings of her examination on his chart and slipped it into a file folder. Then she picked him up and put him into an indoor pen with the other harbor seal pups.

Pearson scooted around the cool cement floor of the pen. He rolled onto a blanket. He touched noses with the other pups. Then he looked up at Holly. "*Krooh*," he cried. It sounded almost like a question.

"Don't worry, little fellow; you're going to be okay," Holly said, as if in answer.

She hoped that she was right.

The harbor seal pups were favorites with everyone who worked at the Center, and Pearson quickly became especially popular.

He was full of energy and high spirits, and he was more active than any of the other pups. When he was inside, he liked to grab the blankets spread on the floor of the pen and drag them about with his teeth. If the gate was left open, he was always ready to slip out and have a look around.

On a diet of rich formula, Pearson began to gain weight. Moving him from the inside pen, where the pups spent the night, to the outside pen and wading pool, where they spent the day, was a job. He was hard to hold. He had to be wrapped in a blanket so that if he wriggled, he would not slip and fall to the ground.

Something New on the Menu

When Pearson had been at the Center for a week, Holly decided it was time to introduce him to fish.

In the sea, a harbor seal pup learns to catch and eat fish by watching its mother. At the age of four or five weeks, it is able to feed on its own.

Without a mother, and living temporarily in captivity, Pearson had to be taught what a fish was and how to swallow it. Eventually, he would have to learn to catch one himself.

Holly started his training with a small herring — an oily fish that is a favorite with seals. Gently, she opened his mouth and slipped the fish in headfirst. Harbor seals have sharp teeth for catching fish but no teeth for grinding and chewing. They swallow their food whole.

Pearson didn't seem to understand what he was supposed to do. He bit down on the fish and then spit it out. Holly tried again. This time, Pearson got the idea. He swallowed the herring in one gulp and looked eagerly for more.

Within a week, he was being hand-fed a pound of fish a day in addition to his formula. This new diet made him friskier than ever. He chased the other pups in the outside pen. He plunged into the small wading pool and rolled in the shallow water, splashing both seals and people.

Another New Home

The people at the Marine Mammal Center did not want any of the pups to die, but sometimes there was nothing they could do to save them. One morning, the smallest harbor seal pup was found dead in the inside pen. Within a week, the other two pups who had been at the Center when Pearson arrived also sickened and died.

Now Pearson was the only pup left, and suddenly he seemed more special than ever. The

volunteers couldn't help regarding him anxiously. He looked healthy, but they knew that looks were no guarantee. They made up their minds to do everything within their power to keep him strong and healthy. He had had good luck so far. His human friends were determined to make it continue.

Alone in his pen, Pearson slipped into the water of the little wading pool and rolled about, but there were no other pups to splash and chase.

Holly felt sorry for Pearson. She decided to move him to another pen. There he would be near a pair of young elephant seals, and he would have a larger pool. It was time for some real swimming.

At first, Pearson wasn't sure what to do in his new tank. It was much bigger and deeper than the old wading pool, but soon he felt at home. As the elephant seals next door watched, he swam eagerly back and forth. Down to the bottom he dove, then up again.

He practiced swimming on his back and on his stomach. He inspected the hose that brought fresh water into the tank. He turned in circles and chased his tail.

It was already May. As the warm spring days passed, Pearson grew steadily stronger. Soon he weighed forty pounds — nearly twenty pounds more than he had weighed when he was brought to the Center.

Hunting Lessons

Pearson's hunting lessons began one morning in June.

For the past weeks, Holly and the rest of the staff had been watching the young seal closely. They had kept track of his weight and had carefully observed his appearance and behavior. As the days passed, everyone had begun to feel reassured. Pearson showed no signs of illness. His body was sleek and fat. He had developed the thick layer of blubber seals need to keep warm in the sea. He no longer needed to be fed formula or to be brought inside for the night. There seemed to be no doubt about it. Pearson was going to live.

However, keeping an animal alive was only part of the struggle. Once that goal had been reached, the next job — preparing the animal for return to the sea — had to be tackled.

In the sea, Pearson's mother would have taught him all he needed to know to survive as a seal. At the Center, that job had to be taken over by his human keepers. Lessons in catching fish were the first step.

One morning, a volunteer brought Pearson's breakfast into his pen. However, instead of feeding it to him by hand, as she usually did, she selected a tasty-looking herring and held it in the water in his tank. She wiggled it, making it look as if it were alive.

Pearson was curious. He swam toward the fish. He was hungry. Quickly he grabbed the herring, but instead of swallowing it at once — as he would have to do when chasing a group of fast-moving fish in the sea — he spit it out. He didn't know how to eat in this strange new way.

It took more than a week before Pearson finally learned to grab a fish in the water and swallow it at once. In another week, he was able to retrieve fish that were tossed into his tank. This made feeding time much easier. It also paved the way for the next step in Pearson's training program — learning to live without human companionship.

Though it was hard, the volunteers gradually stopped spending so much time with Pearson. They fed him, but they did not pause to stroke his smooth gray fur or to talk to him soothingly.

At first, Pearson seemed to miss his human companions. He watched for them. He scooted eagerly to the gate when they came to clean his pen or to bring him his dinner.

Gradually, however, he became more and more absorbed in his own affairs. He rested his head against the rim of the tank. He swam in circles, rippling the water with his flippers. He slept in the warm summer sun.

He also listened to sounds. The cry of a bird or the bark of a dog in the distance would make him lift up his head and open his earholes wide.

Growing and Changing

As the summer went on, Pearson's mind and body slowly changed. He no longer looked like a baby. He weighed more than fifty pounds. His shape was longer and sleeker. His head was slimmer. His coat was a darker shade of gray.

He was no longer very interested in his human keepers. Sometimes he growled when the person cleaning his pen came too near. One day when Holly tried to pick him up to weigh him, he gave her a bad nip on the chin.

These changes in personality were hard to take, but at the same time, the people who worked at the Center knew that they were necessary. They were succeeding in their task of making Pearson independent. Though he had lived almost his entire life in captivity, he was definitely not a pet. Now that his babyhood was over, his natural instincts as a wild animal were beginning to assert themselves. It would soon be time to send him home to the sea.

Holly and the rest of the staff and volunteers had mixed feelings as they began to think about

Pearson's release. On the one hand, they were proud of the work they had done in raising the young seal to be strong, healthy, and independent. On the other hand, though, they would miss him.

It had become a habit, when arriving at work, to ask, "How's Pearson this morning?" Everyone liked to see him swimming round and round in his pool or basking in the warm sunshine. When he was gone, the Center wouldn't seem the same.

It wasn't easy, either, to decide where to let Pearson go. It would be simple to carry him down to the beach near the Center, but that was far from where he had been discovered as a young pup. Finally, a marshy area known as Mowry Slough was chosen. It was a two-hour drive from the Marine Mammal Center, but it was close to where Pearson had been found.

What was more, the Slough — which adjoins the San Francisco Bay — is part of a federal wild-life refuge. Visitors are not allowed to enter without special permission. Sharks are rarely seen in its waters. A group of harbor seals was already living there — perhaps the very group to which Pearson's mother had belonged.

All in all, it was as safe and welcoming a place as could be found for Pearson to start his new life.

"Good Luck, Pearson"

The day of the release — August 18 — dawned cool and foggy. Pearson hardly noticed when Holly entered the pen. It was only when she reached into the tank and grabbed him by the rear flippers that he stopped swimming. He squirmed in protest as she hauled him out, and he puffed angrily as she attached a metal tag through the thin flesh of his rear flipper.

Holly and the volunteer holding Pearson down were sorry to hurt him, but the tag was very important. It had a number on it that would identify him if he were ever found on a beach. A tag was the only way the Center could keep track of an animal after it was released.

Next, Pearson was weighed one last time. Sixty-five pounds, the dial on the scale read. Holly and the volunteer who was helping her to hold Pearson staggered under the load.

The rescue truck holding a metal carrying case had been backed up to the gate of the pen.

Holly grabbed Pearson by the tail. Then, with an effort, she swung him up and into the case. Quickly, the door was shut.

Pearson didn't know what was happening. He scratched frantically at the metal case. He pulled himself up by his front flippers and peered through the barred window.

Holly wished she could explain what was taking place, but she knew that Pearson would not be able to understand. All she could say was, "Don't worry, fellow. It's going to be all right. You'll be swimming again soon. I promise."

The sun came out as the rescue truck traveled over the highways.

When it arrived at the entrance to the wildlife refuge, reporters from a local newspaper and television station were waiting. People were interested in the work that was being done at the Marine Mammal Center. There had already been several news stories about Pearson. Now the reporters wanted one last picture and one last word of farewell.

The woman who had found Pearson when he was a tiny pup was also there. She and a friend were studying the harbor seals living at Mowry Slough. They had brought sleeping bags so that they could spend the night in the marsh, watching Pearson and the other seals after he had been released.

An agent of the Fish and Wildlife Service, which manages the refuge, joined the group as they started over the bumpy dirt road that led to the Slough.

At last the truck stopped. The case was lifted off. In the distance was an inlet of water. A group of harbor seals could be seen dozing on the far bank. Between the road and the water lay the muddy marshland of Mowry Slough. The heavy case, with Pearson inside, would have to be carried through the marsh to the water's edge.

The moment Holly and the volunteers stepped into the tall grass, they knew that this was not going to be an easy release. Thick black mud sucked at their boots. Pearson shifted from side to side within the crate.

The mud became deeper and deeper. Finally, Holly decided that the weight of the case, together with Pearson, was just too much. A large piece of wet canvas had been put inside the case to keep Pearson cool during the journey. Now the door to the case was opened, and Pearson was quickly wrapped in the canvas. He would be carried the rest of the way in this makeshift sling.

Suddenly Holly stumbled. In a second, she was floundering thigh-deep in mud. The canvas dropped. All at once, Pearson was free. Everyone was confused. Some tried to help Holly. Others looked for Pearson. He seemed to have disappeared.

Then out of the reeds at the water's edge, his sleek gray form emerged.

"There he goes!" someone shouted.

Pearson was in the water. He was swimming. He was free. The heads of the harbor seals in the water bobbed down and then up again, watching.

Holly struggled for a footing on the slippery tufts of grass. She hadn't even seen Pearson slip away. Now all that could be glimpsed of him was a round gray head moving through the water.

For a moment, everyone fell silent. The months of patient care and tireless watching and waiting were over. Pearson was on his own.

There seemed to be only one thing to say, and Holly said it. "Good luck, Pearson," she shouted, as the sleek gray head suddenly disappeared beneath the water. "Good luck!"

Author

As a child, living in the country with many different pets, Susan Meyers wanted to become a veterinarian or a zoo keeper. However, her father's script writing and her mother's storytelling influenced her final career choice. Susan Meyers is now a full-time writer — a job she finds "deeply satisfying."

Comprehension Questions

1. Why were Pearson's chances of survival different from those of other orphaned seal pups?
2. How did Pearson get his name?
3. How did the staff prepare Pearson for his return to the sea?
4. Why was Mowry Slough a good place for Pearson to be released?
5. How did Holly probably feel as she watched Pearson swim away?

Vocabulary

Find a word in the list below the sentences that means about the same as the boldface word or words in each sentence. Write the sentence, using the new word in place of the boldface word or words. Then write a sentence of your own using the new word.

1. Pearson was **moving very slowly** along the sand on his belly.
2. He made a **sad** krooh, krooh sound.
3. Many of the staff were **people who work without pay**.
4. Holly Garner is the **person in charge** of the Center.
5. Pearson's new diet made him even **livelier**.
6. Pearson looked healthy, but looks were no **assurance**.

volunteers
plaintive
guarantee
friskier
inching
curator

Using an Index

In your school or public library, find a nonfiction book about marine mammals. Be sure to choose a book that has an index. Look up the main topic seals in the index. Then use the index to answer the following questions.

1. What pages in the book have information about seals?
2. What are the subtopics under the main topic seals?
3. Do any pages have pictures of seals? How can you tell?

Choose one subtopic under seals that particularly interests you. Turn to the pages in the book that discuss that subtopic. Read the information and write down the most important facts.

Seal

by William Jay Smith

See how he dives
  From the rocks with a zoom!
  See how he darts
    Through his watery room
    Past crabs and eels
      And green seaweed,
      Past fluffs of sandy
      Minnow feed!
    See how he swims
      With a swerve and a twist,
    A flip of the flipper,
    A flick of the wrist!
Quicksilver-quick,
Softer than spray,
Down he plunges
And sweeps away;
Before you can think,
Before you can utter
Words like "Dill pickle"
Or "Apple butter,"
Back up he swims
  Past sting-ray and shark,
Out with a zoom,
  A whoop, a bark;
  Before you can say
    Whatever you wish,
    He plops at your side
      With a mouthful of fish!

Synonyms and Antonyms

For the people who lived in the American colonies during the Revolutionary War, it was a **tense** time. Knowing that British soldiers and spies were nearby and the danger of fighting breaking out made people **nervous** and **worried,** like the first two people in the picture above. The words *tense, nervous,* and *worried* mean almost the same thing. They are **synonyms.**

The third speaker uses the word *calm.* This word has the opposite meaning of *nervous, worried,* and *tense.* Words that mean the opposite are **antonyms.**

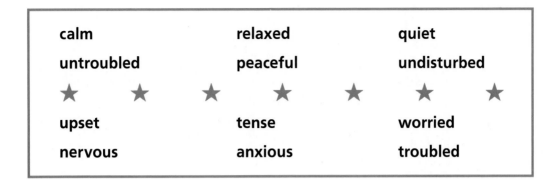

calm	relaxed	quiet
untroubled	peaceful	undisturbed
★ ★ ★ ★ ★ ★ ★		
upset	tense	worried
nervous	anxious	troubled

Look at the chart. The words above the row of blue stars are synonyms for *calm*. The words below the stars are synonyms for *nervous*. The words above the row of stars are antonyms for the words below it. On the chart, find a synonym for *troubled*. Find an antonym for *peaceful*.

Use the words on the chart to finish these sentences. Choose the kind of word that is given in parentheses after each sentence.

1. The ordinarily _____ farmers took up arms to fight the British. (synonym for **quiet**)
2. The soldiers were probably _____ as they marched into battle. (synonym for **upset**)
3. Many Americans, young and old, were _____ because of the fierce fighting. (antonym for **undisturbed**)
4. When victory came, Boston was _____ once again. (antonym for **anxious**)

Something Extra

Use **hot** and **cold** words to make a synonym-antonym chart in your class. Make a row of stars across the middle of your chart. Put **hot** words above the row and **cold** words below it. See how many **hot** and **cold** words your class can gather in a week.

Thank You, Phoebe Fraunces

by Judith Berry Griffin

Phoebe Fraunces had an unusual job for a thirteen-year-old: she was a spy at General George Washington's headquarters. How could she find out, before it was too late, who was plotting to kill him?

In 1776, during the American Revolution, Phoebe Fraunces was sent to General George Washington's headquarters in Mortier House in New York City. Her father, Sam Fraunces, was a free black man and owner of the Queen's Head Tavern in New York City. A trusted Patriot, he had heard of a plot to kill General Washington. Phoebe's job was to help with the household chores while acting as a spy. She was to watch particularly anyone whose name began with T, *the only clue Sam Fraunces had to the identity of the person who was planning to assassinate Washington. Every day Phoebe met her father along the waterfront to tell him anything that she had learned.*

Phoebe soon settled into her job. The work was not as hard as she thought it would be. Mrs. Washington had brought her own quilts and feather beds. It was Phoebe's job to air and turn these every morning as well as to see to the buying of food and the serving of meals. She had to keep the silver cleaned and shining and the furniture dusted and polished. She did not have any special jobs to do for General Washington except to see that his meals were served on time. He was very particular about having dinner served promptly at four o'clock, and Phoebe sometimes had a hard time getting everything finished by then.

General Washington never said very much. He was tall, with a quiet voice. He looked like the kind of man who could win a war. Mrs. Washington was to have a fresh egg each day, and Pompey, who was a lot of company to Phoebe even though he was only eight years old, helped by visiting the hen house early every morning. When the dinner was over, he and Phoebe often stood on the kitchen steps and fed the hens leftover scraps of bread from the table.

Phoebe was a good housekeeper. But she did not forget why she was there. Day after day she watched, and waited, and listened. General Washington came and went. The house was full of people all the time — officers of the Army, friends, members of the bodyguard. Phoebe slipped among them, silent as a shadow, as her father had taught her. Whenever she saw anyone talking softly, she stopped to poke the fire, fill their glasses, light new candles. But still she saw nothing, heard nothing.

Each day at noon she took a basket and went down to the waterfront to do the day's marketing. When she was finished, she would make her way to the edge of the harbor and stand looking out over the ocean. No one took any notice of her, in her clean white apron and cap, a shawl thrown across her

shoulders. Nor did anyone particularly notice the man who always came to stand beside her, his curly hair powdered and pulled back, his brown face plump and smiling.

The two of them would stand together for a few moments, seeming to talk of nothing important. Sometimes Phoebe would throw out a few crumbs to the gulls, which would gather noisily at their feet. After a time they would move off in different directions — Phoebe back to Mortier House, Sam Fraunces back to the Queen's Head.

Phoebe never had anything to report. She was particularly careful to watch every member of the general's bodyguard who came to the house. None was called by a name starting with *T*. They all seemed to be truly fond of the general and laughed and joked with him. Two members of the bodyguard did stand out from the others. One was especially nice. Mr. Hickey was his name. He smiled at Phoebe while she was serving and often came into the kitchen to joke with her and Mary, the cook, while Mary was preparing the meals.

Phoebe was the youngest servant in the house except for Pompey. When the others were talking, she often felt left out. She was glad to have someone to talk to. Hickey seemed much younger than the other men — not much older, in fact, than Phoebe herself. And he seemed glad to talk to her too. Like Phoebe, he seemed not to have many friends. Phoebe often saw him sitting by himself at the edge of the woods.

Mr. Green was another member of General Washington's bodyguard who kept to himself, but he was not like Hickey. He never spoke to Phoebe at all, even when he saw her in the yard. Phoebe would always say, "Evening, sir," but he never so much as looked at her. From what she could tell, he didn't say much to anyone, even at dinnertime when everyone did a lot of talking. Though his name did not begin with *T,* Phoebe made up her mind to watch him very carefully. There was something about him she did not like.

One day when Hickey came to the kitchen, he had a small cloth bag with him. He handed it to Phoebe. "Here," he said. "It's some seed for your precious chickens."

Phoebe was surprised. She did not know anyone had noticed that she fed the chickens. She opened the bag. "But it's good seed, sir!" she protested. "It's too good to feed the chickens!"

Hickey laughed. "It's only the king's true men who'll be missing it," he said. "Let's see if your chickens will get fatter from British grain than from American bread crumbs!"

Phoebe smiled. She did not ask him how he had got the seed. But he began to bring it home to her often. Sometimes he would bring it himself. Other times she would find a bag lying on the table when she came into the kitchen. Sometimes there would be a bright ribbon tied around it. Then Hickey would say, "The ribbon is for you, pretty Phoebe. Compliments of King George III!" Sometimes there would be some other treat inside — always, he said, stolen from those loyal to the King of England.

Soon she was looking forward to his visits every day. And as the days went by and Phoebe still could find no one who seemed to be plotting to take General Washington's life, she thought about asking Mr. Hickey for help. Her father had told her to trust no one. Still . . . perhaps she could trust him. She would wait and see.

Weeks went by. The beautiful house, once so strange to her, was now like a good friend. Phoebe enjoyed using the fine china plates and crystal glasses. She enjoyed serving Mary's deliciously prepared meals to General Washington and his important guests, while Pompey followed solemnly behind with the saltcellar and pepper mill.

She knew she was there to save General Washington's life. But as the days went by and she still heard nothing, she began to wonder if perhaps her father was mistaken. No one seemed to be plotting anything, and it was now the beginning of June. Phoebe had been at Mortier House almost two months.

Then one day when she went to the market, her father was not there. Phoebe stood by the water a long time, waiting and wondering. Should she go to the Queen's Head? Or back to Mortier House? As she was trying to decide, she saw her father hurrying toward her. He looked very worried. For the first time he seemed not to care that people might notice them. He held her by the shoulders and looked into her face.

"Phoebe," he said urgently, "I have heard that General Washington will be leaving Mortier House in a very few days. The person known as 'T' will act before that time. You must find out who it is!"

Phoebe's mind was whirling as she hurried back toward the house. She was frightened, but she was also determined. She *would* save General Washington! She had long ago figured that he would likely be shot. During dinner he always sat in a chair by the window. He would make an easy target for anyone waiting outside.

If only she could get him to change his place away from that window! His good friend General Gates would be a dinner guest at the house this evening. Everyone else was part of the family or a member of the bodyguard. Over and over she said their names. No one's name began with *T*.

As she reached the kitchen door, she saw Hickey sitting on the steps. "Why are you so solemn, pretty Phoebe?" he asked.

"Oh, Mr. Hickey, sir," said Phoebe breathlessly. "I'm so worried. . . ." She paused. She did need help! Should she tell him? Maybe he knew something, had seen something, that had escaped her notice. After all, he was a member of the bodyguard — it was his job to protect General Washington. Her father's words came back to her. "Trust no one," he had said. "No one." She sighed. She would have to keep trying alone.

"Well," said Hickey after a moment. "I've something to bring a smile back to that pretty face. Fresh June peas for the general's dinner — first of the season! His favorite and mine — and enough for us both! Some friends of the king will be mighty hungry tonight!" He handed her a large sack, filled to the brim with pea pods. Phoebe smiled in spite of herself.

"Grown men — soldiers of the American Army — stealing peas!" she said.

Hickey pretended to be hurt. "All right," he said, snatching the sack from her and holding it over his head. "I'll just throw them out to your chickens ——"

"No, no, Mr. Hickey." Phoebe laughed. "Here — I'll fix them myself."

Hickey handed her the sack. "I'll be here to fill my plate at dinnertime," he promised.

All afternoon, as she went about her chores, Phoebe worried. *How* could she get the general's chair away from that window? She would have to stand in front of it, blocking the view from outside. But then, would someone shoot her?

By the time dinnertime arrived she was almost sick with fear. She was in the kitchen with Pompey getting ready to

serve the plates when a voice behind her made her jump. It was Hickey.

"I've come for my peas," he said softly.

"Oh! Mr. Hickey, sir!" she said. "You gave me such a start! I was ——" She stopped and looked at him, even more startled. He looked ill? Frightened? She couldn't tell which.

"Which is my plate, and which is General Washington's?" he said. "It wouldn't do for him to have more than me." He spoke quickly, without smiling this time.

"I never heard of such carryings on over a pile of peas!" Phoebe said. "This is the general's plate, and this is yours!" She turned away to fill Pompey's saltcellar and turned back just in time to see Hickey's hand move quickly away from General Washington's plate and slide into his pocket. Something winked for a second in the light — something shiny, like glass.

"What are you doing to General Washington's plate?" she said. "I told you yours is here!" She picked up the plate. Was it her imagination, or was there something grainy, like sugar, on the peas? Phoebe looked more closely, but as she looked, whatever it was seemed to have disappeared. An instant later she was not sure — had she seen anything at all? She thought of the window again and forgot about the peas. She had to serve General Washington.

Leaving Hickey standing in the kitchen, Phoebe nervously entered the dining room, Pompey following with the salt. As she walked toward the general, Phoebe looked at every face around the table. Some of the guests were talking, some merely smiling. None seemed nervous.

And then she noticed the empty chair. Who was missing? But even as she asked herself the question, she knew. It was Mr. Green. Was he outside the house with a gun, waiting? General Washington was sitting by the window, as she had feared. He sat back easily in his chair, listening to something General Gates was saying. The window was open! As she went past, Phoebe looked outside anxiously. There was not a sound, not a shadow, not a movement. The green grass was smooth and unruffled. Even the leaves in the trees beyond were still.

"Well, Phoebe!" General Washington exclaimed as she stopped beside his chair. "June peas! How did you get them so early in the season?"

"It wasn't me, sir," replied Phoebe, looking past him out the window. "It was your Mr. Hickey who brought them in, fresh today. He says they're your favorite."

"And mine as well!" said General Gates. "Where is Mr. Thomas Hickey? I want to thank him!"

Phoebe started to put the plate down in front of General Washington. Then, in a flash, it came to her whom she was looking for. Mr. Green was not hiding outside the window to shoot at the general. The person who was trying to kill him was here — in the kitchen! Phoebe stood like a stone, the plate still in her hands. She saw Hickey again — Thomas

236

Hickey — laughing and teasing, bringing her candy and ribbons and seed for her chickens — and then bringing June peas for the general and sprinkling them with poison! *T* was for Thomas, member of General Washington's bodyguard!

Still holding the plate, she whirled around. Pompey was waiting behind her. "Run!" she screamed. "Run! Get my father!"

Everyone stopped talking. Pompey looked at her in amazement. "Your — your father?" he stammered.

"Sam Fraunces! At the Queen's Head! Go!" And she stamped her foot. Pompey had never heard Phoebe sound like that before. He dropped the saltcellar and ran through the kitchen door.

Everyone in the dining room sat frozen. All eyes were on Phoebe. "General Washington!" she cried. "Mr. Hickey has put poison in your dinner! I saw him!" There was a gasp from the table.

"What jest is this?" roared General Gates, getting up from his place and reaching for the plate. But before he could take it from her, Phoebe ran to the open window and threw the whole plate out into the yard.

Now the dining room was in an uproar. Chairs over-turned; drinks spilled as the men jumped to their feet in confusion. Some ran toward the window where Phoebe was standing, as if they feared she might try to escape. Others started for the kitchen. Some ran to surround General Washington. No one knew what to do.

It was General Gates who first noticed the chickens in the yard and shouted, pointing out the window, "Look!"

Three of Phoebe's chickens had come to peck at the peas she had thrown outside. Two had already fallen dead. The third was still moving its wings, but as they watched, it, too, grew still. The poison, meant for General Washington, had killed the chickens instead.

"Get Hickey!" bellowed General Gates, and members of the bodyguard rushed to obey. Minutes later Thomas Hickey was dragged in from the yard, his face white with terror. He had not been able to escape. Minutes after that, Sam Fraunces burst into the room. Phoebe was still standing by the window, shaking. He ran to her and held her tightly. Phoebe clung to him, burying her face in his shoulder.

"Well done, Daughter," Samuel Fraunces said quietly.

After the excitement had died down and Hickey had been taken away, General Washington came to speak to Phoebe and her father. "It's nice to know people whom I can trust," he said simply. "Thank you."

General Washington went on to lead the American Army to victory, and the United States was born. So freedom did come to some Americans, but not all. In 1783, when the war was won, General Washington chose to give his victory party at Fraunces's Queen's Head Tavern; there he said good-by to the leaders of his army. And when he became the first

President of the United States, he invited Sam Fraunces to become his official steward. Fraunces held that job until 1796.

Thomas Hickey was tried and convicted of trying to kill George Washington. Seven days later he was hanged. As was usual in those days, everyone turned out to watch. No one knows whether Phoebe was there. No one knows what happened to Phoebe after that. But we do know that she was a good spy.

Thank you, Phoebe Fraunces.

Author

Born and raised in Chicago, Judith Berry Griffin also earned her college degrees there. She has been a teacher and an elementary school principal as well as a writer. Her third book for children, *Phoebe and the General,* a part of which you have just read, was selected as a Notable Children's Trade Book in the Field of Social Studies.

Comprehension Questions

1. How did Phoebe Fraunces find out who was plotting to kill General George Washington?
2. How did Phoebe save General Washington's life?
3. Why did Phoebe notice two of the bodyguards?
4. What do you think was the real reason that Mr. Hickey brought gifts to Phoebe?

Vocabulary

Each word on the right matches a word on the left as either its synonym or its antonym. If **S** is next to a word on the left, find its synonym. If **A** is next to a word, find its antonym.

prompt (A)	seriously
terror (S)	unimportant
urgent (A)	fear
solemnly (S)	tardy
jest (S)	unfaithful
loyal (A)	joke

Writing a Story

Use the library to research one of the following events. Then write a story based on the facts you found.

The Stamp Act
The Boston Tea Party
Paul Revere's Ride
The First Continental Congress

Outlines

What an Outline Is

An **outline** is a plan that an author may use to arrange ideas or that a reader may use to understand and remember ideas. An outline of a piece of writing shows what the most important ideas in the piece are. It also shows in what order the ideas are presented in the piece. It shows how the ideas are connected.

In order to write well, an author needs a good plan, or outline. In the same way, when you read a piece of writing, it is sometimes helpful to make an outline. Making an outline will help you to see how the author has arranged ideas. It will also help you to remember the most important facts in the piece.

In this lesson, you will learn how to make an outline when you read. You will learn to find main topics and subtopics. You will learn to arrange them to show how the ideas in a piece of writing are connected.

Read "Studying the Sea," which appears below. Then read the rest of the lesson to learn how to make an outline of it.

Studying the Sea

People who study the sea use many different tools. Among the most important of these tools are cameras, which take pictures of the sea bottom. Other kinds of tools are *corers,* which have long tubes that bring up bits of mud and sand from the bottom of the sea. Electronic sounding tools send back echoes from the ocean floor. From these echoes, scientists can learn about how deep the ocean is in different places.

These tools are very important. However, the observations made by real live divers are even more useful. Some divers use scuba gear for short trips beneath the surface. Underwater vehicles called *submersibles* make it possible for divers to go deeper in the ocean and stay there longer. In this way, divers can study changes in the ocean floor. They can also study plant and animal life in the sea.

A small submersible vehicle preparing for a deep dive.

Choosing Main Topics

The first step in outlining a piece of writing is to read the title. The title of the piece will become the title of your outline. What is the title of the piece that you have just read? An outline of that piece of writing would have the same title.

The title can also help you write the **main topics** for your outline. The main topics are the most important ideas in the piece. To find the main topics, think of a question based on the title that you expect the piece to answer. A question about the title of the piece above might be *How do people study the sea?*

The next step is to read the piece to find answers to the question. You will almost always find several answers.

Read "Studying the Sea" again. Look for answers to the question *How do people study the sea?*

You may have found the following two answers: *People study the sea by using tools. People study the sea by using the observations of divers.*

These answers will be the main topics of your outline. This is how you would write them in the outline.

Studying the Sea
I. Tools
II. Observations of divers

The first word and every important word in the title begins with a capital letter. There is a Roman numeral and a period before each main topic. Only the first word in a main topic begins with a capital letter. No period is used after a main topic. The main topics are short, using only the most important words of the answers to the question made from the title. The main topics are listed in the order in which they appeared.

Another way to choose the main topics for an outline is to use the paragraph topics. You have already learned that a paragraph topic is the one thing that all or most of the sentences in the paragraph tell about.

The topic of the first paragraph in the piece about studying the sea can be stated as *using different tools*. The topic of the second paragraph can be stated as *using observations made by divers*. Do the paragraph topics give you the same main topics as those in the outline above?

Another help in finding the main topics can be the headings. The author of a long piece of writing may divide it into parts with headings. You can use the important words in the headings as main topics in your outline. Turn back to the piece about Bill Meléndez on page 50. Look at the heading that begins each part. If you were to outline this piece, you could use the most important words in the headings to write your main topics.

Checking Your Main Topics

Once you have listed the main topics in an outline, you should check to see if they are good ones. You can do that by putting the title together with each main topic to make a sentence. The words in the first main topic can be put together with the words in the title to make the sentence *One way people study the sea is by using tools.*

Now put the title together with the second main topic. What sentence can you make? Does it make sense?

Choosing Subtopics

When you are sure that your main topics are good ones, the next step is to outline the **subtopics.** Subtopics are the points the piece of writing gives about the main topics. You can figure out what the subtopics are by turning each of the main topics into a question that you expect the piece to answer. Then read all or part of the piece again to find answers to those questions. You will almost always find several answers to each question.

You could turn the first main topic in the outline into the question *What are some tools that can be used to study the sea?* Read the first paragraph of the piece. Look for answers to that question. You might find the following answers: *cameras, corers, electronic sounding tools.*

What question could you make from the second main topic? You might make the question *How do divers make observations of the sea?* Read the second paragraph of the piece to find the answers.

Your finished outline might look like this:

Studying the Sea
I. Tools
  A. Cameras
  B. Corers
  C. Electronic sounding tools
II. Observations of divers
  A. Scuba gear
  B. Submersibles

Each subtopic is indented under its main topic. This shows that the subtopics tell about the main topic just above them. The subtopics are listed in the same order in which they appear in the piece. Before each subtopic is a capital letter followed by a period. In subtopics, as in main topics, only the first word begins with a capital letter. There is no period at the end. Following these rules for making an outline will help you to show how the main topics and subtopics in the piece are connected with each other.

Checking Your Subtopics

You can check to see if you have chosen good subtopics in the same way that you checked your main topics. See if you can put each subtopic together with the title and the main topic above it to make a sentence. With the three subtopics under the first main topic above, you could make the following sentences: *One tool that can be used to study the sea is a camera. Another tool that can be used to study the sea is a corer. Another tool that can be used to study the sea is an electronic sounding tool.* Does each of these sentences make sense?

Try this test with the other subtopics.

Making an Outline

Review the steps for making an outline. Then read the piece below and make an outline of it.

Fish in Different Parts of the Ocean

The ocean is home to about fourteen thousand kinds of fish. One of the chief reasons why certain fish live in certain parts of the ocean is the temperature of the water. Many fish live in warm, or tropical, waters. Among these tropical fish are angelfish, parrot fish, and barracudas.

North and south of the tropical regions, the water is neither very warm nor very cold. These temperate waters are rich in food fish such as cod, flatfish, and herring.

There are not as many fish in the cold Arctic waters. However, some hardy kinds of fish do live there. Among these fish are eelpouts, sculpins, and sea snails.

Skill Summary

An outline is a plan that shows the most important ideas in a piece of writing and how they are arranged. Remember the following things about making an outline.

- Think of a question based on the title of the piece.
- Use the answers to the question as main topics.
- Check the main topics by putting the title together with each main topic to make a sentence.
- Find subtopics by turning each main topic into a question. Then read the piece again to find answers.
- Check subtopics by putting the title and main topic together with each of its subtopics to make a sentence.

Static Magic

by Doris Spaulding

How can you use static electricity to play some "shocking" tricks?

Reading in Science

A girl in a wool coat slid across the car seat to jump out. "Yeoww!" she yelled as she grabbed the door handle. "I got a shock!"

Such startling contacts with metal may often shock you during cool, dry times of the year. You can cause curious things to happen, though, when you know how to handle the cause of these shocks — static electricity.

You don't need fancy equipment to catch static charges. All you have to do is rub a comb, toothbrush, ballpoint pen, or balloon with the right kind of material. If the air is dry enough, your comb or toothbrush will act as a magic wand, and you'll be able to charm thread, bend water, command table tennis balls, and even make table salt jump up and down.

To get to know static electricity, gather the following materials:

thread	inflated rubber
dinner knife with	balloons
heavy handle	wool cloth
tissue paper	(scarf or sweater)
plastic comb	table tennis ball
(or plastic-handled	table salt
toothbrush or hair-	sheet of paper
brush)	

Later you can demonstrate your static "magic" for friends and family. (For best results, wait for a clear day. Some static tricks fail in damp weather.)

The earliest known form of electricity was a flash of lightning.

Magic Paper Balls

Place a dinner knife on a table with the blade hanging over the edge. Cut two pieces of thread one foot long. Make two small, rounded paper wads of dry tissue. Then tie each of these paper balls to the end of each piece of thread. Fasten both pieces of thread to the end of the knife so they hang down freely, about two inches apart.

Slowly move a comb towards the paper balls. What happens? What did you think would happen?

Rub the comb briskly with wool. Now what happens when you move it towards the paper balls? Hold the comb between the paper balls for a few seconds. Can you explain what happens now?

You have just demonstrated a basic law of electricity. Before you rubbed the comb, it was neutral, or "not charged." The paper balls were also neutral. The comb neither pulled nor pushed them away. When charged, the comb first attracted, or "pulled," the neutral paper balls. Touching the comb made the paper balls receive the same charge as the comb. After the paper balls became charged, the comb pushed them away.

Now hold the paper balls in your hands to remove the charge. Can you guess what happened to the charge? It was discharged to your body and the ground. Try charging the comb on your clothing, hair, or dry hands. Be sure to rub briskly, and don't forget to discharge the comb before testing a different material.

Above: A charged comb attracts neutral paper balls. Below: Charged comb repels charged paper balls.

After you have checked the attraction between charged and neutral objects, use the same idea to do other tricks.

Command a Ball

Bring a *well-charged* comb near a table tennis ball lying on a table. Order the ball to follow that comb! With practice you can make the neutral ball roll about, turn in circles, and roll off the table at your command. Be sure to build up a strong charge on the comb and keep it moving ahead of the ball.

How do you think the ball will respond to the charged comb if you give it the same kind of charge by rubbing it with the same material? Try it.

Below: If you rub a plastic comb briskly with wool, the comb becomes charged. The charged comb then attracts a neutral table tennis ball.

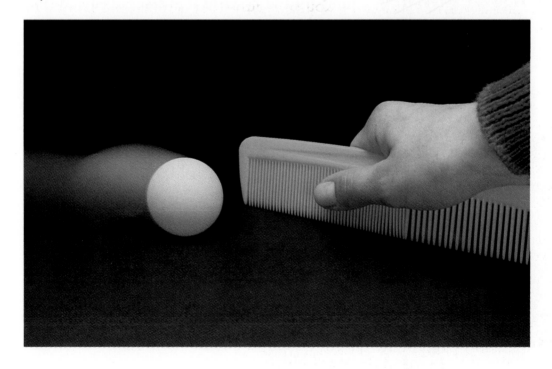

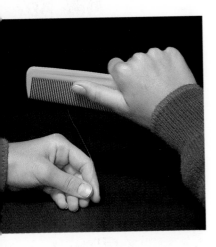

Charm a Thread "Snake"

Hold one end of a three-to-four-inch piece of thread. With your other hand, bring a *charged* comb or brush handle near the free end of the thread. Without touching it, you can make the thread stand up and turn in circles. You can also make the thread "strike" by moving the comb close, then jerking it away. What will happen if you let the thread touch the comb? Try it.

Above: A charged comb attracts a neutral piece of thread. What will happen if the thread touches the comb?

Salt a Comb

Shake half a teaspoon of salt on a sheet of paper. Slowly move a charged comb about a quarter of an inch above it. Then watch the salt jump up and down as it is first pulled and later pushed away by the comb.

Bend a "Waterfall"

Turn on the tap until you get a thin but steady stream of water. Use a *charged* comb, toothbrush, or balloon to see how far you can make the water bend in any direction. Don't let the water touch your magic wand — it will wash off the static charges.

Left: A plastic comb has been charged and then moved near a stream of water. The charged comb attracts the water and makes it bend.

Understanding Static Electricity

This special charge that your rubbing produced is not so hard to understand when you know how materials are put together. Matter, everything in the universe, is made of tiny particles called atoms. Atoms themselves are made up of even tinier pieces that include protons and electrons. Protons and electrons attract each other, but they repel their own kind: Protons push away protons, and electrons push away electrons.

Most of the time, materials are neutral, or "not charged." Neutral atoms have the same number of electrons and protons. For this reason, scientists believe it's a gain or loss of electrons that causes objects to become charged. Here's why: Protons, with a *positive* charge, weigh much more than electrons. They form the center of an atom and never leave it under ordinary conditions. Electrons, with a *negative* charge, are near the outside of an atom where they may be scraped off and even become attached to other atoms.

One way to scrape off electrons is by rubbing. Take an inflated rubber balloon, for example. Ordinarily the electric charges in its atoms are balanced. When you rub it with a wool scarf, some electrons move from the wool to the rubber. The balloon then has a negative charge because it has gained electrons; the wool has a positive charge because it has lost electrons. To see how such opposites attract each other, hold the balloon near the end of the scarf.

Below: (top) Balloon and scarf have an equal number of electrons and protons. (middle) Electrons move from scarf to balloon. (bottom) Balloon has a negative charge. Scarf has a positive charge.

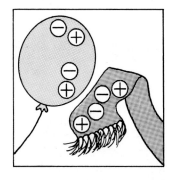

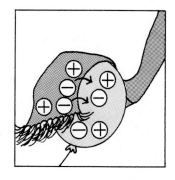

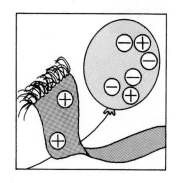

Will materials with the same kind of charge attract each other? Rub two balloons with wool, and try to bring them together. Hard, isn't it? They repel each other. Yet both balloons attract neutral things. This lets you stick the charged balloons on a wall or walk around with them clinging to your body!

After you have played with static electricity, you may want to learn more about it from library reference books. With a little experience, you'll be able to make up your own tricks by scraping electrons onto or off various objects around the house and using them to repel or attract other objects. Wool and polyester clothing should work. If you "comb" your blanket with a nylon comb after dark, you can watch the sparks fly. When you want to do something really shocking, drag your feet across a rug, then touch a metal doorknob. If the air is dry, you're sure to get a big charge out of that!

Below: Charged balloons repel each other, but they stick to a neutral sweater. Why are the balloons attracted to the sweater? Try this trick yourself and see what other materials the balloons will stick to.

Author

A high school biology teacher for many years, Doris Spaulding enjoys working up science tricks. She has written many nature and science articles for children's magazines, such as *Ranger Rick* and *Ebony Jr.!* She has also written two Mini-Books for Houghton Mifflin Company's reading program.

Thinking It Over

Comprehension Questions

1. How can you use static electricity to play tricks?
2. In what kind of weather do static electricity tricks work best?
3. What happens when a *charged* comb is moved towards an *uncharged* paper ball?
4. What happens when a *charged* comb is moved towards a *charged* paper ball?
5. Unlike electrons, protons never leave an atom under ordinary conditions. Why do you suppose this is true?

Vocabulary

Several forms of the word *charge* were used in "Static Magic." Figure out which form of the word in the list fits each incomplete sentence.

discharge   discharged
charge   charges

1. You can _____ a plastic comb by rubbing it briskly with wool.
2. If water touches the comb, it will wash off the electric _____.
3. You can _____ the comb by holding it in your hands.
4. When you hold the comb in your hands, the electricity is _____ to your body.

Now use each form of the word ***charge*** in a sentence of your own.

Writing Directions and Making a Diagram

Think of a simple action that you do all the time, such as brushing your teeth. Write directions for performing this task, as if you were writing them for someone who has never done it. Include a diagram.

A Shocking Creature:
The Electric Eel

by Alvin and Virginia Silverstein

Imagine a fish that can produce a shock large enough to knock you out — or even kill you. One of the most unusual creatures on earth is the electric eel.

Reading in Science

All living things produce electricity. In most animals and plants, the amount of electricity that is produced is so tiny that special machines are needed to discover it. But some fish are able to produce huge amounts of electricity — enough to stun or even kill. The most powerful of these electric fish is the electric eel. It can discharge up to six hundred fifty volts — enough to kill a person.

What an Electric Eel Is

The electric eel lives in the muddy waters of the Amazon and Orinoco rivers of South America. It is not related to other kinds of eels, but it is shaped like them. The electric eel has no back or tail fins as other fish do. It swims with the aid of a long fin that runs nearly the whole length of its body. It can swim backward and forward as well as up and down. Most of the time, though, it lives a lazy life. It does not have to work hard to protect itself or to catch its food.

The electric eel is like a living battery. All of its normal body organs are crowded into the front fifth of its body. The remaining four fifths is packed with more than five thousand tiny electric generators.

How It Uses Electricity

The electric eel uses its electricity in several ways. When it swims, a small "battery" in its tail sends out weak electric pulses at a rate of twenty to fifty a second. The eel uses these electric pulses to find its way. They bounce off objects and come back to special pits in the eel's head. The eel uses electricity in much the same way that bats use sound to find their way around. It's a good thing, too, because as it grows older, its eyes are damaged by electricity and it becomes blind. Scientists think that the electric eel may also use electricity to communicate with other eels.

If an enemy tries to attack the electric eel, or a frog or some other possible prey is in the water nearby, the eel acts quickly. It turns on the powerful "main battery" that fills most of its body. Then it sends out several discharges in a row. An electric eel can send out as many as one hundred fifty pulses a second without showing any signs of getting tired. Fish and frogs are killed by the eel's strong electric shocks, and even a larger animal, such as a horse that has come down to the water to drink, may be stunned and drown. The eel, however, does not seem to be harmed by the electricity — except for the gradual failing of its eyes. In fact, other electric eels are often attracted to a place where one of their kind is discharging. They flock to join in the feast.

How baby electric eels are born is still unknown. During the rainy season of the year, electric eels disappear from their homes. When they return, small baby eels are swimming along with them. The young electric eels produce very little electricity. The larger they grow, the more powerful their electric shocks become. A full-grown electric eel is one fish you want to stay away from!

Authors

Alvin and Virginia Silverstein have been writing together for many years. They have written over sixty books for young people, many of them award winners. *Nature's Champions,* from which the preceding article came, was their favorite book to write.

How the Electric

The electric eel doesn't have a fin along its back like most fish. It has a fin along its stomach, called a "swimming" fin, that it uses to move in a wavy motion. The eel also has smaller fins that probably help it steer. The electric eel spends much of its time lying quietly in the water, moving only to come to the surface for a breath of air. It would drown if it didn't come up for air about every fifteen minutes.

All living things — including people — produce electricity. This electricity is produced in the nerves, glands, and muscles. Over millions of years, some of the electric eel's muscles have developed to produce much more electricity than normal muscles.

The muscles that produce electricity are known as electric organs. There are three electric organs: the main, the Sachs, and the Hunters. The **main organ** sends out a strong charge, and the **Sachs organ** sends out a weak one. The **Hunters organ** seems to help the other two.

Eel Makes Electricity...

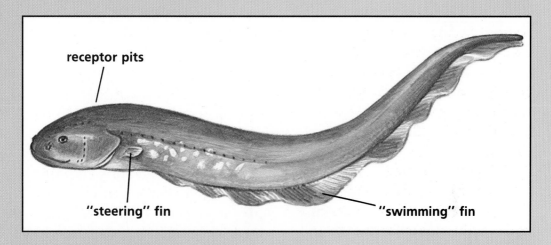

The electric eel can grow to be nine feet long. Its "swimming" fin takes up most of its body. Its receptor pits help it find its way.

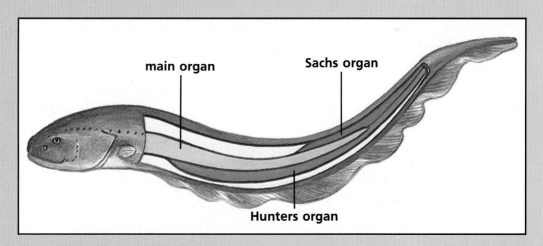

The electric eel has three electric organs. The main organ sends out the most powerful charge. The Sachs organ sets up the electric field. Scientists think the Hunters organ helps the other two.

...and Uses It to Catch Food

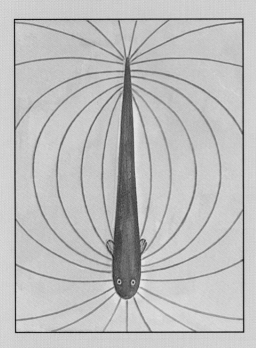

The Sachs organ sets up an electric field around the electric eel.

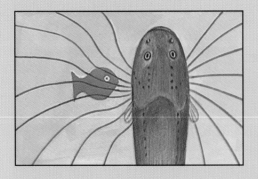

The regular pattern of the electric field is changed when a fish touches it.

The electric eel is a blind, toothless, slow-moving fish. Without its electricity, it would have a hard time defending itself or finding and catching its food.

The electric eel uses an electric field as a pilot uses radar. The **Sachs organ** sends a weak electric charge out the tail, through the water, and back to **receptor pits** in the eel's head. This sets up a weak electric field around the eel. When something touches this field, the regular pattern is distorted. This change in the field tells the eel something is there. The eel can tell what is in its field and how far away it is.

If an object in its field is something the eel would like to eat, its **main electric organ** sends out a huge electric charge. Small fish and frogs are stunned or killed by the shock, and the eel can catch them easily. Larger fish and animals are stunned or scared away.

Comprehension Questions

1. What is unusual about an electric eel?
2. Where do electric eels live?
3. How do electric eels use their electricity?
4. Why is it a good idea to stay away from an electric eel?

Vocabulary

Listed below are words from the selection that have to do with electricity, but the words are written in code. Each number stands for the letter that is in that place in the alphabet. For example, 1 = **A,** 2 = **B,** 3 = **C,** and so on. Figure out what each word is, then use it in a sentence.

Example:
5-12-5-3-20-18-9-3 = **electric**
1. 4-9-19-3-8-1-18-7-5
2. 22-15-12-20-19
3. 2-1-20-20-5-18-25
4. 7-5-14-5-18-1-20-15-18-19
5. 16-21-12-19-5-19
6. 19-8-15-3-11-19

Making an Outline

Look at the incomplete outline below on the electric eel. It is based on the information that is on pages 257–258 of the article you just read. The main topics have been filled in for you. Copy what is written below, then complete the outline by writing the subtopics in their correct order.

A Shocking Creature:
The Electric Eel

I. What an electric eel is
  A.
  B.
  C.
  D.
  E.
  F.
  G.

II. How the electric eel uses electricity
  A.
  B.
  C.
  D.

"The Cat and the Golden Egg"

a story from
*The Town Cats
and Other Tales*

written by Lloyd Alexander

illustrated by Alan Baker

Lloyd Alexander is known as a cat lover as well as an outstanding author of fantasy for young people. His previous books that feature cats include *Time Cat* and *The Cat Who Wished to Be a Man.* In *The Town Cats and Other Tales,* he presents eight tales of cats whose cleverness and common sense help them to get the better of the merely human characters in the stories.

Pescato, one of the "town cats" of the title story; Hillesum, the resourceful "painter's cat"; and Quickset, who uses a "golden egg" and a shrewd knowledge of human weakness to outwit a greedy merchant, are some of the unforgettable felines the reader will meet in *The Town Cats and Other Tales.*

THE
Town Cats
AND OTHER TALES

by Lloyd Alexander
illustrated by Alan Baker

The Cat and the Golden Egg

Quickset, a silver-gray cat, lived with Dame Agnes, a poor widow. Not only was he a cheerful companion, but he was clever at helping the old woman make ends meet. If the chimney smoked, he tied a bundle of twigs to his tail, climbed up the flue, and cleaned it with all the skill of the town sweep. He sharpened the old woman's knives and scissors and mended her pots and pans neatly as any tinker. Did Dame Agnes knit, he held the skein of yarn; did she spin, he turned the spinning wheel.

Now, one morning Dame Agnes woke up with bone-cracking rheumatism. Her joints creaked, her back ached, and her knees were so stiff she could not get out of bed.

"My poor Quickset," she moaned, "today you and I must both go hungry."

At first, Quickset thought Dame Agnes meant it was the rheumatism that kept her from cooking breakfast, so he answered, "Go hungry? No, indeed. You stay comfortable; I'll make us a little broiled sausage and soft-boiled egg and brew a pot of tea for you. Then I'll sit on your lap to warm you, and soon you'll be good as new."

Before Dame Agnes could say another word, he hurried to the pantry. Opening the cupboard, he saw only bare shelves: not so much as a crust of bread or crumb of cheese, not even a dry bone or bacon rind.

"Mice!" he cried. "Eaten every scrap! They're out of hand; I've been too easy on them. I'll settle accounts with those fellows later. Now, mistress, I had best go to Master Grubble's market and buy what we need."

Dame Agnes thereupon burst into tears. "Oh, Quickset, it isn't mice; it's money. I have no more. Not a penny left for food or fuel."

"Why, mistress, you should have said something about that before now," replied Quickset. "I never would have let you come to such a state. No matter; I'll think of a way to fill your purse again. Meantime, I'll have Master Grubble give us our groceries on credit."

"Grubble? Give credit?" Dame Agnes exclaimed. "You know the only thing he gives is short weight at high prices. Alas for the days when the town had a dozen tradespeople and more: a baker, a butcher, a greengrocer, and all the others. They're gone, thanks to Master Grubble. One by one, he's gobbled them up. Schemed and swindled them out of their businesses! Now he's got the whole town under his thumb, for it's deal with Grubble or deal with no one."

"In that case," replied Quickset, "deal with him I will. Or, to put it better, he'll deal with me."

The old woman shook her head. "You'll still need money, and you shall have it; though I must do something I hoped I'd never have to do.

"Go to the linen chest," Dame Agnes went on. "At the bottom, under the good pillowslips, there's an old wool stocking. Fetch it out and bring it to me."

Puzzled, Quickset did as she asked. He found the stocking with a piece of string tied around the toe and carried it to Dame Agnes. She undid the knot, reached in, and drew out one small gold coin.

"Mistress, that's more than enough," said Quickset. "Why did you fret so? With this, we can buy all we want."

Instead of being cheered by the gold piece in her hand, Dame Agnes only sighed, "This is the last of the small savings my dear husband left to me. I've kept it all these years and promised myself never to spend it."

"Be glad you did keep it," said Quickset, "for now's the time you need it most."

"I didn't put this by for myself," Dame Agnes replied. "It was for you. I meant to leave it to you in my will. It was to be your legacy, a little something until you found another home, but I see I shall have to spend it. Once gone, it's gone, and that's the end of everything."

At this, Dame Agnes began sobbing again, but Quickset reassured her, "No need for tears. I'll see to this matter. Only let me have that gold piece a little while. I'll strike such a bargain with Master Grubble that we'll fill our pantry with meat and drink aplenty. Indeed, he'll beg me to keep the money and won't ask a penny; that I promise."

"Master Grubble, I fear, will be more than a match even for you," Dame Agnes replied. Nevertheless, she did as Quickset urged, put the coin in a leather purse, and hung it around his neck.

Quickset hurried through town to the market, where he found Master Grubble sitting on a high stool behind the counter. For all that his shelves were loaded with victuals of every kind, with meats and vegetables and fruits, Grubble looked as though he had never sampled his own wares. There was more fat on his bacon than on himself. He was lean shanked and sharp eyed, his nose narrow as a knife blade. His mouth was pursed and puckered as if he had been sipping vinegar, and his cheeks as mottled as moldy cheese. At the sight of Quickset, the storekeeper never so much as climbed down from his stool to wait on his customer, but only made a sour face. In a voice equally sour, he demanded, "What do you want? Half a pound of mouse tails? A sack of catnip? Out! No loitering! I don't cater to the cat trade."

Despite this curdled welcome, Quickset bowed and politely explained that Dame Agnes was ailing and that he had come shopping in her stead.

"Sick she must be," snorted Master Grubble, "to send a cat marketing, without even a shopping basket. How do you mean to carry off what you buy? Push it along the street with your nose?"

"Why, sir," Quickset answered, "I thought you might send your shop boy around with the parcels. I'm sure you'll do it gladly when you see the handsome order to be filled. Dame Agnes needs a joint of beef, a shoulder of mutton, five pounds of your best sausage, a dozen of the largest eggs ———"

"Not so fast," broke in the storekeeper. "Joints and shoulders, is it? Sausage and eggs? Is that what you want? Then I'll tell you what I want: cash on the counter, paid in full. Or you, my fine cat, won't have so much as a wart from one of my pickles."

"You'll be paid," Quickset replied, "and very well paid. Now that I see your prices, though, I'm not sure I brought enough money with me."

"So that's your game!" cried Grubble. "Well, go and get enough. I'll do business with you then, and not before."

"It's a weary walk home and back again," said Quickset. "Allow me a minute or two, and I'll have money to spare. That is, Master Grubble, if you'd be so kind as to lend me an egg."

"Egg?" retorted Grubble. "What's that to do with paying my bill?"

"You'll see," Quickset answered. "I guarantee you'll get all that's owing to you."

Grubble at first refused and again ordered Quickset from the shop. Only when the cat promised to pay double the price of the groceries, as well as an extra fee for the use of the egg, did the storekeeper grudgingly agree.

Taking the egg from Master Grubble, Quickset placed it on the floor, then carefully settled himself on top of it.

"Fool!" cried Grubble. "What are you doing? Get off my egg! This cat's gone mad and thinks he's a chicken!"

Quickset said nothing, but laid back his ears and waved his tail, warning Grubble to keep silent. After

another moment, Quickset got up and brought the egg to the counter.

"There, Master Grubble, that should be enough."

"What?" shouted the storekeeper. "Foolish cat! You mean to pay me with my own egg?"

"With better than that, as you'll see," answered Quickset. While Grubble fumed, Quickset neatly cracked the shell and poured the contents into a bowl.

At this, Grubble ranted all the more, "Alley rabbit! Smash my egg, will you? I'll rub your nose in it!" Suddenly Master Grubble's voice choked in his gullet. His eyes popped as he stared into the bowl. There, with the broken egg, lay a gold piece.

Instantly, he snatched it out. "What's this?"

Grubble squinted at the coin, flung it onto the counter, and listened to it ring. He bit it, peered closer, turned it round and round in his fingers, and finally blurted, "Gold!"

Grubble, in his fit of temper, had never seen Quickset slip the coin from the purse and deftly drop it into the bowl. Awestruck, he gaped at the cat, then lowered his voice to a whisper, "How did you do that?"

Quickset merely shook his head and shrugged his tail. At last, as the excited storekeeper pressed him for an answer, he winked one eye and calmly replied, "Now, now, Master Grubble, a cat has trade secrets just as a storekeeper. I don't ask yours, and you don't ask mine. If I told you how simple it is, you'd know as much as I do. And if others found out ——"

"Tell me!" cried Grubble. "I won't breathe a word to a living soul. My dear cat, listen to me," he hurried on. "You'll have all the victuals you want. For a month! A year! Forever! Here, this very moment, I'll have a cartload delivered to your mistress. Only teach me to sit on eggs as you did."

"Easily done," said Quickset. "But what about that gold piece?"

"Take it!" cried Grubble, handing the coin to Quickset. "Take it, by all means."

Quickset pretended to think over the bargain, then answered, "Agreed. But you must do exactly as I tell you."

Grubble nodded and his eyes glittered. "One gold piece for one egg. What if I used two eggs? Or three, or four, or five?"

"As many as you like," said Quickset. "A basketful, if it suits you."

Without another moment's delay, Grubble called the shop boy from the storeroom and told him to deliver all that Quickset ordered to the house of Dame Agnes. Then, whimpering with pleasure, he filled his biggest basket with every egg in the store. His nose twitched, his hands trembled, and his usually sallow face turned an eager pink.

"Now," said Quickset, "so you won't be disturbed, take your basket to the top shelf, and sit on it there. One thing more, the most important. Until those eggs hatch, don't say a single word. If you have anything to tell me, whatever the reason, you must only cluck like a chicken. Nothing else, mind you. Cackle all you like; speak but once, and the spell is broken."

"What about my customers? Who's to wait on them?" asked Grubble, unwilling to lose business even in exchange for a fortune.

"Never fear," said Quickset. "I'll mind the store."

"What a fine cat you are," purred Grubble. "Noble animal. Intelligent creature."

With that, gleefully chuckling and licking his lips, he clambered to the top shelf, hauling his heavy burden along with him. There he squatted gingerly over the basket, so cramped that he was obliged to draw his knees under his chin and fold his arms as tightly as he could, until indeed he looked much like a skinny, long-beaked chicken hunched on a nest.

Below, Quickset no sooner had taken his place on the stool than Mistress Libbet, the carpenter's wife, stepped through the door.

"Why, Quickset, what are you doing here?" said she. "Have you gone into trade? Can that be Master Grubble on the shelf? He looks as if he's sitting on a basket of eggs."

"Pay him no mind," whispered Quickset. "He fancies himself a hen. An odd notion, but harmless. However, since Master Grubble is busy nesting, I'm tending shop for him. So, Mistress Libbet, how may I serve you?"

"There's so much our little ones need," Mistress Libbet sighed unhappily, "and nothing we can afford to feed them. I was hoping Master Grubble had some scraps or trimmings."

"He has much better," said Quickset, pulling down one of the juiciest hams and slicing away at it with Grubble's carving knife. "Here's a fine bargain today: only a penny a pound."

Hearing this, Master Grubble was about to protest but caught himself in the nick of time. Instead, he began furiously clucking and squawking, "Cut-cut-cut! Aw-cut!"

"What's that you say?" Quickset glanced up at the agitated storekeeper and cupped an ear with his paw. "Cut more? Yes, yes, I understand. The price is still too high? Very well, if you insist: two pounds for a penny."

Too grateful to question such generosity on the part of Grubble, Mistress Libbet flung a penny onto the counter and seized her ham without waiting for Quickset to wrap it. As she hurried from the store, the tailor's wife and the stonecutter's daughter came in, and, in a moment later, Dame Gerton, the laundrywoman.

"Welcome, ladies," called Quickset. "Welcome, one and all. Here are fine prime meats and fine fresh vegetables on sale today. At these prices, they won't last long. So, hurry! Step up!"

As the delighted customers pressed eagerly toward the counter, Master Grubble's face changed from sallow to crimson, from crimson to purple. Cackling frantically, he waggled his head and flapped his elbows against his ribs.

"Cut-aw-cut!" he bawled. "Cut-cut-aw! Cuck-cuck! Cock-a-doodle-do!"

Once more, Quickset made a great show of listening carefully.

"Did I hear you right, Master Grubble? Give all? Free? What a generous soul you are!"

With that, Quickset began hurling meats, cheese,
vegetables, and bags of sugar into the customers' outstretched baskets. Grubble's face now turned from purple
to bilious green. He crowed, clucked, brayed, and bleated
until he sounded like a barnyard gone mad.

"Give more?" cried Quickset. "I'm doing my best!"

"Cut-aw!" shouted Grubble, and away went a chain of
sausages. "Ak-ak-cut-aak!" Away went another joint of
beef. At last, he could stand no more.

"Stop! Stop!" he roared. "Wretched cat! You'll drive
me out of business!"

Beside himself with fury, Master Grubble forgot his cramped quarters and sprang to his feet. His head struck the ceiling, and he tumbled back into the basket of eggs. As he struggled to free himself from the flood of shattered yolks, the shelf cracked beneath him, and he went plummeting headlong into a barrel of flour.

"Robber!" stormed Grubble, crawling out and shaking a fist at Quickset. "Swindler! You promised I'd hatch gold from eggs!"

"What's that?" put in the tailor's wife. "Gold from eggs? Master Grubble, you're as foolish as you are greedy."

"But a fine cackler," added the laundrywoman, flapping her arms. "Let's hear it again, your cut-cut-awk!"

"I warned you not to speak a word," Quickset told the storekeeper, who was egg-soaked at one end and floured at the other. "But you did, and so you broke the spell. Why, look at you, Master Grubble. You nearly turned yourself into a dipped pork chop. Have a care. Someone might fry you."

With that, Quickset went home to breakfast.

As for Master Grubble, when word spread that he had been so roundly tricked, and so easily, he became such a laughingstock that he left town and was never seen again. At the urging of the townsfolk, Dame Agnes and Quickset took charge of the market and ran it well and fairly. All agreed that Quickset was the cleverest cat in the world. Since Quickset had the same opinion, it was surely true.

Author

Lloyd Alexander was born in Philadelphia and wanted to be a writer from the age of fifteen. He read widely as a child, including the stories of King Arthur and Celtic mythology. "After a good many years of writing for adults," he says, "my happiest surprise came when I began writing for children." His first fantasy for children, *Time Cat*, led to his attempt to create an entire fantasy world, which he did in the five *Prydain Chronicles*, a highly acclaimed fantasy series. His books have won major awards for children's literature, including the Newbery Medal, the National Book Award, and the American Book Award. *The Town Cats and Other Tales*, from which "The Cat and the Golden Egg" was taken, was an American Library Association Notable Book and reflects the author's love of cats.

Illustrator

Alan Baker is an internationally known illustrator whose work has appeared in many children's books, magazines, posters, cards, and advertisements. Born in London in 1951, he now lives in the English countryside. His work has appeared in the Best of British and European Illustrators annuals and has been shown on British and Canadian television. He also teaches a college class in illustration.

Comprehension Questions

1. How did Quickset outwit Master Grubble?
2. Why did Quickset think that he and Dame Agnes must go hungry? What did Dame Agnes say was the real reason?
3. What kind of person was Grubble? Explain your answer.
4. Why did Grubble finally speak out and "break the spell"?

Vocabulary

To each of the words on the left, add a prefix or a suffix to make a word that fits one of the definitions on the right. Match the new word with its definition and write a sentence using the new word.

gold	in a stiff way
paid	the opposite of pleasure
green	made of gold
stiff	somewhat green
pleasure	paid before

Writing Fantasy

Think of an animal you know, and imagine that the animal could talk. Choose one of the topics below, or think of a topic of your own. Write one or two paragraphs telling what the animal would say about the topic.

Things I Would Change If I Were a Person
Why I Prefer to Be an Animal and Not a Person

Catalogue

by Rosalie Moore

Cats sleep **fat** and walk thin.
Cats, when they sleep, **slump;**
When they wake, pull in—
And where the **plump's** been
There's skin.
Cats walk thin.

Cats wait in a **lump,**
Jump in a *streak.*
Cats, when they jump, are sleek
As a grape slipping its skin—
They have technique.
Oh, cats don't creak;
They *sneak.*

Cats sleep **fat.**
They spread out comfort underneath them
Like a good mat,
As if they picked the place
And then **sat.**
You walk around one
As if he were the City Hall
After that.

If male,
A cat is apt to sing on a major scale;
This concert is for everybody—this
Is wholesale.
For a baton, he wields a tail.

(He is also found,
When happy, to resound
With an enclosed and private sound.)

A cat condenses.
He pulls in his tail to go under bridges,
And himself to go under fences.
Cats fit
In any size box or kit;
And if a large pumpkin grew under one,
He could arch over it.

When everyone else is just ready to go out,
The cat is just ready to come in.
He's not where he's been.
Cats sleep **fat** and walk thin.

Magazine Wrap-up

Literary Skill: Character Development

Authors often use a character's words to reveal something about that character. For example, in "Gramp," Simon says, "I'll find him one somewhere. I will. I'll find him one." This tells you that Simon is very *determined* to find a bench for Gramp.

Write the numbers 1–4 on your paper. Read each character's words below. Then find a word in the box that describes the character. Write the word next to the number on your paper.

kind	**self-confident**
greedy	**hot-tempered**

1. Master Grubble in "The Cat and the Golden Egg": "One gold piece for one egg. What if I used two eggs? Or three, or four, or five?"
2. Holly Garner in "Pearson, A Harbor Seal Pup": "Don't worry, little fellow; you're going to be okay."
3. Captain Snard in "Stormalong Goes to Sea": "If you don't shift your weight more to the port side, I'll need a salvage crew more than a cabin boy!"
4. Quickset in "The Cat and the Golden Egg": "In that case, deal with him I will. Or, to put it better, he'll deal with me."

Vocabulary: Sea Talk

Use words from the box to complete the paragraphs below. Copy the paragraphs on your paper.

capsize	**deck**
stern	**bow**
keel	**list**

The moment you step aboard a boat, you begin to learn a new language. The floor beneath your feet is no longer called the floor, but the _____. As you face forward, you see not the front of the boat, but the _____. Behind you is the _____.

With luck, your sail will be smooth, but strong winds can cause the boat to _____ to one side. In such strong winds a small boat might _____, or turn over, but most larger boats have a heavy _____ on the bottom that helps keep the boat steady.

Comprehension Skills: Following Directions and Reading Diagrams

A bowline is one of the most useful knots aboard a boat, and it is very easy to tie. Follow the directions and use the diagram to learn to tie a bowline.

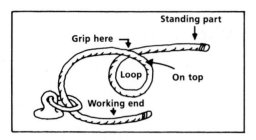

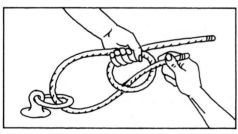

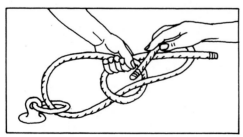

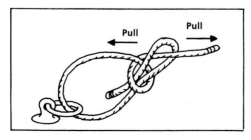

First take a piece of rope or heavy string and make a loop, as shown in the diagram. Your rope should look like a numeral 6, with the loop being the base. Notice that the stem of the 6 is called the *standing part* of the rope and the other end is the *working end*.

Bring the working end up through the loop. Then bring the working end around the standing part and down through the loop beside itself. Finish by pulling the standing part and the loop until the knot is tight.

Practice tying a bowline a few times, and then teach it to a friend.

Books to Enjoy

The Secret Carousel
by Claudia Mills

A carousel, school plays, and a garden she tends with her grandfather enrich Lindy's life.

Sure Hands, Strong Heart: The Life of Daniel Hale Williams
by Lillie Patterson

This noted black surgeon was the first person to successfully perform open-heart surgery.

Raven the Trickster
by Gail Robinson

Here are nine legends of the Native Americans of the Northwest.

Explorations
Magazine Three

Contents

Stories

The Wise Old Woman

Adapted by Yoshiko Uchida

The lord ordered all the older people to leave the village, but when the village was threatened with destruction, he learned a valuable lesson. What did he learn?

Many long years ago, there lived a cruel young lord who ruled over a small village in the western hills of Japan.

"I have no use for old people in my village," he said. "They are neither useful nor able to work for a living. I decree that anyone over seventy-one must be sent away from the village and left in the mountains to die."

"What a terrible decree! What a cruel and unreasonable lord we have," the people of the village murmured. However, the lord punished anyone who disobeyed him, and so those who turned seventy-one were carried into the mountains, never to return.

Gradually there were fewer and fewer old people in the village, and soon they disappeared altogether. Then the young lord was pleased.

"What a fine village of young, healthy, and hard-working people I have," he bragged. "Soon it will be the finest village in all of Japan."

Now there lived in this village a kind young farmer and his aged mother. They were poor, but the farmer was good to his mother, and the two of them lived happily together. However, as the years went by, the mother grew older. Before long she reached the terrible age of seventy-one.

"If only I could somehow fool the cruel lord," the farmer thought; but there were records in the village books, and everyone knew that his mother had turned seventy-one.

Each day the son put off telling his mother that he must take her into the mountains to die, but the people of the village began to talk. The farmer knew that if he did not take his mother away soon, the lord would send his soldiers and throw them both into a dark dungeon to die a terrible death.

"Mother ——" he would begin, as he tried to tell her what he must do, but he could not go on.

Then one day the mother herself spoke of the lord's dreadful decree. "Well, my son," she said, "the time has come for you to take me to the mountains. We must hurry, before the lord sends his soldiers for you." She did not seem worried at all that she must go to the mountains to die.

"Forgive me, dear mother, for what I must do," the farmer said sadly, and the next morning he lifted his mother to his shoulders and set off on the steep path toward the mountains.

Up and up he climbed, until the trees were close together and the path was gone. There was no longer even the sound of birds, and they heard only the soft cry of the wind in the trees. The son walked slowly, for he could not bear to think of leaving his old mother in the mountains. On and on he climbed, not wanting to stop and leave her behind. Soon, he heard his mother breaking off small twigs from the trees that they passed.

"Mother, what are you doing?" he asked.

"Do not worry, my son," she answered gently. "I am just marking the way, so you will not get lost returning to the village."

The son stopped. "Even now you are thinking of me?" he asked.

The mother nodded. "Of course, my son," she said. "You will always be in my thoughts. How could it be otherwise?"

At that, the young farmer could bear it no longer. "Mother, I cannot leave you in the mountains to die," he said. "We are going home, and no matter what the lord does to punish me, I will never desert you again."

So they waited until the sun had set and a lone star crept into the silent sky. Then in the dark shadows of night, the farmer carried his mother down the hill, and they returned quietly to their little house. The farmer dug a deep hole in the floor of his kitchen and made a small room where he could hide his mother. From that day, she spent all her time in the secret room, and the farmer carried meals to her there. The rest of the time, he was careful to work in the fields and act as though he lived alone. In this way, for almost two years, he kept his mother safely hidden, and no one in the village knew that she was there.

Then one day there was a terrible uproar in the village, for Lord Higa[1] of the town beyond the hills threatened to conquer their village and make it his own.

"Only one thing can save you," Lord Higa announced. "Bring me a box holding one thousand ropes of ash, and I will save your village."

The cruel young lord quickly gathered together all the wise people of his village. "You are people of wisdom," he said.

---

[1] **Higa** (hē gä)

"Surely you can tell me how to meet Lord Higa's demands so our village can be saved."

The wise people shook their heads. "It is impossible to make even one rope of ash, sir," they answered. "How can we ever make one thousand?"

"Fools!" the lord cried in anger. "What good is your wisdom if you cannot help me now?"

He posted a notice in the village square offering a great reward of gold to any person who could help him.

All the people in the village whispered, "Surely it is an impossible thing, for ash crumbles at the touch of the finger. How could anyone ever make a rope of ash?" They shook their heads and sighed, "Alas, alas, we must be conquered by yet another cruel lord."

The young farmer, too, supposed that this must be, and he wondered what would happen to his mother if a new lord even more terrible than their own came to rule over them.

When his mother saw the troubled look on his face, she asked, "Why are you so worried, my son?"

The farmer told her of the impossible demand that had to be met if the village was to be saved, but his mother did not seem troubled at all. Instead she laughed softly and said, "Why, that is not such an impossible task. All one has to do is soak ordinary rope in salt water and dry it well. When it is burned, it will hold its shape, and there is your rope of ash! Tell the villagers to hurry and find one thousand pieces of rope."

The farmer shook his head in amazement. "Mother, you are wonderfully wise," he said, and he rushed to tell the young lord what he must do.

"You are wiser than all the wise people of the village," the lord said when he heard the farmer's solution, and he rewarded him with many pieces of gold. The thousand ropes of ash were quickly made, and the village was saved.

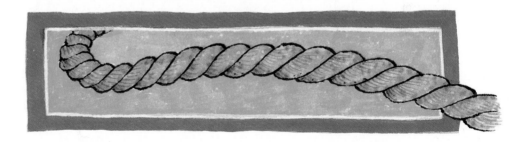

In a few days, however, there was another great uproar in the village as Lord Higa sent another threat. This time he sent a log with a small hole that curved and bent seven times through its length, and he demanded that a single piece of silk thread be threaded through the hole. "If you cannot perform this task," he said, "I shall come to conquer your village."

The young lord hurried once more to the wise people, but they all shook their heads. "A needle cannot bend its way through such curves," they moaned. "Again we are faced with an impossible demand."

"Again you are stupid fools!" the lord said, stamping his foot. He then posted a second notice in the village square asking the villagers for their help.

Once more the young farmer hurried to his mother in her secret room.

"Why, that is not so hard," his mother said with a quick smile. "Put some sugar at one end of the hole. Then tie a piece of silk thread to an ant, and put the ant in at the other end. It will weave its way in and out of the curves to get to the sugar. The ant will take the silk thread with it."

"Mother, you are remarkable!" the son cried, and he hurried off to the lord with the solution to the second problem.

Once more the lord rewarded the young farmer with many pieces of gold. "You are a brilliant man, and you have saved our village again," he said gratefully.

However, the lord's troubles were not over even then. A few days later Lord Higa sent still another demand. "This time you will undoubtedly fail, and then I shall conquer your village," he threatened. "Bring me a drum that sounds without being beaten."

"That is not possible," sighed the people of the village. "How can anyone make a drum sound without beating it?"

This time the wise people held their heads in their hands and moaned, "It is hopeless. It is hopeless. This time Lord Higa will conquer us all."

The young farmer hurried home. "Mother, Mother, we must solve another terrible problem, or Lord Higa will conquer our village!" He quickly told his mother about the impossible drum.

His mother, however, smiled and answered, "Why, this is the easiest of them all. Make a drum with sides of paper, and put a bumblebee inside. As it tries to escape, it will buzz and beat itself against the paper, and you will have a drum that sounds without being beaten."

The young farmer was amazed at his mother's wisdom. "You are far wiser than any of the wise people of the village," he said, and he hurried to tell the young lord how to meet Lord Higa's third demand.

When the lord heard the answer, he was greatly impressed. "Surely a young man like you cannot be wiser than all the wise people of the village," he said. "Tell me honestly, who has helped you with all these difficult problems?"

The young farmer could not lie. "My lord," he began slowly, "for the past two years I have broken the law of the land. I have kept my aged mother hidden beneath the floor of my house. It is she who solved each of your problems and saved the village from Lord Higa."

He shook as he spoke, for he feared the lord's displeasure and anger. Surely now the soldiers would be summoned to throw him into the dark dungeon. When he glanced at the lord, however, he saw that the young ruler was not angry at all. Instead, he was silent and thoughtful, for at last he realized how much wisdom old people possess.

"I have been very wrong," he said finally. "I must ask the forgiveness of your mother and of all my people. Never again will I demand that the old people of our village be sent to the mountains to die. Rather, they will be treated with the respect and honor they deserve and share with us the wisdom of their years."

And so it was. From that day, the old people of the village were no longer forced to leave, and the village became once more a happy, cheerful place in which to live. The terrible Lord Higa stopped sending his impossible demands and no longer threatened to conquer them, for he, too, was impressed. "Even in such a small village there is much wisdom," he declared. "Its people should be allowed to live in peace."

And that is exactly what the farmer, his mother, and all the people of the village did for all the years thereafter.

Author

"Although I was born in California," says Yoshiko Uchida, "a good bit of Japan was inside me all along, for this was the country from which my parents came." Among the many award-winning books she has written are collections of Japanese folktales, such as *The Sea of Gold,* from which "The Wise Old Woman" was taken, and stories of Japanese or Japanese-American children.

Comprehension Questions

1. What lesson did the young lord learn? Explain how he learned it.
2. Why did the lord want to send older people away to die?
3. Why was the farmer unable to tell his mother that he would soon be forced to take her away to die?
4. What made the farmer decide to return to the village with his mother instead of leaving her in the mountains?

Vocabulary

Read these two titles:
"The Wise Old Woman"   "The Smart Elderly Woman"
In the second title, synonyms have been substituted for two of the words in the first title. Below are some sentences from "The Wise Old Woman." Rewrite each sentence, using a synonym for the boldface word. Use a dictionary if you need help.

1. Many long years ago, there lived a **cruel** young lord.
2. "What a terrible **decree**!"
3. A **lone** star crept into the **silent** sky.
4. Lord Higa threatened to **conquer** the village.

Writing a Book Report

Find a collection of folktales in the library. Choose a tale that you like. Write a report on the tale, giving a brief summary and telling what you liked about it.

Best Friends

by Nicholasa Mohr

Felita and Gigi had been best friends for as long as they could remember. Would a class play ruin their friendship?

A wonderful thing happened this new school year. My friends Gigi, Consuela, and Paquito were all put in the same class with me. It had never happened before. Once I was in the same class with Consuela, and last year Gigi and Paquito were together. But this — it was too good to be true! Of course, knowing that Gigi and I were in the same class made me the happiest.

Our teacher, Miss Lovett, was friendly and laughed easily. In early October, after we had all settled into our class and gotten used to the routine of school once more, Miss Lovett told us that this year our class was going to put on a play for Thanksgiving. The play we were going to perform was based on a poem by Henry Wadsworth Longfellow called "The Courtship of Miles Standish." It was about the Pilgrims and how they lived when they first landed in America.

We were all so excited about the play. Miss Lovett called for volunteers to help with the sets and costumes. Paquito and I agreed to help with the sets. Consuela was going to work on make-up. Gigi had not volunteered for anything. When we asked her what she was going to do, she shrugged and didn't answer.

Miss Lovett said we could all audition for the different parts in the play. I was really interested in being Priscilla. She is the heroine. Both Captain Miles Standish and the handsome, young John Alden are in love with her. She is the most beautiful woman in Plymouth, Massachusetts. That's where the Pilgrims used to live. I told my friends how much I would like to play that part. Everyone said I would be perfect . . . except Gigi. She said that it was a hard part to do and maybe I wouldn't be able to play it. I really got annoyed and asked her what she meant.

"I just don't think you are right to play Priscilla, that's all," she said.

"What do you mean by *right?*" I asked. But Gigi only shrugged and didn't say another word. She was beginning to get on my nerves.

Auditions for the parts were going to start Tuesday. Lots of kids had volunteered to audition. Paquito said he would try out for the brave Captain Miles Standish. Consuela said she was too afraid to get up in front of everybody. Gigi didn't show any interest in the play and refused to even talk to us about it.

Finally the day came for the girls to read for the part of Priscilla. I was so excited I could hardly wait. Miss Lovett had given us some lines to study, and I had practiced real hard. She called out all the names of those who were going to read. I was surprised when I heard her call out "Georgina Mercado." I didn't even know Gigi wanted to try out for Priscilla. I looked at Gigi, but she ignored me. We began reading. It was my turn. I was very nervous and kept forgetting my lines. I had to look down at the script a whole lot. Several other girls were almost as nervous as I was. Then it was Gigi's turn. She recited the part almost by heart. She hardly looked at the script. I noticed that she was wearing one of her best dresses. She had never looked that good in school before. When she finished, everybody clapped. It was obvious that she was the best one. Miss Lovett made a fuss.

"You were wonderful, Georgina," she said. "You were made for the part!" Boy, would I have liked another chance. I bet I could have done better than Gigi.

Why hadn't she told me she wanted the part? It's a free country, after all. She could read for the same part I read for. I wasn't going to stop her! I was really angry at Gigi.

After school everyone was still making a fuss over Gigi. Even Paquito had to open his mouth.

"Oh, man, Gigi!" he said. "You were really good. I liked the part when John Alden asked you to marry Captain Miles

Standish, and you said, 'Why don't you speak for yourself, John?' You turned your head like this." Paquito imitated Gigi and closed his eyes. "That was really neat!" Consuela and the others laughed and agreed.

I decided I wasn't walking home with them.

"I have to meet my brothers down by the next street," I said. "I'm leaving. See you." They hardly noticed. Only Consuela said good-by. The rest just kept on hanging all over Gigi. "Big deal," I thought.

Just before all the casting was completed, Miss Lovett offered me a part as one of the Pilgrim women. All I had to do was stand in the background, like a zombie. It wasn't even a speaking part.

"I don't get to say one word," I protested.

"Felicidad Maldonado, you are designing the stage sets, and you're assistant stage manager. I think that's quite a bit. Besides, all the speaking parts are taken."

"I'm not interested, thank you," I answered.

"You know," Miss Lovett shook her head, "you can't be the best in everything."

I turned and left. I didn't need to play any part at all. Who cared?

Gigi came over to me the next day with a great big smile all over her face. I just turned away and made believe she wasn't there.

"Felita, are you taking the part of the Pilgrim woman?" she asked me in her sweetest voice, just as though nothing had happened.

"No," I said, still not looking at her. If she thought I was going to fall all over her like the other kids, she was wasting her time.

"Oh" was all she said, and walked away.

"Good," I thought. "I don't need her one bit!"

At home Mami noticed something was wrong.

"Felita, what's the matter? You aren't going out at all, and I haven't seen Gigi for quite a while. In fact, I haven't seen any of your friends."

"Nothing is the matter, Mami. I've just got lots of things to do."

"You didn't have a fight with Gigi or something, did you?"

"Now, why would I have a fight with anybody?"

"Don't raise your voice, miss," Mami said. "Sorry I asked. Now you just calm down."

The play was going to be performed on the day before Thanksgiving. I made the drawings for most of the scenery. I made a barn, a church, trees and grass, cows, and a horse. I helped the others make a real scarecrow. We used a broom and old clothes. Paquito didn't get the part of Captain Miles Standish, but he made a wonderful fence out of cardboard. It looked just like a real wooden fence. Consuela brought in her mother's old leftover make-up, and she did a good job of making-up everybody.

By the time we set up the stage, everything looked beautiful. Gigi had tried to talk to me a few times, but I just couldn't be nice back to her. She acted as if nothing had happened, as if I was supposed to forget she hadn't told me she was going to read for the part! I wasn't going to forget that just because she was now Miss Popularity. She could go and stay with all her newfound friends for all I cared!

The morning of the play, at breakfast, everybody noticed how excited I was.

"Felita," Papi exclaimed, "stop jumping around and eat your breakfast."

"She's all excited about the school play today," Mami said.

"That's right. Are you playing a part in the play?" Papi asked.

"No," I replied.

"But she's done most of the sets — drawing and designing. Isn't that right, Felita?"

"Mami, it was no big deal."

"That's nice," said Papi. "Tell us about it."

"What kind of sets did you do?" Johnny asked.

"I don't know. Look, I don't want to talk about it."

"Boy, are you touchy today," Tito said with a laugh.

"Leave me alone!" I snapped.

"Okay." Mami stood up. "Enough. Felita, are you finished?" I nodded. "Good. Go to school. When you come back, bring home a better mood. Whatever is bothering you, no need to take it out on us." Quickly I left the table.

The play was a tremendous hit. Everybody looked wonderful and played their parts really well. The stage was brilliant with the colors of my drawings. The background of the countryside, the barn, and just about everything stood out clearly.

No doubt about it — Gigi was perfect as Priscilla. The kids clapped and cheered for the entire cast, but Gigi got more applause than anybody else. She just kept on taking bows.

Afterward Miss Lovett had a party for our class. We had lots of treats. There was even a record player, and we all danced. We had a really good time.

Of course Priscilla, alias Gigi, was the big star. She just couldn't get enough attention. But not from me, that was for sure. After the party, Gigi spoke to me.

"Your sets were really great. Everybody said the stage looked wonderful."

"Thanks." I looked away.

"Felita, are you mad at me?"

"Why should I be mad at you?"

"Well, I did get the leading part, but . . ."

"Big deal," I said. "I really don't care."

"You don't? But — I ——"

"Look," I said, interrupting her, "I have to go. I promised my mother I'd get home early. We have to go someplace."

I rushed all the way home. I didn't know why, but I was still furious with Gigi. What was worse was that I was unhappy about having those feelings. Gigi and I had been close for as far back as I could remember. Not being able to share things with her really bothered me.

We had a great Thanksgiving. The dinner was just delicious. Abuelita[1] asked me if I wanted to go home with her that evening. Boy, was I happy to get away. I just couldn't face another day of Mami asking me questions about Gigi.

It felt good to be with Abuelita in her apartment. We fixed the day bed for me. Then Tío[2] Jorge, Abuelita, and I had some flan. After Tío Jorge went off to bed, Abuelita and I sat quietly for a while. Then Abuelita spoke.

"You are getting to be a big girl now, Felita. You just turned ten years old. My goodness!"

I hugged Abuelita. I loved her the best, more than anybody. I hadn't been to stay with her since the summer, and somehow this time things felt different. I noticed how tired she looked. She wasn't moving as quickly as she used to. Also I didn't feel so little next to her anymore.

"Tell me, Felita, how have you been? It's been a long time since we were together like this." She smiled her wonderful smile at me. Her dark, bright eyes looked deeply into mine. I felt her warmth and happiness.

"I'm okay, Abuelita."

"Tell me about your play at school. Rosa tells me you worked on the stage sets. Was the play a success?"

---

[1]**Abuelita** (ä bo͞o ä lē′tə): Grandmother.

[2]**Tío** (tē′ō): Uncle.

"It was. It was great. The stage looked beautiful. My drawings stood out really well. I never made such big drawings in my life. There was a farm in the country, a barn, and animals. I made it the way it used to be in the olden days of the Pilgrims. You know, how it was when they first came to America."

"I'm so proud of you. Tell me about the play. Did you act in it?"

"No." I paused. "I didn't want to."

"I see. Tell me a little about the story."

I told Abuelita all about it.

"Who played the parts? Any of your friends?"

"Some."

"Who?"

"Well, Charlie Martinez played John Alden. Louie Collins played Captain Miles Standish. You don't know them. Mary Jackson played the part of the narrator — that's the person who tells the story. You really don't know any of them."

I was hoping she wouldn't ask, but she did.

"Who played the part of the woman both men love?"

"Oh, her? Gigi."

"Gigi Mercado, your best friend?" I nodded. "Was she good?"

"Yes, she was. Very good."

"You don't sound too happy about that."

"I don't care," I shrugged.

"But if she is your best friend, I should think you would care."

"I . . . I don't know if she is my best friend anymore, Abuelita."

"Why do you say that?"

I couldn't answer. I just felt awful.

"Did she do something? Did you two argue?" I nodded. "May I ask what happened?"

"Well, it's hard to explain — but what she did wasn't fair."

"Fair about what, Felita?"

I hadn't spoken about it before. Now, with Abuelita, it was easy to talk about it.

"Well, we all tried out for the different parts. Everybody knew what everybody was trying out for, but Gigi never told anybody she was going to try out for Priscilla. She kept it a great big secret. Even after I told her that I wanted to try for the part, she kept quiet about it. Do you know what she did say? She said I wasn't right for it . . . it was a hard part and all that baloney. She just wanted the part for herself, so she was mysterious about the whole thing. As if . . . it was . . . I don't know."

I stopped for a moment, trying to figure the whole thing out. "After all, I am supposed to be her best friend . . . her very best friend. Why shouldn't she let me know that she wanted to be Priscilla? I wouldn't care. I let her know my plans. I didn't go sneaking around."

"Are you angry because Gigi got the part?"

It was hard for me to answer. I thought about it for a little while. "Abuelita, I don't think so. She was really good in the part."

"Were you as good when you tried out for Priscilla?"

"No." I looked at Abuelita. "I was awful." We both laughed.

"Then maybe you are not angry at Gigi at all."

"What do you mean?"

"Well, maybe you are a little bit . . . hurt?"

"Hurt?" I felt confused.

"Do you know what I think? I think you are hurt because your best friend didn't trust you. From what you tell me, you trusted her, but she didn't have faith in you. What do you think?"

"Yes," I nodded. "Abuelita, yes. I don't know why. Gigi and I always tell each other everything. Why did she act like that with me?"

"Have you asked her?"

"No."

"Why not? Aren't you two speaking to each other?"

"We're speaking. Gigi tried to be friendly a few times."

"Don't you want to stay her friend?"

"I do. Only she came over to me acting like . . . like nothing ever happened. And something did happen! What does she think — that she can go around being sneaky, and I'm going to fall all over her? Just because she got the best part, she thinks she's special."

"You think that's why she came over — because she wants to be special?"

"I don't know."

"You should give her a chance. Perhaps Gigi acted in a strange way for a reason."

"She wasn't nice to me, Abuelita. She wasn't."

"I'm not saying that she was — or even that she was right. *Mira*[3], Felita, friendship is one of the best things in this whole world. It's one of the few things you can't go out and buy. It's like love. You can buy clothes, food, even luxuries; but there's no place I know of where you can buy a real friend. Do you?"

I shook my head. Abuelita smiled at me and waited. We were both silent for a long moment.

"Abuelita, do you think it's a good idea for me to . . . maybe talk to Gigi?"

"You know, that's a very good idea," Abuelita nodded.

"Well, she did try to talk to me a few times. . . . Only, I won't know what to say to her. I mean, after what's happened and all."

"After so many years of being close, I am sure you could say 'Hello, Gigi. How are you?' That should be easy enough."

"I feel better already, Abuelita."

I kept thinking of what Abuelita had said, and on Monday I waited for Gigi after school. It was as if she knew I wanted to talk. She came over to me.

"Hello, Gigi," I said. "How are you?"

"Fine." Gigi smiled. "Want to walk home together?"

"Let's take the long way so we can be by ourselves," I said.

We walked without saying anything for a couple of blocks. Finally I spoke.

---

[3]**Mira** (mē′rə): Look.

"I wanted to tell you, Gigi, you were really great as Priscilla."

"Did you really like me? Oh, Felita, I'm so glad. I wanted you to like me, more than anybody else. Of course, it was nothing compared to the sets you did. They were something special. Everybody liked them so much."

"You were right too," I said. "I wasn't very good for the part of Priscilla."

"Look." Gigi stopped walking and looked at me. "I'm sorry about . . . about the way I acted. I didn't say anything to you or the others, because, well, I was scared you all would think I was silly or something. I mean, you wanted the part, too, so I figured, 'Better not say anything.'"

"I wouldn't have cared, Gigi. Honest."

"Felita . . . it's just that you are so good at a lot of things. You draw just fantastically. You beat everybody at hopscotch and kick-the-can. You know about nature and animals — much more than the rest of us. Everything you do is always better than . . . what I do! I just wanted to be better than you this time. For once I didn't want to worry about you. Felita, I'm sorry."

I was shocked. I didn't know Gigi felt that way. I didn't feel as if I was better than anybody at anything I did. She looked so upset, as if she was about to cry any minute. I could see she was miserable, and I wanted to comfort her.

"Well, you didn't have to worry, 'cause I was awful." We both laughed with relief. "I think I was the worst one!"

"Oh, no, you weren't." Gigi laughed. "Jenny Fuentes was the most awful."

"Worse than me?"

"Much worse." Gigi and I burst into laughter.

"And how about that Louie Collins? I didn't think he read better than Paquito."

"Right," Gigi agreed. "I don't know how he got through the play. He was shaking so much that I was scared the sets would fall right on his head."

It was so much fun — Gigi and I talking about the play and how we felt about everybody and everything. It was just like before, only better.

Author

Nicholasa Mohr is well known as an artist and an author of award-winning realistic books about city teenagers. You have just read part of her fourth book, *Felita*, which was chosen as a Notable Children's Trade Book in the Field of Social Studies in 1979. Ms. Mohr grew up in New York City, in a neighborhood much like Felita's.

Thinking It Over

Comprehension Questions

1. How did the class play affect Felita and Gigi's friendship?
2. How did Felita *think* she felt when she realized Gigi was going to audition for the play? How did she *really* feel?
3. Mami realized that something was wrong with Felita because she had certain clues. What were they?
4. Who helped Felita realize why Gigi's actions upset her so much?
5. Why didn't Gigi tell Felita that she was going to audition for the play?

Vocabulary

The following words from "Best Friends" are words that are used in the theater. Make up a Glossary of Theater Terms composed of these words. Make your entries look like those in the Glossary in the back of this book.

set	scenery
lines	narrator
script	audition
part	stage manager

Writing a Play

"Best Friends" can be turned into a play rather easily. Write one scene in the play. Begin by describing the cast of characters and the setting. Then write the dialogue and stage directions, or what the actors are supposed to do.

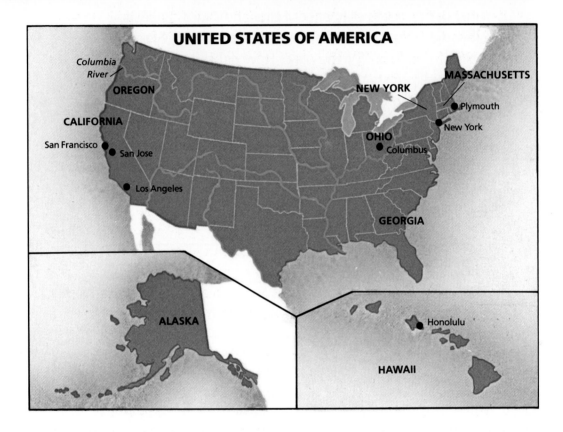

UNITED STATES OF AMERICA

Columbia River

OREGON

CALIFORNIA

San Francisco ● San Jose

● Los Angeles

NEW YORK

MASSACHUSETTS

● Plymouth

New York

OHIO

● Columbus

GEORGIA

ALASKA

HAWAII

● Honolulu

When the Pilgrims first landed at Plymouth Rock, many of the places in the land that would become the United States of America did not have names. The Pilgrims, like others that followed, named their settlement after a place in the country they came from. *Plymouth,* Massachusetts, was named after a seaport in England. Later, other settlers would name *New York* after the town of York in England and the Duke of York.

Many place names in the United States come from Native American languages. The Native Americans had names for their rivers, mountains, and villages. Many times, settlers used the Native American names. *Massachusetts,* for example, got its name from the people who lived there. It means "at the big hill" and refers to the Blue Hills near Boston. *Ohio* means "something great" in the language of the Iroquois. It refers to the Ohio River. *Iowa* comes from a Sioux word meaning "sleepy ones." It was the name the Sioux gave to their enemies who lived in what is now Iowa. The name *Alaska* comes from the language of the Aleuts. It means "great land," or "mainland." On the other side of the country, *Honolulu* means "sheltered bay" in Hawaiian.

Some European settlers made up their own names or named places after explorers or rulers. *Columbus,* Ohio, and the *Columbia River* in Oregon are both named after Christopher Columbus. *Georgia* is named for England's King George.

Spanish settlers often named places after saints. *San Francisco* is named after St. Francis, and *San Jose* is named after St. Joseph. Both these cities are in *California,* which is not named after a saint, but for an island in a Spanish adventure story of the 1500's. In the story the island was supposed to be covered with gold. Later, settlers discovered that the real California, although not an island, was indeed a land filled with gold. *Los Angeles,* also in California, is Spanish for "the angels," and is short for "the Queen of the Angels."

Some place names come from a regional custom or activity. According to legend, the town of Nags Head, North Carolina, acquired its name from the islanders' practice of tying lanterns to the necks of ponies, or nags, at night and then marching them along the sand dunes. The swinging lights looked like boats at anchor. Ship captains were deceived into running aground, and then the islanders seized their cargo.

The names of some places are just plain silly — like *Nameless,* Tennessee, a small settlement that for years went without a name. One day the post office told the people that the place had to have a name to which letters could be addressed. Some people in the community wanted patriotic names, some wanted names from nature, and one man even wanted his own name. They argued for days, until at last one fellow said he didn't like the mail he received anyway. "Forget the post office," he declared. "This is a nameless place if I ever saw one, so leave it be." And that's just what they did!

How do you think these places might have been named: *Mars,* Pennsylvania; *Needmore,* Alabama; *Chili,* Indiana; *Looking-glass,* Oregon; *Truth or Consequences,* New Mexico; *Ore City,* Texas?

MISS LOUISA
and the
OUTLAWS

by Frances B. Watts

Each year, for more than thirty years, Miss Louisa has taught her students the meaning of courage. Even so, today's lesson will stand out from all the others. . . .

CAST OF CHARACTERS

Narrator . . . . .Cynthia Harwood
Miss Louisa, *schoolteacher*. . .Stephanie Pierce
Caroline, *pupil* . . . . .Elizabeth Lennon
William, *pupil* . . . . .Eric Hinton
Annabelle, *pupil* . . . . .Tina Rodriguez
Clara, *pupil* . . . . .Christine Daniels
Regina, *pupil* . . . . .Judy Sakowitz
Benny, *outlaw* . . . . .Clifton Phillips
Dead-Eye Dan, *outlaw* . . . . .James Haggerty
Sheriff . . . . .Maurice Simpson
Ed, *his deputy* . . . . .Samuel Patrick

Presented by the pupils of the Madison School

Narrator: Many years ago, around the turn of the century, a history lesson is beginning in a little one-room schoolhouse in the West. The teacher is Miss Louisa, and her students, Caroline, William, Annabelle, Clara, and Regina, are sitting at attention with their hands folded.

Miss Louisa: For our history lesson this afternoon, you all were to learn the first three stanzas of "Paul Revere's Ride." Caroline, would you come to the front of the room and recite, please?

Caroline: Uh — uh — "Listen, my" — uh — "children, and you shall hear." Uh — uh ——

Miss Louisa *(Sternly):* I see that you haven't studied your lesson, Caroline. You will stay after school and learn the lines before you leave this afternoon. Do you understand?

Caroline *(Mumbling):* Yes.

Miss Louisa: Remember your manners! Yes *what,* Caroline?

Caroline *(Speaking with respect):* Yes, *Miss Louisa.*

Miss Louisa: William, let's see how well you have learned the stanzas.

William: Uh — uh, "Listen, my children, and you shall hear." Uh — uh. "Of the midnight ride of Paul Revere." Uh — uh ——

Miss Louisa: Another shirker! William, you will join Caroline after school. Do you understand?

William *(Mumbling):* Yes.

Miss Louisa: Yes, *what,* William?

William *(With respect):* Yes, *Miss Louisa.*

Miss Louisa *(Sighing):* Students, I realize that this poem may seem a bit dull and uninteresting, but I'm asking you to memorize it in hopes that you will recognize the courage and strength some of our ancestors possessed when they founded our great country. Do you have any idea what courage is?

Pupils *(After a moment's hesitation):* No, Miss Louisa.

Miss Louisa: Well, courage is behaving bravely when you are most afraid. All of us, at some time, have been afraid. Those who discipline themselves and control fear in times of stress are exhibiting courage. Is that clear?

Pupils: Yes, Miss Louisa.

Miss Louisa: Annabelle, do you think that you can recite the lines for us?

Annabelle: Yes, Miss Louisa. *(Reciting):*

"Listen, my children, and you shall hear
Of the midnight ride of Paul Revere."

(As Annabelle recites the poem, Benny and Dead-Eye Dan, two outlaws, enter the schoolroom with drawn guns.)

Benny: Stay where you are!

Caroline *(Fearfully):* Outlaws! It's Benny the Kid and Dead-Eye Dan — the ones who robbed Dodge City Bank last week!

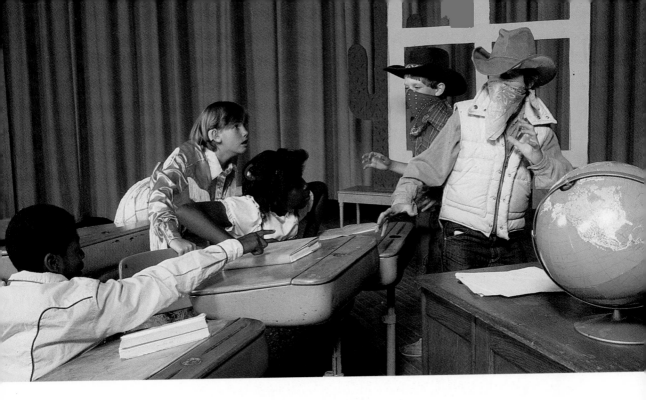

William: It is! It is! Their pictures are up in the post office. Wanted, dead or alive! A hundred dollars reward! *(Pupils scream with terror and run to the back of the room. Miss Louisa raps on her desk with a ruler for attention.)*

Miss Louisa *(Sternly)*: Back to your seats, everyone! How often have I told you never to leave your seats without permission? Sit down at once!

Dan: Nobody's going to get hurt, kiddies, as long as you set there quiet.

Miss Louisa *(With great dignity)*: Watch your grammar in front of my pupils, sir. The proper expression is *sit there quietly* — not *set there quiet*.

Dan *(Baffled)*: Huh? Oh. As long as you *sit there quietly*.

Benny: Just in case somebody tipped off the sheriff that we're in town, my pal Dan and me are going to hide out here till the two-thirty freight train comes through. Then we'll make our getaway. So don't anybody get any bright ideas, like yelling out the window or running for help. See?

Dan: Let's take a load off our feet. We can sit at those two empty desks. May as well be comfortable till train time.

Miss Louisa *(Firmly)*: Just a moment, Daniel! I believe that is your name. You and Benjamin will kindly wipe your feet on the mat in the doorway before you sit down.

Benny *(In confusion)*: Say, what is this? Dan and me got guns. We don't have to take orders from you.

Miss Louisa: It's *Dan and I have guns,* sir. As long as you and Benjamin take refuge here, I shall insist that you obey the laws and rules of our schoolhouse. Kindly wipe your feet, gentlemen!

Dan *(Grudgingly)*: All right. All right. We'll wipe our feet.

Miss Louisa: Mind your manners, sir. When I speak to you, you are to answer, "Yes, Miss Louisa." Do you understand?

Benny *and* **Dan** *(Meekly)*: Yes, Miss Louisa.

Miss Louisa: All right, you may sit down now.

Benny *(Aside, puzzled)*: I don't know why we let this schoolteacher lead us around by the nose, Dan. By all rights, we ought to tie her up in the closet.

Miss Louisa *(Brisk and efficient)*: Well, students, we shall continue our history lesson tomorrow. It is now time for music. Let's have a song — a jolly one. How about "Old MacDonald Had a Farm"?

Regina: We can't sing, Miss Louisa. We — we're too scared!

Miss Louisa: Afraid, Regina? Of what is there to be afraid? As far as we are concerned, we simply have two extra pupils in our room. We will follow our usual schedule.
(Miss Louisa *takes her pitch pipe from her pocket and sounds the key.* Pupils *begin to sing.* Miss Louisa *suddenly raps on her desk with the ruler, interrupting the song, and speaks sternly to* Benny *and* Dan.)

Miss Louisa: Benjamin and Daniel, why aren't you singing?

Dan *(Bewildered)*: Huh? Why should we sing?

Clara *(Earnestly)*: Because, when we have music in this school, everybody sings.

Annabelle: That means *everybody*. It's a school rule.

Miss Louisa: Clara and Annabelle, this is not your affair. *(Firmly)*: When we start to sing again, you will sing. Do you understand?

Benny *(Mumbling)*: Yes.

Miss Louisa: Yes *what*, Benjamin?

Benny: Yes, Miss Louisa.

> (Miss Louisa *blows on her pitch pipe again and waves her arms as she leads the song. The pupils' spirits rise as they sing. The faces of* Benny *and* Dan *are very serious as they sing along with* Pupils. *When the song ends,* Miss Louisa *goes to the window and gazes out with a worried frown.* Benny *and* Dan *jump up and draw their guns.)*

Benny: Stay away from that window, ma'am. We're not giving you the chance to signal for help.

Dan: You may be a schoolteacher, but you can't outsmart us. Nobody has ever outsmarted Benny the Kid and Dead-Eye Dan.

Miss Louisa *(Speaking matter-of-factly)*: It looks a bit like rain. William, will you and Caroline please go out and bring in the flag?

Benny: Do you think we're stupid? Why, the minute those kids leave this room they'll run for the sheriff.

William *(Nervously)*: Don't insist that we go, Miss Louisa! It really doesn't look like rain.

Miss Louisa: There are cumulus clouds forming in the west. A shower could begin at any moment. It is a rule of our school that we never allow the American flag to become wet. One of you may accompany the students — but our flag must not be rained upon! Do you hear?

Benny: Oh, all right then.

Miss Louisa *(Sternly)*: What did you say?

Benny *(Meekly)*: Yes, Miss Louisa.

(Benny *heads toward the door, motioning to* William *and* Caroline *to go ahead of him. They go out the door while* Dan *keeps his gun drawn. After a moment,* Benny, William, *and* Caroline *return. They wipe their feet carefully, and* William *hands the flag to* Miss Louisa, *who folds it and lays it on her desk.)*

Miss Louisa: Now, students, we will have a spelling bee. Regina and Clara may be captains. You may start choosing teams, girls.

Regina: I choose Caroline for my team.

Clara: I choose William.

Regina: I choose Daniel.

Clara: I choose Benjamin.

Benny: Say, what is this? What's going on?

Dan *(With enthusiasm)*: A spelling bee, pal. Ain't you never been in a spelling bee before?

Miss Louisa: *Haven't you ever,* Daniel. Watch that grammar!

Dan: Haven't you ever been in a spelling bee before?

Benny: No, and I'm not going to now. Besides, it'll be train time soon. We have to stay on the alert.

Miss Louisa *(Pauses. Then sympathetically):* Very well, Benjamin. I will excuse you from participating in the spelling bee. Naturally, it would be most embarrassing for you to be spelled down by a group of young children.

Benny *(Blustering):* Who's scared of being spelled down? Look, maybe I haven't had much schooling, but I'm not so dumb that a bunch of little kids can lick me at spelling.

Miss Louisa: I admire your spirit, Benjamin. You won't mind joining Clara's team then.

Benny *(Sighing):* Oh, all right.

Miss Louisa *(Severely):* What's that, Benjamin?

Benny: Yes, Miss Louisa.

Miss Louisa: Clara, please spell *doctor*.

Clara: *d-o-c-t-o-r*

Miss Louisa: Correct. Now, Regina, spell *lawyer*.

Regina: *l-a-w-y-e-r*

Miss Louisa: Good. Now, Benjamin, I would like you to spell the word *thief*.

Benny: Uh — uh. Lemme see. *t — h   t-h-e-i-f*

Miss Louisa: That is wrong, Benjamin. The correct spelling is *t-h-i-e-f*. You may take your seat.

William *(Aside):* Gee whiz! He *is* a thief, and he can't even spell it!

Benny *(Sulkily):* Aw, so what if I'm not a good speller. I still make a good living.

Dan *(Suddenly):* What's that sound? Yeow! There goes the two-thirty freight train!

Benny *(Angrily):* I told you it was time to get out of here! But you had to let that schoolteacher talk us into a spelling bee!

(Suddenly, Sheriff *and* Ed, *his deputy, enter with their guns drawn. They catch* Benny *and* Dan *off guard.)*

Sheriff: Hands up!

Ed: You're covered.

(Benny and *Dan* raise their hands as *Ed* takes their guns. Pupils *cheer as* Sheriff *steers* Benny *and* Dan *toward the door.)*

Caroline: Sheriff, how did you know the outlaws were here?

Sheriff: I didn't know. I gathered that something was wrong, though, when I happened to look out of my office window and saw that the school flagpole was bare.

Ed: Why, you know as well as I do that, unless it's raining, Miss Louisa never lowers the flag until sundown. It's a rule of the school. Remember, Miss Louisa was *our* teacher too.

Miss Louisa: Sheriff, I was hoping you or Ed would notice that the flag was down and would remember that rule. Apparently my pupils remember *some* things that I teach them.

Annabelle *(Laughing)*: Miss Louisa was just like Paul Revere's friend. She used a signal to tell about an enemy!

Miss Louisa: That's right, Annabelle. If Benjamin and Daniel were the slightest bit educated as to the ways of the weather, they would have known that cumulus clouds in the west rarely mean immediate rain.

Benny: I had a hunch that we should have tied that teacher up in the closet the minute we came in!

Dan: Could *you* have tied her up?

Benny: No, I guess I couldn't have at that. There's something about Miss Louisa. Well, you just can't imagine tying her up in a closet. *(Pauses)* She don't scare easy; and before you know it, you're half-scared of *her*.

Miss Louisa: The proper grammar, Benjamin, is *She doesn't scare easily*.

Benny: Yes, Miss Louisa.

Sheriff: Well, we'll take these scoundrels down to jail where they belong. You'll receive the hundred dollars reward in a few days, Miss Louisa.

Miss Louisa: Thank you. I believe it will be just enough money to take the children on an outing to the Dodge City Music Festival. *(Pupils cheer.)*

Ed: Come on, you two. It's jail for you.

Miss Louisa: Now, children, I believe that I will dismiss you for the rest of the afternoon.

Pupils: Hooray! Hooray for Miss Louisa!

(*Pupils* run noisily out the door — all except William *and* Caroline. Miss Louisa *sits limply down at her desk. She holds her head in her hands. After a moment she looks up and sees* William *and* Caroline.)

Miss Louisa: Well, students, why are you still here?

Caroline: You asked us to stay and learn the first three stanzas of "Paul Revere's Ride," Miss Louisa.

Miss Louisa: Oh, so I did. Well, I will excuse you just this once. You see, I'm feeling a bit shaky.

William (*Thoughtfully*): Miss Louisa, you were afraid when the outlaws were here, weren't you?

Miss Louisa: Oh, yes. Very much afraid. I did everything in my power to delay them so that they might miss the train and be captured. Yet, I longed for them to leave before they decided to use those wicked guns on some of us.

Caroline: Well, you didn't act scared — not one bit!

William (*Stoutly*): Naturally, she didn't! She behaved bravely when she was most afraid. That's courage. Remember?

Miss Louisa: Perhaps I taught something today after all. Before you leave, please take the flag and hoist it again. There are several hours yet until sundown. We must abide by the rules of the school, you know.

William (*With admiration*): Yes, Miss Louisa.

Caroline: Yes, indeed. Good-by, Miss Louisa.

Author

Frances B. Watts was a substitute teacher for many years and was always interested in drama and the performing arts. Before her death in 1983, Mrs. Watts had published over twenty-five short plays. She also collaborated with her husband on a number of musical comedies, several of which they saw performed on the stage.

Comprehension Questions

1. Why did this lesson on courage stand out from all the others Miss Louisa had taught?
2. How did Miss Louisa confuse the outlaws by the way she treated them?
3. What reason did Miss Louisa give for wanting to have the flag lowered?
4. What was the real reason?

Vocabulary

In the play you just read, Miss Louisa spoke in a very formal way, while the outlaws spoke very informally. Look at the lines below that were said by Benny in the play. How do you think Miss Louisa would have said the same thing? Substitute more formal words for the boldface words.

Benny: Just in case somebody **tipped off** the sheriff that we're in town, my **pal Dan and me** are going to **hide out** here till the two-thirty freight train **comes through**. Then we'll **make our getaway**. So don't anybody **get any bright ideas**, like yelling out the window or running for help. **See?**

Writing a Letter

Pretend that you were one of the students in Miss Louisa's class. Write a letter to a friend, explaining what happened when the outlaws took refuge in your class.

A Song of Greatness

A Chippewa Indian song transcribed by Mary Austin

When I hear the old men
Telling of heroes,
Telling of great deeds
Of ancient days,
When I hear them telling,
Then I think within me
I too am one of these.

When I hear the people
Praising great ones,
Then I know that I too
Shall be esteemed,
I too when my time comes
Shall do mightily.

Drawing Conclusions

How to Draw a Conclusion

A **conclusion** is something you figure out on your own without being told directly. In order to draw a conclusion about something that you have read, you must use the clues that the author gives you and your own knowledge and experience.

Read the following sentences. See if you can use the clues the author gives you and your own experience to figure out how Emma feels.

Tears rolled down Emma's face as she watched her brother and sister try to win the three-legged race at the picnic. Emma had never seen a funnier race.

Is Emma happy? Or is she unhappy? In the sentences, there were several clues to help you figure out how Emma feels. First you were told that tears rolled down Emma's face. From that clue, you could decide that Emma was crying. You know from your own experience that people who are crying are usually unhappy.

You were also told that Emma's brother and sister were trying to win a three-legged race. You most likely know that a three-legged race is a funny event. In addition, you were told that Emma had never seen a funnier race. You know from your own experience that people usually laugh at something funny.

Why would Emma cry if something were funny? That doesn't seem to fit — unless you think about what you know from your own experience. You know that people *do* cry when they laugh very hard. By combining what the author told you with what you know from your own experience, you can draw the conclusion that Emma is happy.

Whenever you draw a conclusion, check to make sure that it makes sense with all of the information that is given.

Look for Clues Given Directly and Indirectly

You can be given clues in different ways. Sometimes authors state clues directly. At other times, though, authors don't state clues directly. You really have to think to figure out what is happening. Read the following sentence:

The woman stood on the corner and waved frantically at the passing traffic.

You have very little information to help you figure out why the woman was waving at the traffic. Did she see someone she knew? Now read these two sentences:

The woman stood on the corner and waved frantically at the passing traffic. If she didn't get to the airport soon, she would miss her airplane.

Now you have a clue. It's not a direct clue, but it *is* a clue that can help you draw a conclusion. The author told you that if the woman didn't get to the airport soon, she would miss her airplane.

Think about what you know from your own experience. Why might a woman wave frantically at passing traffic if she were worried about missing her plane? Which of these three conclusions can you draw?
a.   The woman was waving at people in a parade.
b.   The woman was trying to catch a taxi.
c.   The woman was waving at a small child in a car.

The most likely answer is that the woman was trying to catch a taxi. In this case, an *indirect* clue helped you draw a conclusion. The author gave you details that you could use to draw a conclusion, but you were not told *directly* that the woman was trying to catch a taxi.

Think About the Order in Which Things Occur

Sometimes, in addition to noting details, you have to think about the order in which things occur to draw a conclusion. Read this passage, and think about the order in which things happen. See if you can figure out how long it takes a tadpole to develop into a full-grown frog.

A grown-up frog goes through several stages in its development. In the early spring, a tadpole, which looks like a tiny minnow, hatches from an egg. Over time the tadpole develops two back legs and then two front legs. Finally the tail of the tadpole is absorbed into the body of the frog. By the end of the summer, most frogs, fully developed and lung-breathing, can live out of the water.

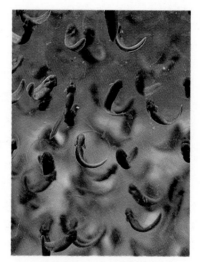

Five-day-old wood frog eggs.

You were told that the tadpole hatches in early spring. You were told the different stages of its development. In the last sentence, you were told that "by the end of the summer," the frog will be fully developed. So how long does it take a tadpole to develop into a full-grown frog?

a. from winter through fall
b. one year
c. from spring through summer

The answer to the question is from spring through summer. You were able to figure that out by thinking about the details the author gave you and the order in which things happened.

Form a Picture in Your Mind

If you can form a picture in your mind about what you read, it will be easier for you to draw conclusions. Reread the paragraph about the frog, and think about the order in which things happen. Try to form a picture in your mind of a tadpole.

The author gave you a big hint by telling you that a tadpole looks like a tiny minnow. If you don't know what a minnow looks like, think about the order in which things occurred. You were told that the tadpole developed legs over a period of time. From this you can tell that a tadpole has no legs at birth. You were also told that the tadpole's tail is absorbed into its body as it grows into a frog. So a tadpole must have a tail.

Form a picture in your mind of an animal with a tail and no legs. Then picture in your mind a fully developed frog. Do you have a better understanding of the paragraph now? Good readers try to form these pictures so they can better understand what they are reading.

Drawing Your Own Conclusions

Read each of the following selections. Decide which is the correct conclusion for each of the questions. Then tell what clues helped you decide upon that answer.

The totem poles carved by the Native Americans of the Northwest tell you about their way of life. On these tall poles, you can see many different figures. The animal most frequently carved on the totem is the frog. Other animals that appear are the bear, starfish, eagle, raven, seagull, whale, wolf, owl, and halibut.

Totem art reached its peak around 1830, when iron tools were acquired by the Native Americans of the Northwest through fur trading. You can see examples of these totems today in several Alaskan communities.

A Tlingit totem pole in Ketchikan, Alaska.

1. How did the Native Americans of the Northwest most likely survive?
   a. by fishing and hunting
   b. by farming
   c. by mining ore
2. Why were many totem poles carved around the 1830's?
   a. Fur traders wanted to buy them.
   b. Iron tools made them easier to carve.
   c. There were more trees at that time.

Although Sam knew that he was not as good a baseball player as the rest of his friends, he decided to try out for the team. He was both pleased and frightened when the coach said, "Congratulations, Sam! You're our right fielder."

Today was the day of the big game. The team that everybody thought was the best was playing Sam's team. Sam just knew that he couldn't help much, but he decided to go out there and do his best.

It was the ninth inning, and the score was tied! Sam stepped up to the plate. He took a deep breath. The pitcher threw the ball, and all of a sudden the crowd jumped to their feet, screaming and shouting. They were still cheering as Sam crossed home plate.

3. What happened to make the crowd cheer?
   a. Sam struck out.
   b. Sam hit a double.
   c. Sam hit a home run.
4. Sam was pleased when he found out he had made the team, but he was frightened too. Why do you think he was frightened?
   a. He was afraid he would not play well enough.
   b. He was afraid he would get hurt playing.
   c. He was afraid his friends would be jealous.

Skill Summary

- Writers don't always state every fact in their writing; they expect you to draw some conclusions on your own.
- To draw a conclusion, think about the clues that the writer gives you and your own experiences. Make sure the conclusion makes sense with the information that was given.
- Look for clues that are given directly and indirectly.
- To draw some conclusions, think about the details that the writer gives you as well as the order in which things happen.
- If you form a picture in your mind about what you read, it will be easier for you to draw some conclusions.

Home from the High Meadow

by William H. Armstrong

Somewhere out on the darkening pasture lands, Tor's ewe was with her new lambs. Why did this search for them mean so much to Tor?

Tor MacLeod had spent most of his life on his grandparents'
farm, where his grandfather Angus raised sheep. This year, for the
first time, Tor had his own four sheep and was eagerly waiting for
their lambs to be born.

As the days passed, Tor grew more and more impatient.
His grandfather's Black-faced Highlands already had so many
lambs that he had to count the marks scratched on the shed
wall to total up the number. Almost every day as the sheep
wandered in at grain time, several ewes would be hanging
back so that newborn lambs could keep up.

When Tor thought of keeping his four prize Cheviots in
the shed, his grandpa had said, "It's better for the lambs if
they're born in some sunny spot by a stone wall; and the ewe
will find the warmest place. This time of year it's much warmer
outside when the sun is high than in the shed."

"But these are my own first lambs," Tor would interrupt.
"Why do all yours have to be born first?"

"Any day now," Angus MacLeod would answer, putting his
hand on the boy's shoulder as they leaned against the shed
gate, "you'll have four, maybe six. Sometimes Cheviots have
twins their first lambing. Cheviots are born small, but they're
active and tough. They're on their feet in half the time it takes
most breeds."

Finally a day came that set Tor's heartbeat racing. When
the flock came in long after sundown, he counted only three of
his ewes among his grandfather's many. He climbed the shed
gate and counted again. When he was sure one was missing, he
found Angus in the barn and said, "One's lambed. She didn't
come in."

Halfway across the night pasture, in search of the missing
ewe, Angus MacLeod was falling behind the boy and dog.
Maybe Tor wanted to handle this alone.

"You don't have to come with me," the boy called without looking back. He had already repeated the same thing several times since they had left the barn.

The man now realized that he was out of place. The joy of finding his first lamb was something a boy would rather not share with anyone. Angus MacLeod understood. "Are you sure?" he called after the boy.

"I'm sure," the boy called, without slackening his ever-quickening strides. The man watched until the boy had disappeared around the corner of the wall beyond the night pasture. He measured the amount of daylight left the boy, then made his way back past the barn to the kitchen.

"Should you have let him go alone?" Una MacLeod asked Angus when she had heard why Tor had not come in with him.

"He'll be all right," Angus replied. "I started with him, but by the time we were halfway across the night pasture, he and Shep were fifty yards in front. He had said about a half dozen times, 'You don't have to go with me.' It finally dawned on me that this was no ordinary venture. He was going to find his very own first lamb. When he's telling the story on the school bus tomorrow, he won't have to say 'Grandpa and me.' He'll say 'I,' like a real shepherd."

Una MacLeod glanced at the wall rack by the kitchen door. "He never remembers to change his good mackinaw and school boots. I hope he doesn't come home carrying a wet lamb in his arms, with that good jacket."

"He'll be careful. Besides, they can't be too far. The Monacan mound pasture and the high meadow have been closed off since last fall. When I was a boy, I used to have to find one up there occasionally. Pa said the sun was warmer there at the bottom of the cliffs than anywhere else on the mountain."

Tor saw his grandfather disappear behind the kitchen door far below. He circled the fields with confidence. He searched along the walls. He startled a fox sparrow from its busy scratching in winter's dead grass and leaves. He put up a covey of bobwhites that had already gone to roost in their tight circle on the ground. They rose with a great flutter in all directions. He sent Shep to search the swales and the far side of the knolls.

Now the bobwhites Tor had scattered began to call each other from all directions to reassemble for the night. It was their covey call, rather plaintive, with a touch of mysterious lure.

By the time Tor reached the gate to the Monacan mound pasture, all was quiet. He knew the birds were back on the ground in their compact little circle, wing to wing, tails in and heads out, so each could take off "like shot out of a cannon," as Grandpa said. "It takes a smart fox to get one."

Years of sliding to and fro, or the rattling of the wooden bolt by summer's breeze and winter's wind, had worn the edges from the bolt slot, so that the gate had been opened either by the wind or some thoughtless hunter.

Tor had gone with his grandfather to look for lost heifers often enough to have learned to look for tracks. In the gateway he found them — one set of sheep tracks going into the Monacan mound pasture and the high meadow. These were two separate fields, but they served as a single summer pasture for sheep and young cattle. So Tor knew the barway between them was always open. They covered a great expanse of acreage, running north all the way to the base of the cliffs of the Hanging Gardens. His grandfather always used a horse when checking the stock here in summer.

Tor knew it was the nature of all animals to give birth to their young in as much privacy as they could find. "They'll go as far as they can," his grandpa always said. "They'll go to the highest spot so they can keep an eye out for the approach of an enemy. This is a carry-over from the days when they were wild."

Tor found himself repeating his grandfather's words aloud. Shep thought he was talking to him. He wagged his tail and moved around to where he could look up into the boy's eyes, as if to question, "What do you want me to do now?"

Tor looked back over the gentle slanted and rolling fields he had crossed. It had grown dark enough now so he could see the lighted windows of the kitchen far away. The evening star glimmered just above the mountains in the west.

He wished he had not come alone. If he had known the gate was open, he would have ridden Little Sorrel, the horse his grandfather had named for Stonewall Jackson's famous war-horse. He tried to pick out the cliffs at the end of the upland. The distance and the dark cut them off; they were too far away.

He'd better go back and get his grandpa with a lantern, he thought. He couldn't find his ewe in the dark. The March wind was beginning to sweep the land. It was cold. Maybe the lamb would be chilled and die if he took time to go back for his grandfather.

If the lamb had been born and was all right, he could find them in the dark. He would hear the mother bleating. He would listen in one spot and then move on to another and listen again.

If he went back, his grandmother would say, "You're chilled through and through, child. Eat your supper and do your schoolwork. Your grandfather will ride Little Sorrel up and look."

Worst of all, Grandpa might say, "You'll never find one ewe in that high meadow tonight. Sometimes it's hard enough to find a whole flock in the daytime. A lamb won't freeze outside tonight. What's happened has happened. We might as well wait till morning."

Tor rubbed his hand over Shep's head for a long time. He patted him gently. Finally he spoke. "We'll go on, Shep." Boy and dog turned from looking back at the faraway glow of the kitchen window, a dim speck, the only light that showed on the whole horizon, and headed north into the backland.

He picked out the stars in the handle of the Big Dipper. The evening star had seemed near and flaming-warm. The stars in the handle of the Big Dipper now appeared far away and starkly cold.

The boy sent the dog in one direction and then another with the command, "Find the sheep, Shep."

As they approached the Monacan mound, he kept the dog by his side. His grandfather had told him the mound was where the Monacan Indians had lived. They were a small branch of the Cherokees, and this was the site of their "long house," where they had held council meetings.

Tor wondered how many chiefs were buried in the mound. He stopped and listened to the distant "Who, whoo, who-oo cooks for you" of a great horned owl. It was answered by the mournful whistle of a screech owl, rising to a tremulous cry, then falling to a low plaintive wail. Grandpa called it the shivers owl — said it ran shivers up and down your spine.

Past the Monacan mound, Tor quickened his pace. There was something in the night cry of the owls that said hurry.

Shep covered the directions where the boy pointed. Tor listened for an excited bark, which would tell him that his sheep was found, but each time Shep returned as quietly as he

went. The light in the kitchen windows had fallen below Tor's view. He wished he would see a lantern crossing the fields below; that would help him keep his directions.

Back in the kitchen Una MacLeod was putting the boy's supper in the warming closet of the stove. Angus stood in the kitchen door listening.

"You must get the lantern and go and help him," Una MacLeod repeated with more determination than the time before. She had said it several times.

"I'll go," Angus replied. "But it's a great adventure for the boy. Pa used to send me out with a feed sack to carry the lambs home in. I forgot to tell Tor to take one. I'll give him a little more time. He knows sheep. The moon'll be up soon, and it's full — the planter's moon. Time to get the ground ready for planting as soon as it dries out."

Angus had lighted the fire in the fireplace to take the chill off. He closed the kitchen door and sat by the fire. Una noticed that he did not remove his boots. She was glad.

Tor missed the gap that led from the Monacan mound pasture into the high meadow. He finally remembered that it was at the crown of a knoll, so he followed the stone wall uphill until he came to it. He had missed it by only a few yards. For an instant he was proud of himself. He would tell Grandpa that he was almost as good as he was about finding his way over the land.

He stood at the gap and called in all directions. When he did it facing the Big Dipper, a faint echo came back to him. He knew that was the direction of the cliffs and the woodland. His voice had echoed off the cliffs. He repeated his grandpa's words to Shep. "They'll go as far as they can. They'll hide in the brush or woods if they can."

The thought of going all the way to the cliffs and the woods sent more shivers up his spine than the screech owl had. He called Shep to his side.

A small arc of gold appeared above the far mountains. In no time at all it was a half circle. Then it was a great bright disk, clearing the mountain, climbing up the sky. By its light Tor could see the stone walls that ran down the ridge. In the distance he could see the outline of the cliffs against the sky.

From somewhere on the mountain, a fox barked at the moon. Tor remembered that his grandpa said they'd never bark when they were hungry — but when they'd feasted on a rabbit or something, they'd sit on their haunches and bay at the moon just like a dog.

Tor suddenly realized that Shep had disappeared on his own. Was it the fox, or had he scented the ewe? Tor wondered if the fox might not have feasted on his lamb. No, the mother would butt the daylights out of the fox. Tor whistled for his dog. A faint echo came back from the faraway cliffs. The echo sounded like somebody had whistled a soft tune.

Shep came bounding back from the direction of the woodland. With the moon up, Tor felt much braver. He heard the bark of the fox again, much closer. Shep stopped and pricked up his ears. "No, Shep," the boy said. Shep dropped back to walk with him.

Tor found himself veering toward the corner of the high meadow. He pointed for Shep to search in that direction. He would go to the top of the last rise and wait for Shep. The stone wall that bordered the high meadow ran just inside the woods. He would stay out in the moonlight and let Shep go into the dark under the hemlocks.

Once long ago, when he was only five or six, his grandpa had shown him one of the trees with great strips of its bark torn off. "A killer bear testing its strength," his grandfather had said. It had probably gotten a whiff of the sheep or cattle, his grandfather had explained, and that had whetted its appetite for the kill. So it tested its claws on the tree. A bear could never catch sheep in the open, though. It could only catch them if it got the sheep in a corner and they were scared stiff with fright.

Shep returned from searching and gave the boy the same disappointed look. Tor now pointed in the direction of the hemlock corner, wondering if he'd feel any better about going in if Shep found her there.

Shep had scarcely started toward the dark woods when Tor heard a sharp clipped bark. The dog was back in an instant, wagging his tail and barking. Tor quieted the dog and moved very cautiously in the direction Shep led. Misgivings replaced the instant excitement he had enjoyed at hearing Shep's bark. They were still in the open. She wouldn't have had her lamb here. Shep moved ahead quietly, as Tor had ordered. Tor peered through the moonlight, pausing with every step to listen.

After not more than a dozen steps, it came to him — the rapid thump, thump, thump of a sheep stomping her foot. Tor picked up Shep's dark form in the moonlight, and there right in front of him was the ewe. Tor moved closer and saw a white ball directly under her. She stomped her foot at the dog and boy but moved to one side, then turned and put her nose against the white ball and bleated. The white ball divided in half; each half bounced in a different direction.

Tor could scarcely believe his eyes or the action that followed. His ewe had twins. He had thought only in terms of one tiny new lamb, still wobbly on its rubbery legs.

In the barn lot his ewes were so tame he could rub his hand over the soft wool, scratch their heads, and they would follow him, asking for more. Now the ewe was wild, moving in a circle, trying to keep her lambs together and away from boy and dog. The lambs were several hours old and, as was characteristic of Cheviots, quite capable of trying to keep out of reach of the stranger who had just appeared. Shep moved in a wide arc outside the circle of ewe, lambs, and boy.

Tor tried to turn the ewe in the direction of home, but she would not lose sight of her lambs. She walked backward or circled or went from side to side. When the boy realized that they were getting nowhere, he caught the lambs and held them in his arms. Now the mother moved back and forth in front of him, never letting the lambs out of her sight. The lambs squirmed in his arms. When the ewe had run under his feet, and he had tripped and nearly fallen on the lambs several times, he decided there had to be a better way.

He had seen his grandfather walking calmly, a grain sack over his shoulder, with two wooly heads sticking out of slits he had made in the sack, and the ewe walking behind, bleating as she followed. "Why didn't we remember to bring a grain sack?" Tor spoke aloud to Shep, who was still staying well out of the way.

One lamb squirmed free and bounced off its mother's back to the ground as she darted in front of Tor. He was afraid to squeeze the other tightly enough to hold it. So he put it gently on the ground.

He began to unbutton his mackinaw. He would tie it into a bag and carry them that way. He felt in his pockets for string. He always had several pieces — but tonight, when he needed it for something important, he had none.

For the first time during the whole night he began to sniffle. He blew his nose, and an idea was born. Better than tying his mackinaw into a bag, he would cut his handkerchief in half, tie the end of each sleeve, put a lamb in each, with its head sticking out, and carry them on his back. "The way the Monacans would carry papooses," he said to Shep. He cut the hem of the handkerchief with his knife and ripped it the rest of the way. He was already cold without his jacket, but that didn't matter.

It worked. With lambs and jacket on the ground in a heap, the frantic mother dancing wildly, Tor stuffed one lamb in tail-first, held his knee on it while he got the other in, hung them low over his back so the mother could see them, and started for home. The ewe followed on his heels, bleating with each step. Shep dropped behind to drive but found that unnecessary. His only problem was keeping up.

Halfway across the Monacan mound pasture, Tor saw the moving light of a lantern far below on the horizon. He was no longer cold. The moonlight on the fields and the bleating of his ewe brought the world alive and made it beautiful.

When man and boy came together, the man held the lantern high and studied the boy's precious burden. "How'd you ever think of that," he asked, "and how'd she ever get into the upper land?"

"The gate was open," the boy replied. Then after a long pause he added, "On the way up I was thinking of the Monacans, so I thought of this."

"Want me to carry them the rest of the way?"

"No, they aren't a bit heavy."

The man thought of taking his jacket off to put around the boy; but then he thought better and didn't. Instead he blew out the lantern.

Over the fields drenched in moonlight, a man and a boy walked in silence. The thoughts of each too meaningful for words — one too wise, the other too happy.

Author

Ever since his school days in Virginia, where he grew up on a farm, William H. Armstrong has had the creative-writing urge. He has written award-winning books for young people, as well as educational textbooks for adults. For many years Mr. Armstrong has raised purebred Corriedale sheep near his hillside home, which he built with his own hands.

Thinking It Over

Comprehension Questions

1. Why did the search for his ewe mean so much to Tor?
2. Angus MacLeod felt it was important for Tor to find the ewe by himself. Why do you think he felt that way?
3. What problem did Tor encounter when he finally found his ewe? What helped him think of a solution?
4. When Angus MacLeod met Tor on his way back home, he thought of putting his jacket around Tor — but then he decided not to. Why do you think he made that decision?

Vocabulary

*Sometimes I am the opposite of **dark**,*
*and sometimes I am the opposite of **heavy**.*
What am I?

The answer to this riddle is a word that has more than one meaning. Can you figure out what the word is? Make up similar riddles for the words below.

yards	**faint**	**drive**
stock	**crown**	**brush**

Writing a Dialogue

Imagine Tor's conversation with a friend the day after he found his first lambs. What do you suppose he said about his adventure? What do you suppose his friend asked him? Remember what you've learned about quotation marks, and write the dialogue as you imagine it.

The Case of the Golden Opportunity

by William and Loretta Marshall

A letter offering Jack a golden opportunity was intended for someone else. How would Jack find that person in time?

Friday, Dec. 10

Today the most exciting thing happened since I
started keeping this journal. I had just gotten
home from playing football when Mom said I had a
letter. I never get letters, and here was a letter addressed to Mr. Jack Huff! Actually, my name
is John Ryan Huff, Jr., but everyone calls my dad
John, and they call me Jack. Anyway, there was
this letter addressed to me. Here it is:

Dear Jack,

*I'm a friend of Michael's and have just seen him this
past weekend at the gold diggings in Alaska. When he
heard I had a stopover here, he asked me to deliver a
message to you. You weren't home when I called, so I'm
sending this letter. He wants you to wire him $2000 by
Monday. He has a chance to buy an interest in the claim.
He says you won't regret it — you'll all get rich. But he
has to have $2000 by Monday. Send it by wire to Fair-
banks. Your sister Eva will pick it up there.*

Sincerely,
Tim

When I read the letter, I got all excited about
getting rich and everything until I remembered
that I don't know anyone named Michael, except
the little boy next door, and I don't have a sister named Eva. I don't have any sister. Besides,
I don't have $2000. Actually, it has taken me two
years to save $23.56, and I need at least another
$5.00 before I can buy the electronic football

game I want. If I had $2000, I would be super
rich! If I were rich, I would go to a real Broncos
football game. I guess the letter really wasn't
for me after all but for some grown—up Jack Huff
with $2000 and a sister named Eva.

I feel sorry for Michael out there in the dig—
gings waiting for the money. If I had it, I'd send
it to him — but I don't even know his address.

Saturday, Dec. 11

All night I kept worrying about Michael and Eva
and the other Jack Huff missing out on their big
chance on the gold mine. So I got up real early
and looked over the letter for clues. There isn't
an address or whole name, except mine, on the
letter anywhere.

I inspected the stamp because I saw this movie
on TV where the stamp solved the whole thing.
This was just a plain old stamp, though. I looked
at the postmark, and it was mailed on Thursday,
right here in Denver. The way I figure it is that
Michael and Eva are married, and this friend of
Michael's named Tim flew here from Alaska and
mailed me this letter by mistake. He probably
looked up Jack Huff in the phone book, and my dad
was the only John Huff in the book. (I know be—
cause I looked it up to see, and there's no other
John, Jack, or J. There are about a zillion other
Huffs, though — two columns of them.)

When the mail carrier came, I asked her what
the post office would do with the letter, and she
said it would go to the dead—letter office.
That's not going to help Michael or Jack at all.

So I decided it was up to me. After all, I'm the one who got the letter. First, I tried to find Tim. I called the airport and asked if any passengers named Tim had come from Fairbanks, Alaska, on Thursday. They said even if I knew his last name, that was confidential information. Besides, there aren't any flights directly from Fairbanks, and Tim might have been on any one of about a zillion flights, because Stapleton Airport is the seventh busiest in the whole world. I thought I'd better forget about finding Tim.

I thought about trying to call Michael and Eva in Alaska; but if they had a phone, they probably would have called Jack themselves. Besides, I don't know their last name or where they live in Alaska — and Alaska is BIG. (I know because I looked it up in an atlas.) You can't very well call up a state that has 589,757 square miles and 521,019 people and ask to talk to Michael!

I decided to concentrate on finding Jack — at least he's right here in Denver somewhere. After lunch, I started calling every one of the zillion Huffs (except the four who are my uncles and cousins) and asking for Jack and if they knew someone named Michael in Alaska. I was surprised at how huffy some Huffs can get! Hee-hee. I'm only about halfway through, but Mom says I have to go to bed anyway.

Sunday, Dec. 12

First thing in the morning I started calling, but after the third person yelled at me for waking him up at dawn on Sunday, I decided to wait.

After lunch I called Huffs all day long, but no one I talked to knew Jack or Michael in Alaska. One lady I called said that of course she knew Jack Huff, but she never listened to Alaskan stations. I think she was a little mixed up, but she did thank me for calling. Well, as I was saying, I called Huffs all day, except of course during the Broncos game. My dad and I always watch the game together, and I'm sure Jack and Michael would understand.

Besides, I didn't want anyone else to yell at me. No one did, but no one knew Jack or Michael either.

So here I am at 9:00 on Sunday night, and I'm no closer to helping them than when I started. I feel terrible. Dad says I did all I could. Too bad. It wasn't enough. THAT'S IT! *Enough—Hough!*

It was right there in the phone book — Jack M. Hough. I called, and it was Michael's brother-in-law. He was so happy that I called. When I told him how I had been calling all the zillion Huffs for two days (except during the Broncos game), he thanked me a lot and said that he and Michael (Scott is his last name) would always be grateful that they hadn't missed their golden opportunity. I feel great.

Friday, Dec. 17

I can't believe it! Jack Hough called tonight and asked if Dad and I would like to go to the Broncos game on Sunday with him. Would we! Tim's letter turned out to be my golden opportunity too.

Authors

Writing stories for children is a brand-new career for William and Loretta Marshall. Both have studied art. Mrs. Marshall is a painter and has taught art in college. Her husband has designed programs and catalogs and was the director of the Colorado Historical Society for sixteen years.

Thinking It Over

Comprehension Questions

1. How did Jack find the person for whom the letter was intended?
2. What golden opportunity was offered in the letter?
3. How did Jack know the letter was intended for an adult?
4. What did Jack mean when he said, on page 364, "Tim's letter turned out to be my golden opportunity too"?

Vocabulary

Find the homophone that is used incorrectly in each of the sentences below. Rewrite the sentence using the correct word.

1. Their was this letter addressed to me.
2. He herd I had a stopover here.
3. He wants you to wire him $2000 buy Monday.

Writing a Schedule

Make a schedule that shows how Jack spent Friday through Sunday. Use your imagination when times are not given.

Maps

Road Maps

A **road map**, or highway map, gives information about roads, cities, recreational areas, and other concerns of travelers. Travelers use road maps to find out how to get where they want to go and to locate points of interest. The map of Oregon on page 367 is a road map.

Compass Rose

In reading a map, direction is important. Many maps have a **compass rose** with the letters *N*, *S*, *E*, and *W*, which stand for the directions *north*, *south*, *east*, and *west*. Some maps use only an arrow pointing north to show direction. North is usually at the top of a map. The compass rose above the map of Oregon on page 367 shows which direction is *north*, *south*, *east*, and *west*.

Legend

Most maps have a **legend**, or key, which explains what each symbol on the map stands for. Mapmakers use symbols, such as different colors, kinds of lines, shapes, and drawings, to show many types of information. Map symbols are used to stand for natural features of the land, like lakes and deserts. Symbols are also used to stand for features made by people, such as cities, recreational areas, highways, and roads.

Look at the road map of Oregon and find the legend. You can see from the legend that the first three symbols stand for

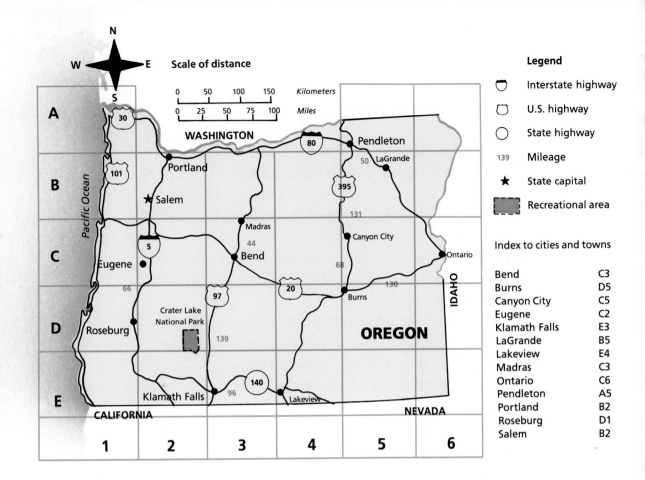

different kinds of highways. Both symbols and route numbers are used to mark highways. The symbol for an interstate highway, which is usually a divided highway that goes from state to state, is a route number printed on a shield-shaped symbol with a band across the top. A U.S. highway, which also goes from state to state, but is usually a two- or four-lane undivided highway, is shown with its route number on a differently shaped shield without a band. A state highway, which is within a state only, has its route number printed inside a circle.

Look at the map and find the highway that goes between Salem and Roseburg. The shield with the band and the route number 5 shows that this is an interstate highway. Now find the road that goes between Pendleton and Canyon City. From the symbol on that road, you can see that Route 395 is a U.S. highway. Look at the road that goes between Klamath Falls and Lakeview. The symbol for that road shows that it is State Highway 140.

The next symbol on the legend is a number printed in red. This red number stands for the distance between two cities or towns on this road map. If you look at the number beside U.S. Highway 97, you will see that the distance between Madras and Bend is forty-four miles.

Another symbol, the star, shows the state capital. Look at Salem and notice the star that shows you that Salem is the capital of Oregon.

The names of the largest cities are shown in large type. Find Portland. You can see that the type used to show Portland is larger than the type for Burns, a smaller city.

The last symbol in the legend is a green box, which stands for a recreational area. If you look at the map of Oregon, you will see a green area in the southwest part of the state. That is Crater Lake National Park.

Scale of Distance

Look again at the map of Oregon. Above the map is a **scale of distance.** You can use the scale of distance on a map and a piece of paper to find the real distance on the earth's surface between any two points on that map.

To find the distance between Salem and Portland, place the edge of a piece of paper along an imaginary line between the two dots that stand for the cities. Make a mark on your paper next to each dot. Now place your paper below the scale of distance, with the left dot under the *0* on the miles line. By reading the number on the scale closest to the right-hand dot on your paper, you find that the distance from Salem to Portland is about forty-five miles.

Grid and Map Index

Road maps also have **grids** to help you find cities and towns. Look at the letters and numbers around the outside of the map. Notice the blue lines that cross the map and form a grid. If you wanted to find LaGrande on this map, you could do it by using the grid and the **index** of cities and towns, located below the legend.

Look at the index, and find the city of LaGrande in the alphabetical list of cities and towns. After it, you will see *B5*. Find the letter *B* along the left side of the map and place your left index finger on it. Now find the number *5* at the bottom of the map, and place your right finger on it. Move your right finger up the map and your left finger across the map until your fingers meet. LaGrande will be in that square of the grid.

Political Maps

Political maps show political divisions of the earth's surface, such as countries and states. They also may show major cities, rivers, lakes, and sometimes major highways. Color is often used to show different political divisions and to show the difference between land and large bodies of water.

Look at the political map of Mexico and part of the United States on page 370. Like other maps, a political map has a compass rose, a scale of distance, and a legend. Find the compass rose, the scale of distance, and the legend on the map.

The information included on a political map is shown by the symbols explained in the legend. As with any map, you must study the symbols in order to read and understand the information presented on a political map.

You can see that the first symbol in the legend is a red line. A red line shows an international boundary, a boundary

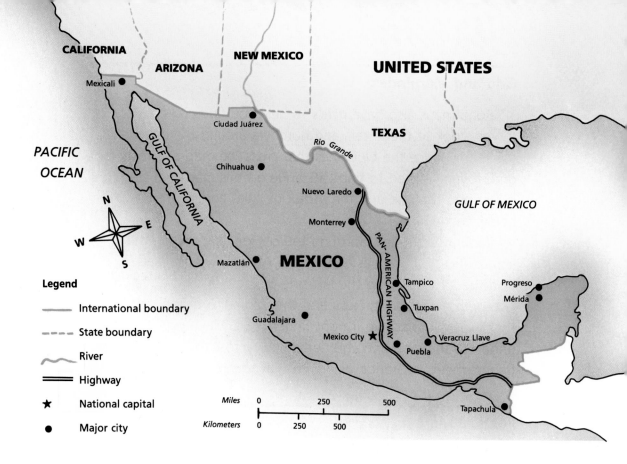

Legend

—— International boundary

- - - - State boundary

~~ River

═══ Highway

★ National capital

● Major city

Miles 0   250   500

Kilometers 0   250   500

between countries. Look at the map and find the international boundary between Mexico and Arizona. The second symbol is a broken red line, which shows a boundary between states. Look at the map and find the boundary between the states of New Mexico and Texas.

The next two symbols in the legend are lines that stand for rivers and highways. A blue line stands for a river. A double black line stands for a highway. Look at the map and find the Pan-American Highway. Then find the Rio Grande River.

The last two symbols in the legend stand for cities. The star shows you which city on the map is the national capital. Find the star on the map. What is the capital city of Mexico? The heavy, dark dots stand for other large cities. The dot shows that Mazatlán is an important city, but not the capital of Mexico. What is another large city in Mexico?

Reading Maps

Answer each question below.

1. According to the map of Oregon on page 367,
   a. in which direction would you drive on State Highway 20 to go from Bend to the Pacific coast?
   b. what grid number and letter does the index of cities and towns tell you to look for to find the city of Klamath Falls?
   c. how many miles would you drive to get from Burns to Canyon City?
   d. which city is at A5 on the map?
   e. which highway would you take to drive from Ontario to Burns?
2. According to the map of Mexico and part of the United States on page 370,
   a. which city is farther north, Mexicali or Ciudad Juárez?
   b. which river forms part of the border between the United States and Mexico?
   c. which states border Mexico?
   d. which large body of water borders Mexico on the west?
   e. in which direction is the city of Puebla from Tampico?

Skill Summary

- A road map, or highway map, gives information about roads, cities, recreational areas, and other concerns of travelers.
- A political map shows political divisions of the earth's surface, such as countries and states.
- When reading road maps and political maps, use the compass rose, the legend, and the scale of distance.

The Heroine of Kapiti

Kapiti

Retold by Shirley Climo

Te Rau was the best swimmer on Kapiti Island, but how could she use this skill to save her people?

On the south side of the world, where Christmas comes in summer and snow falls in July, are two islands we now call New Zealand. Long ago, before Dutch explorers discovered these islands from their tall-masted sailing ships, the Maori[1] people had paddled there in their dugout canoes. When the Maoris saw the snowy mountain peaks rising up from the mists of the Pacific Ocean, they named these new-found islands Aotearoa[2], or "Land of the Long White Cloud." Here they settled, put out their eel pots, planted their sweet potatoes, and lived happily — or almost happily — because then, as now, people often quarreled among themselves.

Many tales are told about the battles of those early days, but this legend is based on a true incident and tells of a young Maori woman who lived in the mid-1800's.

Like a school of flying fish, the swimmers skimmed across the water. Then one pulled ahead of the rest with such strong and smooth strokes that her arms scarcely ruffled the surface of the sea.

"Te Rau[3] has won!" called a young girl who was watching the race from the beach. She hugged the baby she was carrying and ran with her to the water's edge.

Te Rau waded to shore, shaking the salty water from her long black hair. She picked up her feather cloak and pulled it about her wet shoulders. Then she took the baby from the excited girl.

"Are you pleased with your mother, my child?" she asked. Her daughter just snuggled against the soft feathers of Te Rau's cloak and closed her eyes.

---

[1] **Maori** (mou′ rē)

[2] **Aotearoa** (ä ô tě ä rô ä)

[3] **Te Rau** (tě   rä ōō)

The girl danced around Te Rau, scuffing the sand with her toes. "I am pleased," she announced, "and proud to be your sister." She looked scornfully at the other swimmers, mostly men and boys, who were just now coming ashore. "You are the best swimmer on Kapiti Island. Perhaps in all the ocean!"

Te Rau laughed. "The ocean is large; and you forget *mango,* the shark."

"Don't speak of sharks!" cried the girl, catching hold of Te Rau's hand. "I wish I were as brave as you."

Te Rau put her arm around her sister. "Then you must open your eyes to what you can do," she said, "and close your ears to those who would keep you from trying."

Te Rau knew that others were not so pleased with her swimming feat. Some of the men she had beaten grumbled as they passed her. Some of the old women who sat by the sea, soaking the leaves of the flax bush to soften them for weaving, shook their heads.

"Boldness doesn't become a woman," called one, loudly enough that Te Rau might hear.

"Such foolishness is not fitting," agreed another.

"There is a proverb," said a third. "'A fish in water; a woman on land.'" Then she added more kindly, "Come, Te Rau, you have played the part of fish. Now learn to weave flax."

"So I shall, soon enough," replied Te Rau, smiling down at her sister, "but there are other skills to practice too."

Then the women muttered among themselves. Te Rau's ways were brash, and she was no longer one of their people. She had married a young warrior from the North Island of Aotearoa. Now his people and home were hers as well. She had returned to the small island of Kapiti to visit her father, Chief Te Rauparaha[4]. He would choose the right name for her baby daughter — just as he had called her Te Rau-o-te-Rangi[5], or "The Leaves of the Sky," because her hair was as dark as the midnight sky and her voice as true as the bellbird that sings at dawn.

Now Te Rau looked away from the women and up at the sky. Already the sun was slipping toward its ocean bed. So she climbed the tangled path through the trees to her hut, where she put the baby down upon her mat of ferns.

"Now you, too, must rest," she said to her sister, "for sleep brings strength."

The girl shook her head and shivered, though no breeze blew through the woven reeds of the walls.

---

[4]**Te Rauparaha** (tĕ rä o͞o pä rä hä)

[5]**Te Rau-o-te-Rangi** (tĕ rä o͞o ô tĕ räng ē)

"What troubles you?" asked Te Rau.

"Take me back with you to Aotearoa," begged her sister. "I don't want to stay on Kapiti."

"This is your home," answered Te Rau, "and I cannot return until my little one is named."

"Misfortune comes here," whispered the girl. "I know it. For three nights I have had a dream, and it is always the same. Evil beings come by sea and turn the waters red. The wind carries the sounds of their wails." Her voice rose, and the baby stirred.

"Sssh!" warned Te Rau. "The god of the sea is our friend. The red of your dreams is but the sun reflected on the water; the cries you hear are no more than the calls of gulls."

Then Te Rau sat, cross-legged, upon the floor and softly sang an ancient charm to quiet her daughter and her sister:

"O eyes that see
be you closed in sleep,
tightly sealed, in sleep, in sleep . . ."

Lulled by the singing, the children slept; but Te Rau was restless and strangely troubled by her sister's words. She left the hut to walk alone beside the sea. The men had long since left their games, and the women had gone to uncover their earthen ovens for the evening meal. Waves licked lazily against the shore, and the hills of distant Aotearoa looked little larger than pebbles. However, when the moon climbed into the sky, its light showed dark shapes moving silently upon the sea.

"Porpoises," said Te Rau aloud. "They, too, race with one another."

She stood still, watching them. Then — suddenly — Te Rau realized these were not ocean creatures at all. War canoes floated upon the waves, waiting for daybreak to attack Kapiti.

Te Rau ran to give warning. Hushed and fearful, the villagers gathered at the shore and stared at the shadows on the sea. Dozens of canoes dotted the water, and each held eighty warriors. Without help from Aotearoa, the people of Kapiti would be destroyed.

Chief Te Rauparaha picked up his club. "I cannot spare a man to go for help," he said. "Every warrior is needed to protect the *pa*[6]. We must do the best we can."

"Spare a woman," urged Te Rau. "Let me go, Father."

The chief shook his head. "They would see even the smallest canoe — and sink it immediately."

"I shall swim."

---

[6]**pa** (pä): A fort or protected settlement.

"Aotearoa is too far, and there are sharks and a strong undertow."

"That is so," agreed Te Rau, "but I, too, must do the best I can."

Some who heard her words raised their voices to protest, and others clicked their tongues against their teeth in disapproval. This was not woman's work. Chief Te Rauparaha slapped his club upon the earth for silence.

"Go," he said to Te Rau, "and may the god of the sea go with you."

Te Rau hurried back to her hut. Both children were still sound asleep.

"Grow strong; grow brave," she whispered to her sister.

Then Te Rau looked down at her own child. She could not leave her behind. Te Rau took off her feather cloak and wrapped it about her baby. She tied it securely with thongs and hung hollow gourds from the lacings. Should she fail, perhaps her daughter would float safely to shore. Then Te Rau strapped her to her back, walked swiftly to the shore, and stepped into the sea.

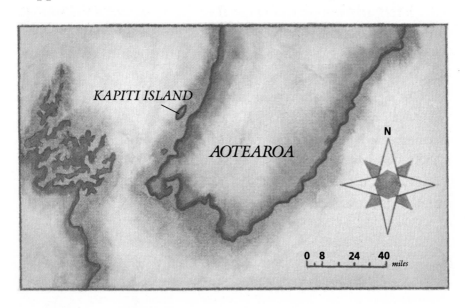

Without a sound, without a splash, Te Rau glided past the enemy canoes. She swam strongly at first, and her baby slept as if rocked in a cradle; but as Te Rau pushed beyond Kapiti's calm lagoon, the current grew greater. Sprays of foam broke over her head, and rip tides tugged at her legs. Te Rau knew that she must win this race or lose her life.

Soon there was nothing to mark her way through the dark water, for mist hid both the shore behind her and the hills ahead. Then, suddenly, a sea gull circled in the gray above her.

"A good omen!" gasped Te Rau. "The gods have sent a gull to guide me." She swam slowly, following the flight of the bird. Just as dawn reddened the clouds overhead, Te Rau felt the sands of Aotearoa beneath her feet. Struggling for breath, she shouted the alarm.

The night guards awakened the village, and at once warriors in boats set out for Kapiti. As in her sister's dreams, Te Rau listened to their cries borne upon the wind. When the battle noises ceased, she knew the war canoes had been driven off. Kapiti was safe. Only then, with her baby in her arms, did Te Rau sleep upon the sand.

Te Rau swam to save Kapiti in the year 1842. Today the island is a peaceful place, a sanctuary for gulls and other sea birds.

Author

Although she began her career by writing radio scripts, most of Shirley Climo's recent writing has consisted of books and magazine stories based on folklore. After a five-week trip with her family to New Zealand and the South Pacific, she wrote this version of a local legend she heard there.

Comprehension Questions

1. What did Te Rau do to save her people?
2. What did some of the people of Kapiti think of Te Rau's swimming?
3. Why was Te Rau visiting Kapiti?
4. Why did Te Rau's sister ask Te Rau to take her to Aotearoa?
5. What kind of swimmer was Te Rau?

Vocabulary

Kapiti is an island — a land surrounded by the sea. Some of the words from the story listed below are related to the land, others to the sea. Make a chart of these words listing *land* and *sea* words. Use the Glossary or a dictionary if you need help. When you have finished, choose two words from each list and write a sentence for each. Think of other *land* and *sea* words to add to each list.

flax	**porpoises**	**lagoon**
canoes	**gourds**	**ferns**
shark	**undertow**	**rip tide**
pa	**reeds**	**bellbird**

Making a Time Line

This story tells about one of the major events in Te Rau's life. Make a time line showing the major events of *your* life. Choose a few events to illustrate.

How to Read

Social Studies

When you read your social studies textbook, you may be learning about geography, history, and government. How can you read, understand, and remember so many different kinds of information?

You have learned how to use SQRRR — survey, question, read, recite, review — to help you read and study. This lesson will give you some other ways to help you read a social studies book.

How to Use Headings

Before you read anything, it helps to ask yourself, "What was the author's reason for writing?" The social studies author's reason for writing is to present facts in a way that will help you to understand and remember them. One way the author does this is to use **headings**.

Each part of a textbook lesson has a heading that tells you what the main topic is. Suppose that you are reading a lesson about the desert and the first heading is "Weather." What is the main topic of the first part?

How to Use Graphic Aids

Maps, charts, tables, time lines, and pictures are all kinds of **graphic aids** that you might find in a social studies textbook. They can help you to understand more clearly the information in the book. They can also tell you things that the words do not.

Maps are very important in social studies because they show where certain places are and where things happened.

In social studies, it is important to understand the order in which events in history took place. A **time line** shows this order in a way that is easy to understand and remember. Important events and the dates on which they happened are shown in order on the time line.

How to Remember Sequence

Dates are important in social studies because they help you to understand the order, or **sequence**, in which events took place. As you read, notice how much time there was between events and what events were happening at the same time. In social studies, often one event leads to another. That is why it is important to remember the order of things that happened.

Certain words can also help you to understand sequence. Look for words such as *before, after, next, finally, the following year,* and *many years later.*

How to Get the Main Ideas

Headings can help you to figure out the **main ideas** of the paragraphs in your lesson. Boldface words and important names and dates are also useful.

When you have found the main ideas, look for the details that support them. You may find it helpful to make an **outline** of the main ideas and important details in the lesson.

How to Review Social Studies

Most textbook lessons have **questions** at the end. These questions review the main points of the lesson. Answer the questions after you have read the lesson to review the important points or to prepare for a test.

Summary

Besides SQRRR, some other ways to help you read, understand, and remember social studies are the following:

- Use headings.
- Use graphic aids.
- Use dates and clue words to understand sequence.
- Look for the main ideas and the details that support them.
- Use the questions at the end of the lesson to review.

Preview

Next you will read "New Zealand." This piece will tell you something about the setting of "The Heroine of Kapiti." "New Zealand" is like a lesson you might read in a social studies book. As you read it, think about how the author has organized the material, and use the ways of reading that have been described in this lesson.

After you have read "New Zealand," be ready to describe how the material was organized and the ways that you used to read it.

NEW ZEALAND

A glacial valley in the Mount Cook region of New Zealand.

An Island Country

If it is winter as you read this, children in New Zealand are enjoying their summer vacation. This is because New Zealand lies south of the equator. During our winter, the earth's **axis**, an imaginary line that runs through the earth from the North Pole to the South Pole, is tilted away from the sun. That is when the southern half of our planet is warmest. The coolest month in New Zealand is July. Which month do you think is the warmest in New Zealand? Why?

The half of the earth below the equator is called the **Southern Hemisphere**. There, halfway between the equator and the South Pole, is the island country of New Zealand. It is in the Pacific Ocean, southeast of Australia. It is about one thousand miles long, but only two hundred eighty miles at its widest point.

From the map, you can see that New Zealand is made up of two main islands and a few smaller ones. What are the names of the two main islands?

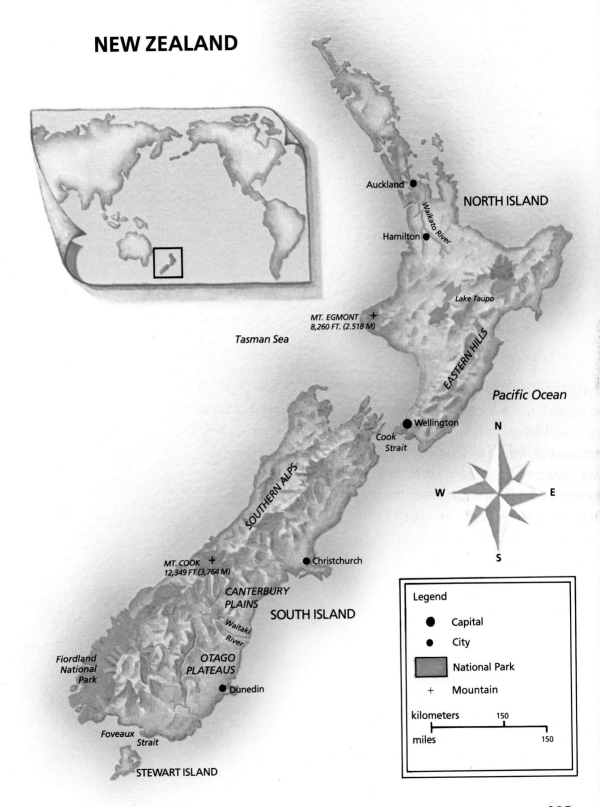

NEW ZEALAND

Auckland

Waikato River

NORTH ISLAND

Hamilton

Lake Taupo

MT. EGMONT
8,260 FT. (2.518 M)

Tasman Sea

EASTERN HILLS

Pacific Ocean

Wellington

Cook
Strait

N

SOUTHERN ALPS

W   E

MT. COOK
12,349 FT (3,764 M)

Christchurch

S

CANTERBURY
PLAINS

SOUTH ISLAND

Waitaki
River

Fiordland
National
Park

OTAGO
PLATEAUS

Dunedin

Foveaux
Strait

STEWART ISLAND

Legend

● Capital

● City

▨ National Park

+ Mountain

kilometers ⊢——150——⊣
miles ⊢————————150⊣

385

Two Main Islands

A long chain of mountains runs down the west coast of South Island. These snow-capped mountains are called the Southern Alps.

As you can see from the map, mountains cover most of South Island. To the east, between the mountains and the sea, lies a low, flat area called the Canterbury Plains. Here wheat, barley, oats, and other grain crops are grown. The Otago Plateaus in the southeast are regions of rolling hills and plains.

Cook Strait separates South Island from North Island. North Island is mountainous, but its mountains are not as high or as rugged as those of South Island. They are used for grazing sheep and cattle.

There are many volcanoes on North Island, some of them still active. Auckland, New Zealand's largest city, is built on **extinct** (no longer active) volcanoes.

Although North Island is the smaller of the two main islands, almost three quarters of the people live there. What do you think is the reason for this? (Remember that New Zealand is in the *Southern* Hemisphere.)

Left: A view of Sutherland Falls at Fiordland, South Island. Right: A sheep ranch, or station, at Hastings, North Island.

Not only do more people live on North Island, but over half of New Zealand's three million people live in the five largest cities. These cities are Wellington (the capital), Auckland, and Hamilton on North Island and Christchurch and Dunedin (dŭn ēd′n) on South Island. Find these cities on the map on page 385. What do the locations of these cities have in common?

Discovery and Settlement

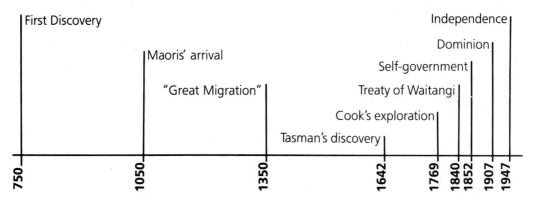

The time line above shows important dates in New Zealand's history.

New Zealand was first discovered more than a thousand years ago by people from Pacific islands to the northeast. These bold sailors traveled long distances hundreds of years before most European sea captains dared to sail out of sight of land. People think these first discoverers came to New Zealand around A.D. 750.

About three hundred years later, people again started coming to New Zealand from other islands in the Pacific. They were the ancestors of the Maori (mou′ rē) people who live in New

Zealand today. These people continued to come until 1350. In Maori history, 1350 is called the year of the "Great Migration." That year people came in seven great canoes, and each canoe had a name. Maoris today still trace their families back to one of the seven canoes.

European explorers thought there was a large continent in the southern part of the Pacific Ocean. In 1642, while searching

More Sheep Than People

New Zealand has a mild and rainy climate. This makes it a good place for sheep ranching. Even the steep sides of the mountains are used. Here, sure-footed sheep can graze where farm machinery cannot go.

New Zealand has about eighteen times as many sheep as it has people. The sheep are raised on large ranches called **stations**. During the summer, the sheep feed on the lush grass in the mountains. In late fall, they must be rounded up, or **mustered**. Then they are herded down to spend the winter months on the warmer lower slopes.

On a large station, thousands of sheep may be scattered over many mountain acres. The musterers cannot use horses on the steep mountainsides. With the help of well-trained dogs, they herd the flock, or **mob**, on foot.

The real work, however, begins in spring. Once again, the sheep are mustered. This time the mobs are herded down from the lower slopes to fenced-in pens. The lambs to be fattened for meat are separated from the others. The remaining thousands

Below: A mob of sheep being mustered at a station in Todds Valley. Right: The spring is a busy time for shearers, like this man, who travel from station to station, clipping thousands of sheep.

for that continent, the Dutch sea captain Abel Janszoon Tasman (ä′bəl **yän**′sən **täz**′mən) discovered the western coast of New Zealand. He tried to land but was driven off by Maori warriors. Since he never sailed around New Zealand, he did not know that it was an island. He thought that he had found the mysterious southern continent.

More than a hundred years later, in 1769, the English Captain James Cook arrived in New

are moved into sheds where their thick wool is clipped, or **sheared**. This job is done by workers called **shearers**.

Once the wool is sheared, it must be sorted, graded, pressed, and baled. Trucks and railroad cars then take the wool to stores

on the coast, where it will be sold to buyers from all over the world. New Zealand is one of the world's largest **exporters** of wool.

New Zealand is also the world's largest exporter of sheep meat. Also, in addition to its millions of sheep, New Zealand has large herds of dairy cattle. Together with lamb and wool, butter and cheese make up over four fifths of New Zealand's income from exports.

Although New Zealand earns most of its income from agriculture, more than three quarters of its people live and work in cities. Many of them work in factories that process farm products. Wool is turned into cloth, carpets, and clothing. Leather goods are made from the hides of the animals. Meat, too, is processed before being shipped to other countries.

Zealand. He, too, came to find out whether it was part of a southern continent. Instead, Cook found that New Zealand was made up of two islands with a **strait**, or narrow body of water, between them. If you look at the map on page 385, you will see the strait that is named after Captain Cook.

Captain Cook sailed back to England to tell the king what he had found. Whalers, seal hunters, and traders came from Europe,

Australia, and America. Later, people came looking for gold. The Maoris fought against the strangers, but this did not stop more from coming.

In the early 1800's, people came to settle in New Zealand. They intended to farm. The Maoris, however, refused to give up their lands. Fighting between the two groups went on for many years. Finally, the Maori chiefs asked Great Britain for protection.

Government

On February 6, 1840, Captain William Hobson and a group of Maori chiefs signed the Treaty of Waitangi (wä ē täng ē). This treaty gave the Maori people all the rights of British subjects. In exchange, the Maoris gave Britain the right to rule New Zealand. New Zealand thus became a colony of Great Britain.

In 1852, the British Parliament granted New Zealanders the right of self-government. In the years that followed, many settlers came to build new lives for themselves. They also came to help build a new country.

In 1907, New Zealand became a **dominion** within the British Empire. This means that it became a free country, but a country loyal to the king or queen of England. Then, in 1947, New Zealand was granted complete independence.

In New Zealand, the people elect a House of Representatives that makes the laws. Instead of a president, there is a **prime minister**. The prime minister is the leader of the **majority party**. This is the political party with the most seats in the House of Representatives.

Saving the Past

In the early days, both Maori and European settlers cleared vast areas of forest to build homes and set up farms. Many of the trees and plants that grew in New Zealand were **unique** — they grew nowhere else in the world. The famous kauri (kä o͞o rē) forests were almost totally destroyed. Today, the trees are protected, and the kauri forest is growing back.

New Zealand's rare birds that were hunted for food and feathers, as well as for sport, are all protected now. Many live in one of New Zealand's ten national parks. The kiwi (kē wē) is perhaps the most popular of all New Zealand birds. It has, in fact, become New Zealand's national symbol.

The tree fern is one of many interesting plants native to New Zealand. It grows on the west coast of South Island and most of North Island.

Comprehension Questions

1. Sheep are sheared in the spring. Name the spring months in New Zealand.
2. On which of the two main islands do most of the people of New Zealand live? Why do you think they live where they do?
3. Who were the first people to discover New Zealand? Who was the first European?
4. What were some of the reasons why people came to New Zealand after Captain Cook's voyage? Why did people come in the early 1800's?
5. What are the chief exports of New Zealand?
6. Who is the head of New Zealand's government?

Activity

Choose one of the following topics about New Zealand. Research the topic and present an oral report to your class.

Education
The Arts
Animal and Plant Life
Natural Resources
Sports and Recreation

Sensory Images

Some movies can really make you feel as if you are in the picture. Some sentences can also. They do this by using *sight, sound,* and *touch* words to create images, or pictures, in your mind. These images help you to *see,* to *hear,* and to *feel* what is being described.

Read the following paragraph:

A **powerful** wind suddenly **whipped** out of the east, driving **dark, black** rain clouds before it. In the distance, angry thunder **rumbled** and **rolled** while forks of lightning **streaked** the sky.

The words *dark, black,* and *streaked* are sight words. They help you to see the sky. *Rumbled* and *rolled* are sound words. They help you to hear the thunder. *Powerful* and *whipped* are touch words. They help you to feel the wind.

Read the following paragraphs and find the words or groups of words that help you to see, hear, and feel. List the words on a sheet of paper. Make three columns, one headed *sight,* one headed *sound,* and one headed *touch.* What images do these words create in your mind?

When people stand in the rain, they get wet, and Jamie was soaked. He was standing outside my bedroom window, waving his arms and grinning up at me, while rain slid down his hair and dripped off his ears. "Hey, Mary!" he cried. "Come on out! The water's great!"

I opened the window and reached out to feel the rain pelting straight down from the sky. It was only a summer shower, but it had come, sudden and welcome, after weeks and weeks of dry, burning heat. The sharp, stinging coolness of each drop made my skin tingle.

"Come on!" yelled Jamie, just as a crack of thunder rattled my windowpane.

"Right!" I kicked off my sandals and wiggled my toes. My feet were just itching to play in the mud.

Look at the picture. Write one or two paragraphs to describe it. Use words from the chart or other *sight, sound,* and *touch* words that you can think of to describe the sights, sounds, and feelings in the picture. Try to create images with your words.

Sight	Sound	Touch
white	laugh	frosty
tall	pat	warm
round	plop	smooth
bright	chatter	wooly
powdery	crunch	damp

"The Stormy Rescue"

an excerpt from
The Midnight Fox

written by Betsy Byars

illustrated by Cherie Wyman

For a boy who hates — and fears — animals, the prospect of spending a summer on a farm is not a pleasant one. Tom's summer on Aunt Millie and Uncle Fred's farm would have been just as bad as he expected — except for the black fox.

From the first day he sees her, Tom's whole life centers around watching the fox and following her, undetected, to her den where she cares for her cub.

When Uncle Fred sets out to kill the fox, Tom is inspired to an act of bravery that is totally against his usually timid nature.

The story of *The Midnight Fox* is told by a sensitive and imaginative boy, looking back on an event that occurred five years earlier.

The Midnight Fox

by Betsy Byars

illustrated by Cherie Wyman

The Stormy Rescue

  Ten-year-old Tom, a quiet, unathletic, and somewhat timid city boy, was spending the summer on the farm with Aunt Millie and Uncle Fred while his parents were in Europe. His aunt and uncle's sons, Bubba and Fred Jr., had long since married and left the farm, and their daughter Hazeline was planning her wedding. Bored and lonely, Tom found that time hung heavy — until the day he saw the black fox. Fascinated, he stalked the beautiful wild creature for two months, asking little more of life than the chance to watch her hunting, tending her young, free and at home in the woods. When the fox began to steal Aunt Millie's chickens, Uncle Fred went out hunting for the thief and found her den. Grief-stricken, Tom couldn't bear to think of what would happen to the fox.

As Uncle Fred began to dig, I closed my eyes and pressed my hands against my eyelids, and I saw a large golden sunburst, and in this sunburst the black fox came running toward me.

I opened my eyes and watched Uncle Fred. He dug as he did everything else — powerfully, slowly, and without stopping. His shovel hit a rock, and he moved the shovel until he could bring the rock out with the dirt. At my feet the gravelly pile of earth was growing.

I turned away and looked across the creek, and I saw for the fifteenth and last time the black fox. She moved anxiously toward the bushes, and there was a tension to her steps, as if she were ready to spring or make some other quick, forceful movement. She barked, and this bark was a high clear call for Uncle Fred and me to follow her.

There was a grunt of satisfaction from Uncle Fred. I turned to see him lift out, on the shovel, covered with sand and gravel, the baby fox.

He turned it onto the sack, and the baby fox lay without moving.

"He's dead," I said.

Uncle Fred shook his head. "He's not dead. He's just play-acting. His ma taught him to do that."

We both looked down at the little fox without speaking. I knew that if I lived to be a hundred, I would never see anything that would make me feel any worse than the sight of that little fox pretending to be dead when his heart was beating so hard it looked like it was going to burst out of his chest.

I looked over my shoulder, and the black fox was gone. I knew she was still watching us, but I could not see her. Uncle Fred was probing the den with his shovel. I said, "I don't think there are any more. She just had one."

He dug again, piled more earth on the pile, then said, "You're right. Usually a fox has five or six cubs."

"I think something happened to the others."

He bent, folded the ends of the sack, and lifted the baby fox. I took the shovel, he the gun, and we started home, the baby fox swinging between us. The dog joined us as we crossed the creek and began to leap excitedly at the sack until Uncle Fred had to hold it shoulder-high to keep it from him.

We walked back to the house without speaking. Uncle Fred went directly to some old rabbit hutches beside the garage. Bubba had once raised rabbits here, but now the cages were empty. Uncle Fred opened one of the cages, shook the baby fox out of the sack, and then closed the wire door.

The baby fox moved to the back of the hutch and looked at us. His fur was soft and wooly, but his eyes were sharp. Nervously he went to one corner.

Aunt Millie came out and looked. "Just like a baby lamb," she said. "It's a sweet little thing, isn't it?"

"That's not the way you were talking yesterday," Uncle Fred said.

"Well, I'm not going to have anything after my chickens," she said. "Not *anything*! I'd be after you with the broom if you bothered my chickens." They laughed. Her spirits seemed greatly improved now that the fox was doomed, and she called, "Hazeline, come on out here and look at this cute little baby fox."

"No."

Uncle Fred went into the shed, returned, and snapped a lock over the cage latch.

"You think somebody's going to steal your fox?" Aunt Millie laughed.

"I wouldn't put it past a fox to open up an unlocked cage to get her baby."

Aunt Millie shook her head in amazement, then said, "Well, you men have got to get washed up for supper."

We went into the house, and I said to Uncle Fred, "What are you going to do with the baby fox?"

"That's my bait. Every hunter alive has got some way to get a fox. They've got some special trap or something. Mr. Baynes down at the store makes up a special mixture that he says foxes can't resist. My way is to set up a trap, using the baby fox for bait. I'll sit out on the back porch tonight and watch for her."

"Oh."

"It never fails. That is one bait a fox can't resist."

"Are you getting sick?" Aunt Millie asked at supper that night.

"I guess I'm a little tired."

"Well, I should think so! Helping with the pump out in the broiling sun all morning and then tracking that fox all afternoon. It's a wonder you don't have heat stroke. You eat something though, hear? You have to keep up your strength."

"I'm just not hungry."

"It's the heat. But, listen, you drink your tea. You *will* have heat stroke sure enough if you let your body get dried out."

I finished my tea and went up to my room. I did not even look out the window, because I knew I could see the rabbit hutch by the garage, and I never again wanted to see that baby fox cowering against the wall.

Hazeline came out of her room and looked in at me on the bed. "You feeling better?"

I nodded. "You know that fox I was telling you about? The black one?"

"Sure."

"Well, your dad has her baby out in the rabbit hutch, and he's going to shoot her."

"I know it. I heard. But, listen, don't let it upset you."

"Hazeline, I don't want anything to happen to that fox."

"Tommy, listen. All wild animals die in some violent way. It's their life. Wild animals just don't die of old age. They get killed by an enemy or by the weather, or they have an accident, or they get rabies or some other disease, or they get shot. That's the way nature is."

"I know that," I said quickly, because I did not want to hear any more.

"You just forget the fox. Tomorrow maybe we can go to the picture show in Clinton or something."

"All right."

I got up and went down the steps and walked to the tree in front of the rabbit hutch. I could not explain why I did this. I didn't want to see the baby fox again, and yet here I was.

He did not see me. He was busy biting the wires of his cage with great fury and determination. I could hear the clicking of his sharp, tiny teeth against the wire, but he was making no progress. Then he stopped. He still had not seen me, but he had heard or smelled something, and he raised his head and let out a short cry. He waited, then after a moment he began biting the wires again.

I remained by the tree watching him, listening for the quavering cry that he uttered from time to time.

"Don't get your fingers in the cage," Uncle Fred warned behind me. "He may not be able to cut wire yet, but he sure could hurt a finger."

"All right."

"In a bit, when it starts getting dark, you can sit up here with me and watch for the fox."

It seemed to get dark quickly that night. Uncle Fred was already out on the back porch. He had brought out a chair and was sitting with his gun beside him, pointing to the floor. I never saw anyone sit any quieter. You wouldn't have noticed him at all, he was so still.

I stood behind him inside the screen door. Through the screen I could see the tiny fox lift his black nose and cry again. Now, for the first time, there was an answer — the bark of his mother.

I looked toward the garden, because that's where the sound had come from, but Uncle Fred did not even turn his head. In a frenzy now that he had heard his mother, the baby fox moved about the cage, pulling at the wire and crying again and again.

Just then there was the sound of thunder from the west, a long rolling sound, and Aunt Millie came to the door beside me and said, "Bless me, is that thunder?" She looked out at the sky. "Was that thunder, Fred?"

"Could be," he said without moving.

"Look!" Aunt Millie said. "I swear I see black clouds. You see, Tom?"

"Yes'm."

"And feel that breeze. Honestly, when you think you have reached absolutely the end of your endurance, then the breeze comes. I could not have drawn one more breath of hot air, and now we are going to have a storm."

We stood in the doorway, feeling the breeze, forgetting for a moment the baby fox.

Then I saw Uncle Fred's gun rise ever so slightly in the direction of the fence behind the garage. I could not see any sign of the fox, but I knew that she must be there. Uncle Fred would not be wrong.

The breeze quickened, and abruptly the dishpan that Aunt Millie had left on the porch railing clattered to the

floor. For the first time, Uncle Fred turned his head and looked in annoyance at the pan and then at Aunt Millie.

"Did it scare your fox off?" she asked.

He nodded, then shifted in the chair and said, "She'll be back."

In just this short time, the sky to the west had gotten black as ink. Low on the horizon, forks of lightning streaked the sky.

"Now, Fred, don't you sit out here while it's thundering and lightning. I mean it. No fox is worth getting struck by lightning for."

He nodded, and she turned to me and said, "You come on and help me shut the windows. Some of those upstairs are stuck wide open. Just hit them with the heel of your hand on the side till you can get them down."

I started up the stairs, and she said again, "Fred, come on in when it starts storming. That fox will be back tomorrow night too."

I went upstairs and started hitting the sides of the windows. I closed two, and the third one just banged down all by itself. Then I sank to the bed.

I had no intention of going to sleep when I lay down on the bed; I did not think I would ever be able to sleep again, but that is what I did. I fell right asleep and did not even move until four hours later, when I awoke. It was one o'clock in the morning.

The storm was in full force, or perhaps it was a second storm, but the house was quiet. I got up and went out into the hall. I could not hear anything but the sound of the rain and Hazeline's transistor radio, which was sputtering with static beside her on the pillow.

I went down the stairs, one by one. I did not make a sound. I was just stepping into the hall when, without warning, the hall light went on. Aunt Millie was standing there in her bathrobe, squinting at me.

"What's wrong?" she asked.

"Nothing. I just didn't know what time it was."

"Well" — she looked closely at her watch — "it's just past one o'clock."

"I went to sleep in my clothes."

"Well, you get on your pajamas and get back to bed. This is the first good sleeping night we've had, and you mustn't let it go to waste."

"Sure."

"Well, go on back up the steps." She watched me go up two steps, and then she said, "Goodness, we've gotten on so well all summer, I'd hate for anything to happen now, right before your parents get home."

"Aunt Millie, did Uncle Fred get the fox?"

"No."

"Is he still out on the porch?"

"In this rain? No, he is fast asleep in his bed like you ought to be."

She waited until I was up the stairs, and then she turned out the light. I went into my room, and she called, "Are you getting in bed?"

I lay down. "Yes."

"And go to sleep."

I lay in bed for a long time, still in my clothes, and then I got up very carefully. I walked over to the window and looked out at the tree Aunt Millie had said Bubba and Fred Jr. used to just run up and down all the time like monkeys. I could imagine them climbing up, laughing, racing, going out on all sorts of perilous limbs just to be first at the window. I opened the window, pushed out the screen, reached out, and felt for the smooth spot Aunt Millie had told me their feet had worn into the bark of the tree.

I took off my shoes and knelt on the windowsill. There was an enormous flash of lightning that turned the whole world white for a moment, and then I climbed out onto the nearest branch and circled the trunk with my arms.

I thought that I could never get one step farther. I thought that I could never move even one muscle or I would fall. I thought that in the morning, when Aunt Millie came up to see why I wasn't at breakfast, she would find me here, pressed into the tree, still frozen with fear.

The rain was hard and slanting directly into my face. Finally I got up just enough courage to turn my face out of the rain. Then the lightning flashed again, and I saw the ground about a million miles below. I held the tree so tightly that the bark was cutting into my cheek.

I don't know how long I stayed that way. If I had tried to look at my watch, just that little movement would have thrown me off balance. After a while, though, I began to sort of slip down the tree. I never let go of the main trunk for a second. I just moved my arms downward in very small movements. Then, slowly, when I was practically kneeling on the first limb, I let my foot reach down for the next one.

If there were smooth spots on those branches, my feet never found them. They only touched one rough limb after another as, slowly, I kept inching down the tree, feeling my way, never looking down at the ground until, finally, my foot reached out for another limb and felt the cold wet grass. It shocked me for a moment, and then I jumped down, landing on my hands and knees.

I got up and ran to the rabbit hutch. The baby fox was huddled in one corner of the pen where there was some shelter from the rain. The lightning flashed, and I saw him watching me.

"I'm going to get you out," I said.

He crouched back farther in the hutch. In the next flash of lightning I looked on the ground for a rock, and I saw at my feet a small dead frog. I knew that the black fox in all this rain had brought that frog here to her baby. She was right now watching me somewhere.

There were bricks stacked in a neat pile under the hutch, and I took one and began to bang it against the lock. I was prepared to do this all night if necessary, but the lock was an old one and it opened right away.

The noise had scared the baby fox, and he was now making a whimpering sound. I unhooked the broken lock, opened the cage, and stepped back against the tree.

The baby fox did not move for a moment. I could barely see him, a small dark ball in the back of the cage.

He waited, alert and suspicious, and then, after a moment he moved in a crouch to the door of the cage. He cried sharply. From the bushes there was an answering bark.

He crouched lower. The lightning flashed again, and in that second he jumped and ran in the direction of the bushes. He barked as he ran. There was an immediate answer, and then only the sound of the rain. I waited against the tree, thinking about them, and then I heard the black fox bark one more time as she ran through the orchard with her baby.

I thought, "Someday I will be in a famous museum, walking along the marble floors, looking at paintings. There will be one called 'Blue Flowers,' and I will look at that for a while. The next one will be 'Woman on the Beach,' and I will look at that for a while. Then I will glance at the name of the next painting, and it will be 'Fox with Baby at Midnight'; and I will look up, and my heart will stop beating because there it will be, just the way it was this night, the black fox and her baby running beneath the wet, ghostly apple trees toward a patch of light in the distance." And I thought, leaning against that tree in the rain, "If there is a picture like that, I hope sometime I will get to see it."

Suddenly the rain began to slacken, and I walked around the house. I had never been so wet in my life, and now that it was over, I was cold too. I was tired. I looked up at the tree, and there didn't seem to be any point in climbing back up, when in just a few hours everyone

would know what I had done anyway. I went up on the porch and rang the doorbell.

In all my life I have never felt so foolish as I did barefooted, soaking wet on that slick porch at two o'clock in the morning, waiting for someone to come and answer the door.

It was Aunt Millie in her cotton robe who turned on the porch light and peered out through the side windows at me.

I must have been an awful sight, for she flung open the door at once and drew me in.

"What are you doing out there? What are you doing?"

"Who is it?" Uncle Fred asked as he came into the hall. He was pulling his pants up over his pajamas.

"It's Tom," Aunt Millie said.

"I meant who's at the door."

"Tom," she said again.

"Tom?"

"Yes, he was just standing out there on the porch."

They both turned and looked at me, waiting for an explanation, and I cleared my throat and said, "Uncle Fred and Aunt Millie, I am awfully sorry, but I have let the baby fox out of the rabbit hutch." I sounded very stiff and formal, and I thought the voice was a terrible thing to have to depend on, because I really did want them to know that I *was* sorry, and I didn't sound it in the least bit. I knew how much Uncle Fred had looked forward to the hunt and how important getting rid of the fox was to Aunt Millie, and I hated for them to be disappointed.

There was a moment of silence. Then Aunt Millie said, "Why, that's perfectly all right, isn't it, Fred? Don't you think another thing about that. You just come on to bed. You're going to get pneumonia standing there in that puddle." She started for the linen closet. "I'll get you some towels."

Uncle Fred and I were left in the hall alone, and I looked up at him.

"I'm sorry," I said again.

He looked at me, and I knew he was seeing through all the very casual questions I had been asking all summer about foxes and seeing through the long days I had spent in the woods. He was remembering the sorry way I had tried to keep him from finding the fox's den and the way I had looked when we did find it. I think all those pieces just snapped into place right then in Uncle Fred's mind; and I knew that if there was one person in the world who understood me, it was this man who had seemed such a stranger.

He cleared his throat. "I never liked to see wild things in a pen myself," he said.

Aunt Millie came down the hall and threw a towel over my head and started rubbing. "Now get upstairs. I am not going to have you lying in bed with pneumonia when your mother arrives."

We went upstairs, she rubbing my head the whole way, me stumbling over the steps, and Hazeline calling from her room, "Who was that at the door?"

"Tom," Aunt Millie said.

"Who?"

"Me," I said.

"Oh."

We went into my room. "There," Aunt Millie exclaimed at the sight of my open window, "I knew it! I knew you'd be out there on that tree at the first opportunity." She shut the window with a bang. "There is no explaining a boy."

She turned down my bed, went out, and came back with a glass of milk.

"I'm sorry about your turkey and hen," I said.

"Oh, that! I bet you think I'm awful, carrying on the way I did."

"No."

"It was more the heat than anything else, like Fred said. Just don't think about it any more. That fox and her baby are miles away by now, and they'll never come back to bother my birds. That's one thing about a fox. It learns."

She turned out the light and said, "It is starting to rain again. I declare, we are going to be flooded out." Then she went downstairs.

The next week I spent in the woods, assuring myself that the black fox had gone. I sat on the rock over the ravine; I lay by the creek; I went back to the den again and again to look at the ruins; I sat by the field where the mice ran. I never once saw or heard the black fox, and I knew I never would again.

Author

Betsy Byars began her career by writing magazine articles. As her children grew, she became interested in writing books for young readers and now has more than twenty to her credit. She won the Newbery Medal for her book *The Summer of the Swans* and the Dorothy Canfield Fisher Award for *The Eighteenth Emergency*. *The Midnight Fox,* from which this story was taken, received the Lewis Carroll Shelf Award. Of this book Mrs. Byars says, "This is my favorite book because it is very personal. A great deal of my own children and their activities went into it, and a great deal of myself."

Illustrator

Born in the Midwest in 1949, Cherie Wyman spent her childhood years fishing, building tree houses, playing ball, and drawing. By the age of twelve, she had begun to draw portraits of her friends and family. Her art teachers were the great masters, whom she studied from a book given to her by her grandfather. Cherie Wyman now lives in Minneapolis, where she divides her time between her artwork and remodeling her fifty-year-old house.

Thinking It Over

Comprehension Questions

1. What did Tom do about his uncle's plan for the fox?
2. How did Tom feel as he climbed down the tree?
3. Why did Tom decide to ring the doorbell and admit right away what he had done?
4. How did Aunt Millie and Uncle Fred respond when Tom confessed what he had done?
5. Was Tom glad or sorry that he never saw the fox again? Why?

Vocabulary

The words listed below were used to describe the baby fox locked in the rabbit hutch.

nervously	**quavering**	**alert**
cowering	**whimpering**	**suspicious**
fury	**huddled**	**in a frenzy**

Write one or two paragraphs about a person or animal trapped in a difficult situation — like the baby fox in the hutch. Use some of the words listed above. Use your Glossary or a dictionary if you need help with the meaning of the words.

Writing a Letter

Pretend that you are Tom. Write a letter to your parents in Europe. Explain to them how you felt about the fox and why you let the baby fox go.

Magazine Wrap-up

Literary Skill: Setting

"Home from the High Meadow" took place from dusk until night on the darkening pasture lands surrounding Tor MacLeod's house. Where and when a story takes place is called the story's setting.

The setting for "Home from the High Meadow" played an important role in the story. If it had not been night, and if there had not been such a large area of pasture to search, Tor would not have had such a hard time finding his ewe.

What was the setting for each of the following stories? Where and when did each story take place? If the author has not directly told you the setting, use clues in the story to figure it out.

"The Wise Old Woman"

"Miss Louisa and the Outlaws"

"The Case of the Golden Opportunity"

"The Heroine of Kapiti"

Vocabulary: Antonyms

Each sentence below was taken from a selection in Magazine Three. Change each boldface word to a word that has the opposite meaning. Then write the new sentence on your paper.

1. I was very **nervous** and kept **forgetting** my lines.
2. I lay in bed for a **long** time, still in my clothes, and then I got up very **carefully.**
3. As the days passed, Tor grew **more** and **more impatient**.
4. The **cruel young** lord **quickly** gathered together all the **wise** people of the village.

418

5. The gate had been **opened** either by the wind or some **thoughtless** hunter.

Comprehension Skill: Summarizing

Imagine that you work in a library and your job is to write short summaries of stories. Write a brief summary of one of the following selections from Magazine Three.

''The Wise Old Woman''

''Home from the High Meadow''

''The Heroine of Kapiti''

Books to Enjoy

Man from the Sky
by Avi

Jamie searches for a mysterious man with a satchel, whom he saw parachute from a plane.

A Boy's Will
by Eric Christian Haugaard

Patrick sets out to warn Captain John Paul Jones after discovering an English plot to ambush the American fleet.

Just Like a Real Family
by Kristi Holl

June's special social studies project — adopting a foster grandfather — brings a new interest to her life.

Goodbye, My Island
by Jean Rogers

This Inuit girl's story, based on fact, tells of the last summer her people spent on King Island, Alaska.

Explorations
Magazine Four

Contents

The Boy Who Drew People Upside Down

by Jean Friedman

Young Marc was a dreamer who used his school paper for drawing rather than for his assignments. His parents believed he was wasting his time as well as his paper. How could he convince them that his dreams were important?

Marc Chagall
The Market Place, 1917
Oil on Canvas, 66 × 97.3 cm.
Metropolitan Museum of Art, New York
Bequest of Scofield Thayer, 1982

A young boy trudged through the falling snow to the old wooden synagogue, where boys from the town gathered to study. It was early morning in the town of Vitebsk[1] in Russia.

As he walked through the narrow streets, he looked at the way the snow had turned the dirty cobblestones white and covered the wooden houses and sheds and fences of the town. The houses seemed wide awake and watchful — as though they, too, could observe the townspeople hurrying back and forth and hear the cackling of the roosters that were being sold over in the marketplace.

He wished he had time to sit down and sketch the scene, but it was late. Besides, drawing had already gotten him into trouble.

Last night he had sat in his room for hours watching the snowflakes whirl around the gas lamps in the street, causing strange halos to form around the glowing lights. He had looked at the people hurrying to their houses, dark against the snow and hunched from the cold. He loved to see their strange shapes and especially those of the carts

---

[1]**Vitebsk** (vē′tĕpsk′)

drawn by the horses or mules. As he watched, he drew pictures, using paper from his schoolbook and some old paper bags his mother had given him.

Then his mother had knocked on his door. "Marc, it's almost dinner time. What are you doing?" He had shown the pictures to his mother. She had sighed, "Yes, my son, I see. More pictures."

She had turned the pictures over and had seen his homework, half completed, on the other side. "You know that paper is expensive, and I have no more to give you. You will have to take these papers to school with you tomorrow."

She had handed the pictures back to him and looked at him again. "Your duty is to learn the law and the history of our people. You are our eldest son, and you have responsibilities."

As Marc approached the synagogue, his heart thumped louder and faster. His teacher, the rabbi, was a serious scholar and made no allowance for frivolity or inattention. What was he going to think of the drawings? Marc hesitated at the heavy, wooden door, then opened it and went in.

The other students were already seated at the long tables and benches, their books opened, ready for work. They tittered as he walked by, but they kept their faces hidden behind their books. No one wanted to risk a reprimand from the rabbi.

The rabbi looked up from his text and nodded in Marc's direction. "Marc, what will I do with you? You are late, and even when you are here, you are not really here. You are far away in some other world — dreaming." The rabbi paused. "Did you do your homework assignment?"

"I read the chapter," Marc answered quietly.

"Did you answer the questions?" asked the rabbi. Marc looked at his wet shoes and mumbled something.

"Speak up," instructed the rabbi.

"I ran out of paper," Marc said.

The rabbi sighed. "Ah, you've been drawing again. Bring up these drawings that are so much more important than your lessons. Let me see them."

Marc fumbled in his notebook and handed the papers to the rabbi, who was now standing over him in his long black robe.

"Well," the rabbi said after examining the drawings, "I think we had better talk about this after class."

Marc Chagall
I and the Village, 1911
Oil on Canvas, 192.1 × 151.4 cm
Collection, The Museum of Modern Art, New York.
Mrs. Simon Guggenheim Fund.

The rest of the day passed slowly for Marc. Finally in the late afternoon, when all the other boys had left, the rabbi walked across the room to Marc's bench and sat down beside him. He pulled out Marc's pictures and studied them again. "These are fine drawings, Marc, but why do you have these people flying over the town, and why does this house have an eye in it?"

"The people are flying because they are happy. It is the way they feel," answered Marc. "Sometimes I draw people upside down or sideways. It just depends on what I see. This house has an eye because, even though it is silent, it sees everything that goes on."

"Ah," said the rabbi, "you have quite an imagination. We must talk more about your drawings, but you must also do your lessons. I will give you paper — but only on the condition that you use it for written work."

As Marc walked home, he thought about what the rabbi had said. Why was his teacher helping him? Did this mean that the rabbi thought drawing could be as important as studying? Marc wondered what his parents would think.

When he reached home, his mother met him at the door. On her head was a brightly colored kerchief. She looked beautiful.

She helped Marc pull off his coat and hung it on a chair near the wood-burning stove. Dinner was almost ready, and the delicious smell of chicken soup filled the whole house. Marc loved Friday night when everything was made so bright and clean. It was the one time during the week that the white tablecloth was used, candles were lit, and a special meal was prepared.

As his mother lit the candles, Marc thought of how alive the candles' flames looked. They seemed to be reaching up toward the moon — like people with outstretched arms.

When Marc's father came home, the children gathered around the table. Then Marc's mother ladled steaming soup into each bowl. Chicken would come later, with hot potato pancakes and shredded carrots sweetened with honey. Everyone seemed happy.

"Son, what happened at school today?" Marc's father asked suddenly. "I met the rabbi on my way home, and he said he wanted to stop by here later to discuss your work."

"My work?" Marc repeated. He looked at his father. "The rabbi

428

Marc Chagall
Vitebsk Seen from Mount Zadunov, 1917
Oil on Canvas, 24³⁄₈ × 32¹⁄₄ in.
Private Collection

saw some of my drawings and said he would give me extra paper for my lessons. That way I will have more paper for drawing." Marc tried to sound casual, but he stuttered over the last word.

"Marc, dear," his mother's voice was gentle, "don't you realize that the rabbi cannot afford to buy you supplies? I am sorry that we cannot give you as much paper as you want, but he doesn't have the money, either." Her voice was sad.

Marc's father interrupted. "We will wait until the rabbi comes before we discuss this further."

Marc didn't enjoy the rest of his supper. He wondered what he had done that would make the rabbi want to stop by the house tonight to discuss his work with his parents.

When the rabbi finally came, he didn't look angry at all. He smiled at Marc and murmured a greeting to the family. Then he addressed Marc's parents.

"May we talk privately? With Marc, of course."

The rest of the family left the room, and the four of them sat down around the table.

"I will come straight to the point," the rabbi said. "Marc's work could be better, but I didn't come to discuss his schoolwork. He will never be a scholar."

When Marc saw the disappointment on his father's face, he felt like running out of the room.

"This does not surprise me," Marc's father answered. "In spite of what my wife and I tell him, our son spends most of his time dreaming and painting."

"That is why I asked to come by tonight," the rabbi said, looking at Marc's parents. "I believe that Marc has a special talent, something rare and unusual. He has the gift of making dreams come alive. He doesn't just draw objects; he draws the souls of things." The rabbi paused. "Marc must learn the importance of our ancient laws and traditions, but once he has, he too will be a kind of teacher."

Marc's father was looking intently at the rabbi now, waiting for his next words. His mother lowered her head, but Marc could see that she was smiling to herself.

"I have given a great deal of thought to this matter," said the rabbi, "and I would like to make a suggestion. As soon as Marc completes his studies, he should be apprenticed to the town painter and portrait artist, Juda Pen. There he can begin to learn the craft of painting and will be able to use his talent for earning a living. Meanwhile, I would encourage Marc in his artwork."

Marc was astounded. Did he hear the rabbi correctly? There was a look of surprise — and pride — on his father's face, as though he too were only beginning to realize what the rabbi was saying.

For the next hour Marc's father asked the rabbi about his son's studies and possible living arrangements; the rabbi said he would act as a go-between if Marc and his parents were agreeable. Marc could scarcely breathe a response; he was overcome with happiness.

Finally the rabbi stood up. "It is late and time that I left. You will have much to talk about." At the door he turned to Marc and smiled. His eyes twinkled as he shook hands with Marc's father. "This dreamer of yours," he said, "who can say how far he will go?"

Marc turned to his father as the door closed. "Papa," Marc asked, looking into his father's eyes, "do you think I will be able to earn a living with my drawings and paintings?"

Marc's father placed his hand gently on Marc's shoulder. It was a moment both would remember.

"Marc, my son, you have a gift, and you must use it. Love it, and work hard at it."

Marc did finish school and went on to study painting in Paris. He never lost his lyrical, even mystical, vision of things around him. His paintings are filled with the images of his childhood in the Russian town of Vitebsk. Marc Chagall[2] became one of the great painters of this century.

---

[2]**Chagall** (shə gäl′)

Author

Jean Friedman has had a lifelong interest in art. Painting has helped her to express her own imagination. When she was at Hunter College in New York, she studied Marc Chagall's life and his painting. In the story you have just read, she has tried to make his art and his background come alive.

Thinking It Over

Comprehension Questions

1. What caused Marc's parents to change their attitude toward their son's drawing?
2. What did the rabbi mean when he said to Marc, "Even when you are here, you are not really here"?
3. Why, according to Marc, were the people in his drawings flying? Why did the house have an eye?
4. What was Marc thinking about as he walked home from school?
5. What plan did the rabbi have for Marc?

Vocabulary

Marc Chagall used pencils and paints to create pictures. A writer uses words. For example, the author of "The Boy Who Drew People Upside Down" described the houses as **wide awake and watchful** and candles as **reaching up toward the moon — like people with outstretched arms**.

Choose two of the items listed below. Write some words or phrases to describe them — to create pictures in your mind.

> **cars rushing by on the highway**
> **a river, stream, or pond**
> **your pet**
> **your favorite place**
> **your favorite food**

Writing Facts and Opinions

Look at the painting by Marc Chagall on page 427. After you have studied the picture, write two paragraphs about it. In the first paragraph tell some facts about the painting — for example, what objects are shown or what colors are used. In the second paragraph, give some opinions about the painting — for example, what you think the artist was trying to say or how you feel about the painting.

Making Dreams Come Alive:

The Art Of Marc Chagall

by Ernest Raboff

Self-portrait with Seven Fingers, 1912

In the story you have just read, the rabbi said of young Marc Chagall, "He has the gift of making dreams come alive. He doesn't just draw objects; he draws the souls of things."

Look at these two famous paintings by Marc Chagall. Try to see how he used his gift to paint memories of his childhood.

The explanations with the paintings were written by an artist named Ernest Raboff. They tell what he sees and feels when he looks at the paintings. Look for the colors and objects that Raboff points out in each painting. Do you agree with his explanations? What else do you see in the paintings?

"Peasant Life" is the story of a small village, told for us in paint by a great storyteller. Chagall shows the pleasant everyday life of the village's rural people.

Notice the farmer's well-fed horse. This is the peasant's most important fellow worker and his loved companion.

The cottage, with its windows and shutters, the gas lantern, and the tree form the setting for this picture story. The horse and cart are ready to take the village family, with their many farm products, to market. The dancing couple completes Chagall's colorful picture of peasant life.

The "Green Violinist" is one of Chagall's painted memories of his uncle, who played the violin, and of his birthplace in Vitebsk, a town in Russia.

The fiddler, the violin, the violet clothes, and the soaring dancer create a sense of music through the artist's use of color. The green face and hand make the old tune seem as new as a fresh green spring. While the dark violet colors may reflect the sadness of the long, hard Russian winter, we are warmed by the glow from the orange violin.

Descriptive Language

Have you ever read a story that made you feel as if you were *in* the story? Some stories give you such a clear picture of the characters, events, and setting that you feel as if you can really *see* them. You can *feel* the dragon's breath of the hot desert sun or *hear* the hero's heart pounding like a hammer.

Authors choose their words very carefully to help their readers form clear pictures. Often they do this by making comparisons or using words in different ways.

In this lesson you will learn to recognize and understand some of the ways authors use words to make stories more interesting, keep your attention, or describe something more clearly.

Understanding Similes and Metaphors

In "The Boy Who Drew People Upside Down," the author said that the candles on the dinner table were "reaching up toward the moon — like people with outstretched arms." Have you ever thought of how candles and people could be alike? The author wanted to tell you that the candles were like people in the way they seemed to be reaching up.

One way an author may compare two different things is to use a **simile**. A simile points out one way in which the two things are alike. Similes always use the word *like* or *as*. Those words can help you recognize a simile.

Another kind of comparison that an author may use is called a **metaphor.** In a metaphor, two things are compared by saying that one thing *is* the other: The candles are people with outstretched arms. A metaphor does not use *like* or *as*.

What things are being compared in the following metaphor?

Please open a window! This room is an oven!

When you read descriptive language, make sure you understand what the author is telling you. The first step is to figure out what things are being compared. The metaphor above compares a room and an oven.

The next step is to figure out in what ways the things could be alike. A room and an oven could be alike in several ways: each could have a box-like shape; each could have a door; each could be very hot.

How do you figure out the meaning the author intended? To figure out the meaning of a simile or metaphor, use the sense of the sentence, and what you already know about the subject, just as you would for a word that you do not know. In the example above, *Please open a window!* tells you that the room must be very hot — as hot as an oven.

Understanding Personification

There is another interesting use of words in "The Boy Who Drew People Upside Down." When Marc was walking to school, the author said that the houses "seemed wide awake and watchful." Can a house be wide awake? Can it be watchful? Only living things can be awake; only human beings can be watchful. The author is using **personification** to describe the houses. Personification is a way of describing something that is not human by giving it human characteristics.

Why do you think the author described the houses in this way? Like similes and metaphors, personification is used to make writing more interesting.

Read the following sentence:

The trees whispered in the wind.

What thing or things are being given human characteristics? What human characteristic is being given to the trees? Only humans can whisper, so *The trees whispered* is an example of personification.

Not only can a thing, like a tree, be described through personification, but also a feeling or an idea can be described in this way:

Curiosity gnawed at Jane until she opened the package.

Curiosity is a feeling. In this example it is being given the human characteristic of gnawing. The author wanted to describe how Jane's curiosity bothered her.

To understand personification, first ask yourself what thing, such as a tree or curiosity, is being given human characteristics. Next, ask yourself what those human characteristics are. Finally, use the sense of the sentence and what you already know to figure out what picture the author was trying to give you.

Understanding Idioms

Read these two sentences:

The boss will be tied up in a meeting all morning.
We were late because traffic was tied up for blocks.

What two words are used in both sentences? Do the words *tied up* have their usual meaning — "bound with rope or string"? Neither the boss nor the traffic was bound with rope. In these sentences, the words *tied up* are used as an **idiom**. An idiom is a group of words with a meaning that is different from the meaning the words usually have.

You may have heard someone say, "My parents will *hit the ceiling* when they see this terrible report card. I'll really be *in the doghouse.*" Will your friend's parents be so upset about the report card that they will pound their heads on the ceiling? Of course not. To *hit the ceiling* is an idiom that means "to be very angry." Will your friend's parents make him or her sleep in the doghouse? That's not likely either. *In the doghouse* is an idiom. What do you think it means?

If you do not know the meaning of the idiom *in the dog-house,* you can figure it out from the sense of the sentence. The report card is terrible. Your friend's parents will be angry. Therefore, your friend will probably be in trouble. The idiom *in the doghouse* means "in trouble."

To understand an idiom, therefore, you must first know that a group of words is used with a meaning different from the words' usual meaning. Then, if you do not understand the idiom, use the sense of the sentence and what you already know to figure out its meaning.

Understanding Descriptive Language

Each of the numbered items has an idiom, a simile, or a metaphor. For each item, tell what words are used as an idiom or what two things are being compared. Then tell which of the three choices below the item gives the meaning of the idiom or comparison.

1. This loaf of bread is like a rock!" said Hilda. "We'll never be able to cut it!"
   a. The loaf of bread is hard.
   b. The loaf of bread is round.
   c. The loaf of bread is lumpy.
2. "I bend over backwards, but no matter how much I try I still can't please Millie," said Anne.
   a. do exercises
   b. do tricks
   c. try very hard
3. "This room is a pig sty," said Dad, as he stepped over the mound of clothes on the floor.
   a. The room is muddy.
   b. The room is messy.
   c. The room is noisy.

4. "I'm so far behind in this race," thought Jack. "I guess I might as well throw in the towel."
   a. wipe my face
   b. take a shower
   c. give up

Read the following paragraph. Find four examples of personification. For each one, tell what thing or idea is being given human characteristics and what those characteristics are.

What a hot day! The flowers are too tired to hold up their heads. On days like this, my stubborn old car takes forever to get started. It gasps and chokes as if it's about to take its last breath. I don't blame it, though. I feel the same way. When the heat of an August day grips me with its heavy hands, I just want to climb into a tub of cold water and not come out until fall.

Skill Summary

Writers use words in different ways to make their writing interesting and colorful.

- **Similes** and **metaphors** are comparisons. A simile uses the word *like* or *as;* a metaphor does not.
- **Personification** is a way of describing an object, a feeling, or an idea by giving it human characteristics.
- An **idiom** is a group of words that has a meaning that is different from the usual meaning of the words.

Life in the Desert

Many people think of the desert as a harsh environment — which indeed it is. However, it is also a place of great beauty and the home of many kinds of plants and animals, as well as human beings, who have adapted to life in its hot dry climate.

One Day in the Desert

Reading in Social Studies

by Jean Craighead George

July 10, at the turn of the century, would be
a memorable day in the Sonoran Desert. . . .

Injured mountain lion approaching ki.

At daybreak on July 10, a mountain lion limped toward a Papago Indian ki[1], a small structure of grass and sticks on the bank of a dry river in the Sonoran Desert of Arizona. Behind it rose Mount Scorpion, a dark red mountain. In all directions from the mountain stretched the gray-green desert. It was dry, hot, and still.

The cactus wrens began to sing. The Gila woodpeckers squawked to each other across the hot air. The kit foxes, who had been hunting all night, went into underground dens. The bats flew into caves on the mountain and hung upside down for the day.

The lion was hungry and desperately thirsty. A bullet had torn into the flesh of his paw, and for two weeks he had lain in his den halfway up the mountain, nursing his wound. As the sun arose this day, he got to his feet. He must eat and drink.

The desert stretched below him. He stopped and looked

---

[1]**ki** (kē): House.

down upon the dry river, called an arroyo. It was empty of water, but it could be a raging flood in the rainy season after a storm. He twisted his ears forward. Bird Wing and her mother were walking along the bank of the dry river. They entered the ki.

The lion smelled their scent on the air and limped toward them. He was afraid of people, but this morning he was desperate.

He growled as he came down the mountain. Near the top of the mountain were pools where beaver and fish lived and which the mountain lion normally visited to hunt and drink. But today he went down, for it took less energy than going up.

The rising sun burned down from space, heating the rocks and the soil until they were hot, even through the well-padded feet of the lion. He stood in the shade of a rock at 8 A.M., when the temperature reached 80° Fahrenheit.

This day would be memorable. Bird Wing, her mother, the lion, and many of the animals below Mount Scorpion would be affected by July 10. Some would survive, and some would not — for the desert is ruthless.

All deserts are lands of extremes: too hot, too dry, too wet. Yet they abound with living things that have adjusted to these excesses. To fight dryness, plants store water in their tissues or drop their leaves to prevent evaporation from their broad surfaces. They also grow spines, which do not use much water and cast shadows on the plant to protect it from the blazing sun. They thicken stems and leaves to hold water.

The animals adapt by seeking out small shelters out of the terrible heat. They seek out burrows in the ground where it is cool, cracks and caves in rocks, or the shade. Because of the dryness, the thin desert air does not hold heat. Shady spots can be 20° Fahrenheit cooler than out in the sun.

A few animals adapt to the harsh conditions by manufacturing water from the starch in the seeds they eat. The kangaroo rat is one of these. Others move in the cool of the night.

The coyote hunts in the dark, as does the deer, ringtailed "cat," desert fox, raccoon, and lion. The honeypot ant, on the other hand, has such a tough outer skeleton that it can walk in extremely hot sunshine.

On July 10 the wounded mountain lion was forced to

Coyote under saguaro cactus.

hunt in the heat of the day. He could not wait for darkness. He made his way slowly down the Papago trail toward the ki.

By 9 A.M. he was above the ki, on a mountain ledge. The temperature climbed another degree. He sought the shade of a giant cactus and lay down to rest.

The scent of lion reached the nose of a coyote, who was cooling off under the dark embankment of the dry river not far from the Papago ki. The coyote lifted her head, flicked her ears nervously, and got to her feet. She ran swiftly into her burrow beneath the roots of the old saguaro cactus that grew beside the ki.

The huge cactus was over one hundred years old, stood twenty-five feet tall, and weighed more than three tons. The last of its watermelon-red fruits were ripe and on the ground. Bird Wing and her mother were going to gather them and boil them in the water they had carried in buckets from the village. The fruit makes a sweet, nourishing syrup.

At 11 A.M. they stretched out on their mats in the ki. It was much too hot to work. The temperature had now reached 112° Fahrenheit.

Roadrunner passing family of peccaries.

The old cactus was drying up in the heat. It drew on the last of the water in the reservoir inside its trunk and shrank ever so slightly, for it could expand and contract like an accordion.

The mountain lion's tongue was swollen from lack of water. He got to his feet again.

A roadrunner, a ground-dwelling bird with a long neck and legs, saw the lion pass his shady spot in the grass. He sped down the mountain, over the riverbank, and into the dry riverbed. He stopped under the embankment where the coyote had been. There he lifted his feathers to keep cool. Bird feathers are perhaps the best protection from both heat and cold, for they form dead-air space, which is one of the best insulations.

The roadrunner passed a family of seven peccaries, piglike animals with coarse coats, tusks, and almost no tails. They stay alive in the dry desert by eating the water-storing prickly pear cactus, spines and all. They were now lying in the cool of the paloverde trees, which grow in bushes. Like the pencil-straight ocotillo and almost all the desert leafy plants, the paloverdes drop their leaves when the desert is extremely hot and dry. On July 10 their leaves began falling faster and faster.

The scent of the lion reached the old boar. He lifted his head and watched the great beast. The lion turned away from the peccary family and limped toward the Papago ki. All the pigs, big and little, watched him.

A warm, moist wind that had been moving northwest across the Gulf of Mexico for a day and a night met a cold wind blowing east from the Pacific coast mountains. The hot and cold air collided not far from the Mexico-Arizona border and exploded into a chain of white clouds. The meeting formed a stiff wind. It picked up the desert dust and carried it toward Mount Scorpion.

As the lion limped across the embankment under which the roadrunner was hiding, the air around him began to fill with dust.

A kangaroo rat was asleep in her labyrinth under the leafless ocotillo plants. She awakened when the temperature reached 119° Fahrenheit. Her bedroom near the surface of the desert floor had become uncomfortably hot. Her body was drying out. She scurried along a tunnel, turned a corner, and ran down a slope toward a room under the giant cactus. She stopped at her pantry to eat seeds before retiring to the cool, deep chamber. While she slept, her system changed the starch of the seeds into water and revived her dry body.

At 12:30 P.M. the lion walked into the paloverde bushes. The peccaries squealed in fright and trotted out into the terrible sunshine. In a cloud of dust, they ran into the dry riverbed and

Kangaroo rat in tunnel.

frightened the roadrunner. He ran out from under the overhang and flew into the saguaro forest on the far side of the dry river. The pigs hid under the embankment where the roadrunner had been.

The injured lion could not chase the pigs. He lifted his head, smelled the sweet piglets, and climbed up the trail till he was at the ki. Bird Wing and her mother were sleeping. He stared at them and crouched. Slinking low, he moved to a bucket, drank long and gratefully, then lay down in the doorway of the ki.

The temperature climbed one more degree. The birds stopped singing. Even the cicadas, who love hot weather and drum louder and faster in the heat, could no longer stand the fiery temperature. They stopped making sounds with their feet and wings and sat still. The Gila woodpecker flew into his hole in the giant saguaro. Below him, in one of his old nests, sat the sparrow-sized elf owl. He opened his beak and lifted his feathers.

Bird Wing was awakened by thirst. She tipped one of the water buckets and drank deeply. The desert was so quiet she became alarmed.

Gila woodpecker (left) and elf owl.

Clouds were racing toward Mount Scorpion. They were black and purple. Constant flashes of lightning lit them from within. Bird Wing crept to the back of the ki and lay down beside her mother. She closed her eyes.

At 1:20 P.M. the temperature reached 121° Fahrenheit.

This hour on July 10 was the hottest hour on record at the bottom of Mount Scorpion.

Even the well-insulated honeypot ants could not stand the

heat. They ran toward the entrance of their labyrinth near a pack rat nest by the ki. Some managed to get underground in the caves, where sister ants hung from the ceilings. The last two ants ran across the hot soil to get home. They shriveled and died in seconds.

The pigs under the embankment dug into the earth to find coolness.

The clouds covered the sun.

Instantly, the temperature dropped four degrees.

The thunder boomed like drums.

The kangaroo rat felt the earth tremble. She ran to her door,

Honeypot ants clinging to cave ceiling.

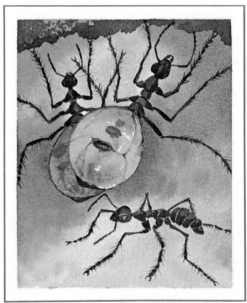

smelled rain on the air, and scurried to a U-shaped tunnel. She went down it and up to a room at the top. There she tucked her nose into her stomach to sleep.

The temperature dropped five more degrees. A rattlesnake came out of the pack rat's nest and slid back to her hunting spot at the rear of the ki. The cicadas sang again.

A thunderclap exploded sharply. Bird Wing awoke. She saw the lion stretched in the doorway. She took her mother's arm and shook her gently until she awoke. Signaling her to be quiet, she pointed to the mountain lion. Bird Wing's mother parted the grass at the rear of the ki and, after pushing Bird Wing out, backed out herself.

The rattlesnake buzzed a warning.

The sky darkened. Lightning danced from saguaro cactus to saguaro cactus. Bird Wing's mother looked at the clouds and the dry river.

"We must get out of here," she said. "Follow me up the mountain." They scrambled over the rocks on hands and feet without looking back.

Huge raindrops splattered onto the dust. Bird Wing and

Bird Wing and her mother sheltered from storm.

her mother reached an overhanging rock on the mountain. Lightning flashed around them like white horsewhips.

The thunder cracked and boomed. Then water gushed out of the sky. The rain fell in such torrents that Bird Wing and her mother could not see the dry river, the ki, or the old saguaro. They sat quietly, waiting and listening.

A flash of lightning shot out of a cloud and hit the old saguaro cactus. It smoked, split, and fell to the ground. The elf owl flew into the downpour. Her wings and body became so wet that she soared down to the grass beneath the paloverde bushes. The Gila woodpecker stayed where he was, bracing himself with his stiff tail.

The crash of the saguaro terrified the coyote. She darted out of her den under the tree and back to the dry riverbed. The pigs dug deeper into the embankment. The roadrunner took to his feet and ran up the slope beyond the giant saguaro forest.

The rain became torrents, the torrents became waterfalls, and the waterfalls cascaded out of the sky until all the moisture was wrung from the clouds. They drizzled and stopped giving rain. The storm clouds rumbled up the canyon above the dry riverbed.

The sun came out. Bird Wing and her mother did not move. They listened. The desert rocks dripped, and the cacti crackled softly as they swelled with water. Cactus roots lie close to the surface, spreading out from the plants in all directions to absorb every possible drop of water. The roots send the water up into the trunks and barrels and pads to be stored.

A drum roll sounded up Scorpion Pass.

The pigs heard it and darted out from under the embankment. They struggled up the bank and raced into the saguaro forest.

The lion got to his feet. He limped through the door.

The coyote rushed out of the dry riverbed. The wet elf owl hooked her beak around a twig of a paloverde and pulled herself upward toward higher limbs.

Water came bubbling and singing down the dry riverbed. It filled the riverbed from bank to bank, then rose like a great wall, a flash flood that filled the canyon. It swept over the embankment, over the ki, over the old saguaro cactus. It rose higher, thundered into the paloverdes, and roared over the rocks at the foot of the mountain. It boomed into the valley, spread out, and disappeared into the dry earth.

The coyote was washed out from under the embankment. She tumbled head over heels, swam to the surface, and climbed onto an uprooted mass of prickly pears. On this, she sailed into the valley and was dropped safely onto the plain when the water went into the ground. Stunned, she shook herself and looked around. Before her, the half-drowned pack rat struggled. Recovering her wits, the coyote pounced upon him.

The lion was lifted up by the flood and thrown against a clump of ocotillo. He clung to it for a moment, then, too weak to struggle, slipped beneath the water.

The flash flood that had trickled and then roared, trickled and then was gone. The banks of the arroyo dripped. Bird Wing and her mother walked to the spot where their home had been.

Mountain lion caught in flood.

There was no sign of ki, pack rat nest, saguaro, or lion.

"But for the lion, we would be dead," said Bird Wing.

Her mother picked up a stick and turned it over in her hand. "We will rebuild our ki up the mountain above the flood line," she said. Bird Wing nodded and gathered sticks too.

The kangaroo rat sat in her room above the U-trap that had stopped the water from reaching her. She waited until the flood waters seeped into the ground. Then she began to repair her labyrinth.

The pigs came out of the saguaro forest and rooted for insects among the millions of seeds that had been dumped on the land by the flood. The land was greening; the sky was blue. The roadrunner came back to the saguaro forest, ran down a young snake, and ate it. The owl did not call. The rattlesnake did not rattle. They had not survived the wrath of the desert on this day, July 10.

Bird Wing walked to the arroyo edge. The earth trembled at her feet. She looked down. Plugs of sand popped out of the wet bank, like corks. In each hole sat a smiling spadefoot toad. These are creatures who must grow up in the water. Then what were they doing in the desert? Waiting for just this moment.

They hopped into the brilliant sunshine and leaped into the puddles in the arroyo. Quickly they laid eggs, and quickly they ate and dug backward into the sand with the spades of their feet. Far underground, their skins secreted a sticky gelatin that would prevent them from drying up. This is how they survived in the hot, waterless desert.

The warm sunlight of late afternoon heated the water in the puddles, speeding up the development of the toad eggs. They had to hatch into polliwogs and change into toads before the

Spadefoot toad leaping for water.

blazing heat of the sun dried up the puddles.

At 7:33 P.M. soft blue and purple light swept over the beautiful desert. In the puddles polliwogs swam.

Author

Jean Craighead George comes from a family of naturalists, and she has built her own life around observing nature and writing about it. Her outstanding nature books for young people have received acclaim and won many different awards. Among her more than thirty books is *All Upon a Sidewalk,* which was named an Outstanding Science Trade Book for Children.

Comprehension Questions

1. Why was July 10 a memorable day in the Sonoran Desert?
2. How do animals adapt to the extreme heat and dryness of the desert?
3. How do plants adapt?
4. The mountain lion usually hunted at the top of Mount Scorpion, and not at the bottom. How would things have been different for the lion if he had gone up, rather than down, the mountain to hunt on July 10?
5. Why did Bird Wing say, on page 453, "But for the lion, we would be dead"?

Vocabulary

Play "Mountain Lion" with the names and descriptions of animals from "One Day in the Desert." On 3" x 5" cards, write the following names and descriptions. (Note that there is one extra name card.)
Names: Gila woodpecker, honey-pot ant, roadrunner, peccary, kangaroo rat, cicada, spadefoot toad, mountain lion.
Descriptions: squawking noise and stiff tail; tough outer skeleton; long neck and legs; coarse coat and tusks; body changes starch into water; drums louder and faster in heat; skin secretes a sticky gelatin.

Find another player. Deal all the cards. If you have any "pairs" of a name and description for the same animal, lay those cards on the table. Then take turns drawing a card from each other's hand, laying any pairs on the table. The player who is left with the "Mountain Lion" card loses.

Researching a Topic

Pretend that you and your classmates are opening a special exhibit about the desert at a local museum. Use the appropriate reference source to research and prepare one of the following for the exhibit.

- a map of the Sonoran Desert
- a report about desert land and climate
- a report about how deserts develop and change
- a diagram of a desert animal's home
- a diagram of a desert plant
- a glossary of desert animals
- a glossary of desert plants

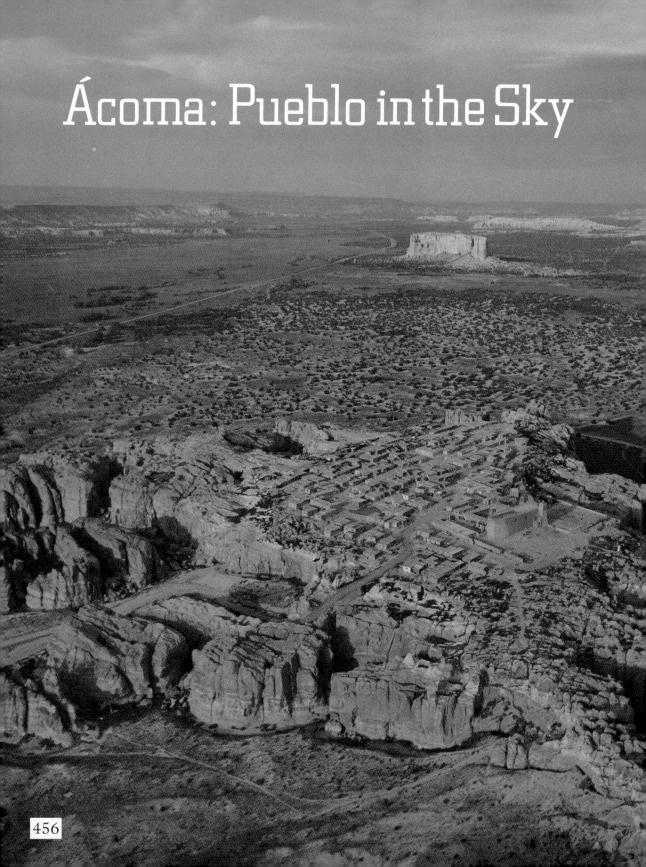

Ácoma: Pueblo in the Sky

Left: Rising up out of the New Mexican desert is the pueblo of Ácoma, the Sky City. It is built atop a mesa, or flat-topped hill. In the distance is Katzimo, also called the Enchanted Mesa. Above, top: Houses in Ácoma are built of adobe in three stories and joined together. The first story is usually used for storage. The second story is reached by climbing a ladder. Above, bottom: Ácoma Indians, like this woman, built the pueblo in the sky and have lived there for centuries. It is the oldest continuously inhabited town in the United States.

Saukin!

by Bobette Gugliotta

All summer long, Carl had been unable to do what he wanted to do most: become friends with his cousin Horace — and climb Katzimo. How could it be any different on his last day in Ácoma?

Carl Bibo was born in 1912, the youngest son of Solomon Bibo, a German-Jewish immigrant, and Juana Valle Bibo, an Ácoma Indian. When he was thirteen, Carl went to spend the summer with his Indian relatives in the pueblo of Ácoma, the Sky City that was built on a mesa. He quickly made friends with Aunt María, her son Wilbert, Aunt Plácida, and her daughter Helen. Helen's brother Horace, who was Carl's age, was another matter. Sometimes, Horace almost seemed to like Carl, but at other times, he seemed to hate him. Carl was determined to make friends with Horace, just as he was determined to climb Katzimo, the huge mesa that towered over Ácoma. Now the summer was nearly over, and both Horace and Katzimo seemed out of Carl's reach. A few days before he was to leave, a race was held as part of a festival. Horace was one of the runners, and he had his heart set on winning. Just before the finish line, however, with the race nearly won, Horace collapsed and was taken home unconscious.

The day after the race, there was still no change in Horace. When Carl saw Wilbert for a moment and asked about the sick boy, Wilbert said, "Horace hasn't moved or talked yet."

On the second day, Carl began to wander, covering areas on the surface of Ácoma that he had never seen before. In a remote corner, far from the dwelling places of the town itself, he came upon a rock mound, built high with hundreds of tufted prayer sticks wedged in the cracks. He stood there looking at it a long time, then walked down the path to the base of Ácoma in search of scrub cedar. When he found some, he broke off a branch and whittled a prayer stick. Returning to the place where he had found the rock mound, he carefully inserted the prayer stick into one of the cracks, saying silently to himself that it was for the recovery of Horace. Except for Horace, everyone in Ácoma had treated him with unfailing kindness. He felt that the least he could do was to show

respect. He began to understand his mother's gentle ways and her tolerance of other customs and religions.

On the third day, Carl climbed up the southern portion of the mesa. When he reached the top, it was close to sunset. From his perch, he could see Katzimo in the distance. It looked magical, like a solid mass of gold. He knew it was only a trick of the sunset, but he stared at it, fascinated as ever. Then suddenly he felt his temper rise when he realized how many times, since coming to New Mexico, he had looked in frustration upon this same glorious, unattainable sight.

Picking up handfuls of dirt, he flung them into the air while he shouted, "Katzimo, you're nothing but a bunch of dust and rock! What's so great about that?"

The only answer he received was that the sun disappeared and Katzimo changed to a muddy brown with deep purple shadows at the base. As he climbed down, the thread of a plan kept running through his mind.

Early the next morning he got up, stuck some bread and jerky in his pocket, and slung a water bottle and rope over his shoulder. Planning to be gone most of the day, he left a note so that if anyone came back to check they'd know he was all right. Last night the usual food had been left for him when he returned to Aunt María's house. But since María and Wilbert were away again all night, he had to assume that Horace was still sick and that the family was continuing the customary watch by his bedside.

The side of Katzimo that faced Ácoma was less than three miles away. Yesterday Carl realized that he had never really explored the base of the big rock. Although he knew it was impossible for him to walk all the way around in one day, he wanted to be able to say when he went home that he had scouted a portion of it. This was what he told himself anyway when he started out. He had just begun picking his way through the talus when it began to rain. The place he was in had no ledges to stand under, nothing that gave cover. Sliding through the mud, he tripped over pieces of rock as sharp as knives. He fell down twice, cutting his knee and tearing a hole in his pants. The minute he reached a spot where there was an opening that looked like a cave, the rain stopped.

Standing there, he got the feeling that it was all on purpose. It was another way for Katzimo to tell him to stay away. Soaking wet, with hair plastered down around his head, he turned and shook his fist at the mesa. He was glad nobody was there to see him. Seeking the shelter of the cave, he took off his clothes and wrung them out. Then he put them back on, figuring they'd dry faster on than off. He began to walk again, looking up and down the steep sides of the mesa, finally

admitting to himself that he was looking for some place where he could make the beginning of a climb.

It was late afternoon when he worked through to the southern end, where he'd never been before. As he stumbled around a curve, he suddenly came upon a big gorge, or cove, cut like a V upside-down into the body of Katzimo. He crawled about midway up the slope on hands and feet. Then, as the going got tough and he looked up seeking a first handhold, he almost lost his balance and fell backward in surprise. There, against the steep wall that led straight to the top of Katzimo, was a rope ladder, sand-colored against sand-colored stone. It was impossible to see from below, because at a distance it blended into the rock.

Carl must have stared at it for five minutes, trying to figure out who had put it there and if it had been there a long time. It was getting so dark that he couldn't see if it was fastened at the top or if it went only part way up. Was it rotted so that a person who tried it might drop down onto the jagged rubble? He knew there wasn't enough time left in the day for him to find out. Even if he made it to the bottom of the ladder, he'd never get back to the Sky City again by sunset, and he was afraid somebody might report to the family that he hadn't come home for his supper. He didn't want anyone to worry about him. Nor did he want anyone to know what he was trying to do. It was hard to leave, but he knew he'd better come back at dawn the next morning, fresh after a night's sleep, ready to try again.

Ácoma was quiet when he got back. The few people he saw were disappearing into their houses for the evening meal. As he passed Aunt Plácida's house, he could see no sign of activity. When he climbed the ladder to Aunt María's, it was the same as before. Nobody was there. Carl was so keyed up that he didn't feel tired, but he was hungry. It didn't take him long to see that food had been laid out and that there was a note placed beside the jug of goat's milk.

Picking it up, he read, "Dear Carl, Aunt Juana and Uncle Solomon sent a message that they have to leave sooner than expected because of business in San Francisco. They'll be coming to pick you up tomorrow at noon. You'd better gather your things together. I'll see you later. Cousin-sister Helen."

As Carl mopped up the gravy from his frijoles, he got the feeling again that every time he came close to doing what he had wanted to do all summer, Katzimo won and he lost out. No matter how early he got up in the morning, there wouldn't be time to make a try up that ancient trail to test the rope ladder to see if it would hold and be back again ready to leave by noon.

When he finished supper, Carl began to stack his gear in a corner of the room. Picking up the medicine bowl Helen had made for him, he looked around for something to pad it with so it wouldn't break on the ride back to San Francisco. The minute he touched it his fingers began to tingle. It was the same feeling he had when his hand went to sleep and he felt prickles all over the skin. The bowl felt warm too, almost alive. It was as though it were sending a message to him. He put it down quickly on top of his clothes, afraid he might drop it. As soon as he let go, he knew what he was going to do. There was no other way and no other time. He had to do it now.

Once he made up his mind, he worked fast, not wanting any of the family to catch him before he left. He wrote a note saying he was camping out and would see them in the morning. Then he shot out of the house. There was a full moon coming up, and he knew that would be a help. He took the long way round to get to the trail, not wanting to pass Aunt Plácida's house in case any of the relatives came out.

When he reached the base of Katzimo, he kept away from the talus and walked around on the plain until he came to the gorge where the trail was. The moon was ascending the sky now, bursting with white light. "Even if I don't make the climb," Carl thought, "it was worth coming just to see Katzimo." The gorge was bleached to the same silver as the moonlight, but on either side the big rock had turned to thick black velvet. It looked as though a spotlight had been deliberately focused on the ancient trail.

Carl shook his head to break the spell. Bending over, he started through the talus on all fours, feeling his way with his hands so he wouldn't fall or twist an ankle before he got where he wanted to be. When the rock smoothed out and he was at the start of the climb where the slope was gradual, he stood up.

"Now," he said out loud. He didn't feel scared because for the first time he thought maybe he could do it. Then it happened. The back of his neck prickled and a chill shot through his shoulders. Something or somebody was standing behind him. He didn't move and it didn't move, but he knew it was there all the same. He waited but there wasn't a sound. At last he whirled around, and the two of them stood stock-still, staring at each other.

Carl spoke first. "Where did you come from?"

"From Ácoma, same as you."

"I thought you were sick."

"I was, but when I woke up this morning I felt good as new, and it was all over. The rest of the day we had ceremonies to give thanks because I was well. Nobody in the family leaves until they are over. Didn't you think our doctors were as good as your doctors? Didn't you think they could cure me, or didn't you want them to?"

"Horace hasn't changed a bit," Carl thought. "He's as nasty as ever."

"Why did you follow me?" Carl asked.

"I wouldn't follow you anywhere if I could help it. I had my own plans, but it wasn't hard to figure out what you wanted to do."

"I don't get it," Carl said. "Listen, why don't you run along back to Ácoma and leave me alone? Get a good night's sleep. Maybe your temper will be better in the morning."

"You've got it all wrong, the way you do with everything, cousin-brother." Horace stressed the last two words sarcastically. "You're the one who is going home. I'm the one who is going to climb Katzimo tonight. That's my rope ladder up there."

Carl took a deep breath, trying to hold his temper. "Why don't we both climb it?"

"No."

Carl tried another tack. "You were pretty smart to make that ladder." When he said these words, he couldn't believe the change that came over Horace. He looked at Carl with such anger in his eyes that it was all Carl could do not to turn and run.

"Don't ever say that to me again!" Horace shouted. His thin face splintered, and Carl was afraid he was going to cry. Then

the whole thing backed up on Carl as he remembered the abuse he'd taken from Horace all summer long.

"Don't scream at me!" Carl screamed back. "It's always me who's trying to keep the peace. You can't even be pleasant the last night I'm here. Who do you think you are? I said you were smart to make that ladder. So you *weren't* smart. You were dumb, dumb, dumb ——"

Suddenly Carl knew he'd better shut up fast because Horace started to cry. It wasn't like other people crying — it hurt to watch him because he was so ashamed of it. He half-twisted his body, turning his face away, putting his hands over his eyes. There wasn't any sound. That was the worst part.

"All right, you win," he said. "After all, you've been pretty fair at that. You've let me know where I stand ever since I came to Ácoma. Sometimes I used to think you liked me, but then you'd change right back to hating." Carl didn't even turn around to take a last look at Katzimo. He never wanted to see it again. He began to walk away, then stopped and called back over his shoulder, "There's only one thing I want to know. Why was it such an insult to say that you were pretty smart to make that ladder?"

This time Horace didn't shout. Carl could barely hear him. "Because that's what *he* said."

"That's what who said?" Carl turned around and took a few steps back so he could hear the answer.

"It's not *exactly* what he said."

Carl walked up close to Horace. "You don't like me and that's all right, but there's got to be a reason."

Then Horace began to talk. "When I was in school in Santa Fe, I had a friend in town, an Anglo. We did everything together. We went fishing up the Pecos River; we went swimming. Once in a while, another boy would come along, a friend of his, an Anglo too. One day they were waiting for me on the street corner after school. They were talking and didn't see me when I came up behind them. I heard the other boy say, 'If you can't work that problem in your arithmetic book, why don't you ask Horace?' and my friend said, 'Well, maybe I will. He's pretty smart — for an Indian.'"

They were both quiet for a while after Horace stopped talking. Finally, Horace said slowly, "I suppose you think that was a stupid thing to get mad at?"

"No, I don't. The half of me that's Anglo is Jewish. The other half is Indian. I've heard remarks like that on both sides. It hurts."

For a long time they didn't say anything more. Then Horace walked a few steps toward the gorge, put his hands on his hips, and stood looking up at the ancient trail.

"I was lying before when I said I was going to climb Katzimo tonight. The ladder isn't fastened. It's just hanging there. I came here because I wanted to see if it was still here. Before I got sick, I was able to toss it up a ways, and it caught on a rough knob of rock. It would take two people to peg it in place. One would have to help the other from below." Horace looked back. His eyes met Carl's. For the first time, each of the boys knew what the other was thinking.

"Come on. Let's go," Carl said. "It's my last chance this summer."

"You first. I'll back you up, tell you what to do, where to put your hands, how to fasten the ladder. You'll have to work holes in the rock before you can push the wooden pegs in. I carved some before the race. I've got them in my pocket. I brought a hammer too."

"How come, if you didn't plan to climb Katzimo tonight?" Carl asked.

Horace shrugged his shoulders. "It's hard to explain. There was this feeling ——"

"I know; I had it too."

As they climbed up the incline, Carl wanted to suggest that he be the one to back Horace up. Horace had been sick, and he was so much shorter and lighter that Carl knew that if he slipped back on him, Horace would surely roll over and over down the slope and onto the sharp talus below. But he felt that this was no time to even hint that he, Carl, might be stronger, so he kept quiet.

It seemed to take forever, but at last they reached the ladder. Things went along slowly and smoothly at the start. With Horace handing him pegs and hammer in the dark, Carl was tall enough to be able to stand on the slope of the gorge, in relative safety, while he fastened the first few rungs into place. But soon he could reach no higher.

"Now comes the first hurdle," he said to Horace. "Let's see if it will hold me."

"I'm right behind, backing you up."

Carl tried the first rung carefully with one foot, stepped on it, and climbed up to the second. The rungs held. "Now comes the next big test," Carl called back. "You'll have to move onto the first rung or you won't be able to hand me the pegs and hammer. Let's hope the ladder is strong enough for both of us."

Though Horace was light, Carl could feel the strain as Horace stepped on. There was the scrunch of wood moving against stone, and the rung Carl was on quivered as a peg settled into place. But it stayed firm. Carl didn't realize he'd been holding his breath until he let it out with a whoosh and gulped another. "So far, so good," he said to himself.

Step by step, rung by rung, they climbed higher. Carl began to breathe a little easier. But when they got within a few feet of the top, Carl suddenly felt so clumsy that he was scared he'd drop the pegs down on the rocks below.

"Listen, Horace," he whispered, although there was nobody to hear them, "do you have any extra pegs with you?"

"No, just the one you're holding now and the last one to go on the other side. Why? What's the matter?"

"I don't know for sure. I'm afraid I might drop one of the pegs. If I did, we'd be only a couple of feet short of reaching the top."

"Go ahead," Horace said. "It's got to be all right."

Carl fumbled the peg into the hole, hammered it in, and slipped the loop on the side of the rope ladder over it. One more to go. Reaching back, Carl felt Horace put the last peg into his hand.

"Here goes," Carl said. This peg didn't fit in easily. It jutted out at an angle. Carl had to hold it in place with his left hand so he could rap it with the hammer he held in his right. There wasn't much elbow room in the narrow crevice, and it was almost impossible to swing with enough strength to drive the peg home. This time Carl wasn't afraid he'd drop the peg but that it might break in two because he couldn't hit it straight.

It was getting colder. An icy wind slashed along the top of Katzimo and blew dust in his eyes. His hands were slimy with sweat, but he didn't dare wipe them off for fear he might lose his balance. Horace, on the rung below him, was absolutely motionless. Taking a firm grip on the hammer, Carl whacked the peg as best he could, then tried it with one finger. It wobbled in the socket.

"I'm going to have to do it again," he warned Horace, trying to keep a quiver out of his voice. "Hold tight."

Carl pushed away the sudden vision he had of the long drop down to the base of Katzimo. Lifting the hammer, he drove down hard. Then, carefully, with thumb and forefinger he tested the peg once more. It didn't turn in the socket. It was firm. He slipped the loop over it and said to Horace, "Let me climb this last rung and get on top. Then I can give you a hand up. I won't feel safe until we're both on solid ground."

In a minute, he was sprawled out on the top, hanging onto a boulder with one arm and reaching down with the other to Horace. They clasped hands, Carl pulled, and thin as Horace was, he seemed to fly up.

They sat there side by side in the dark, breathing hard, waiting for their hearts to stop banging against their ribs.

"How do you feel?" Carl asked.

"Free," Horace said, then, "light."

Carl knew what he meant.

"I had to do it," Horace said. "Not like you, just because you wanted to, but because every Ácoma boy must climb Katzimo some time."

"You mean it's a part of a ritual?"

Horace nodded in the dark.

"I didn't know, or I wouldn't have gotten in your way."

"It's a good thing it happened." Horace didn't explain any further, and Carl didn't ask him to.

Carl dozed for a while — he couldn't help it; he was so tired. It seemed as though he had just closed his eyes when he felt a tap on the shoulder. Horace stood there in a world that glowed with rose-pink light.

Motioning to Carl, Horace walked to the edge of the mesa. Carl followed him, and they stood together watching the day come alive. As the enormous valley yielded to the demanding light of day, it seemed to Carl that all the wonders of nature lay revealed before him and that he and Horace were the first people ever to see them. "I know there will never be anything like this again," Carl thought. "Even if I climbed Katzimo a dozen times, things like this only happen once." Sadness touched him, and for the first time, he knew the sense of loss that comes with the fulfillment of a cherished dream.

"Hold out your hand," Horace said abruptly.

Carl looked at him for a minute, then thrust out his hand.

Horace turned it over, palm up, fished in his pocket, then dropped two rough agate stones shaped like arrowheads in it. "I found them on the other side of Katzimo," he said.

Carl was about to say, "I don't have anything for you," but he kept quiet. He could tell by Horace's face that he didn't want anything in return; he only wanted to give something.

"Thank you," Carl said.

"Thank you, *saukin*!"

"What does that word *saukin* mean?" Carl asked.

"It's a good word," Horace replied. "In the Ácoma language, it means 'friend.'"

Author

Bobette Gugliotta is part of the Bibo family, whose lives became linked with the Ácoma Indians in the 1800's. In New Mexico, Mrs. Gugliotta met newfound relatives and taped a conversation with Carl Bibo, who became the hero of her book *Katzimo, Mysterious Mesa*. Besides her books for young people, she writes for magazines and newspapers.

Comprehension Questions

1. How were things different for Carl on his last day in Ácoma?
2. On page 465, Horace must have watched Carl for a little while before Carl realized he was there. What expression do you think Horace had on his face as he watched Carl?
3. How did Carl react to Horace's story about his former friend?
4. How did Carl's reaction to Horace's story help him to become Horace's friend?

Vocabulary

"Climb Katzimo" by figuring out the words that are defined below. Each word was used in the story "Saukin!" and contains the letter **i**, like the words *climb* and *Katzimo*. The blanks tell you how many letters are in each word and where the letter **i** belongs. The first one is done for you.

1. opposite of liquid   <u>s o l i d</u>
2. tremble   __ __ i __ __ __
3. carry out   __ __ __ i __ __
4. narrow crack   __ __ __ i __ __
5. bitterly mocking   __ __ __ __ __ __ i __
6. still   __ __ i __ __ __ __ __

Writing a Composition

Write what you imagine Carl wrote in a composition entitled "How I Spent the Summer of 1925."

Unfamiliar Words

**"I wish my desk weren't in such disarray! I can't find anything!
Nothing is where it's supposed to be!"**

What does the girl in the picture mean when she says that she wishes her desk weren't in such **disarray?** One way to figure out what the word *disarray* means is to look at the picture. Another way is to use other words and sentences near the word. Read what the girl says again. The words *can't find anything* and *nothing is where it's supposed to be* tell us that *disarray* means "confusion" or "lack of order."

What clues to the meaning of **impudent** can you find in the following sentence?

Pam said, "My little brother is so **impudent!**"

You can tell that the word *impudent* describes a person because Pam uses it to describe her brother. Does it describe something good or something bad about a person? Let's read on.

"I wish he wouldn't act so rudely. Yesterday, for example, he turned the TV up full blast when I was trying to study," Pam went on. "Then he stuck his tongue out at me when I asked him to turn it down."

The first sentence tells us that Pam doesn't like the way her brother acts and that he acts rudely. The second sentence gives an example of what he does that Pam doesn't like. Using these sentences, you can tell that *impudent* means "disrespectful and rude."

Choose the correct meaning of each boldface word. Use other words and sentences as clues.

1. My dog Rufus is a great example of **fidelity.** He always greets me when I get home, and he stays by my side wherever we go.
   a. happiness
   b. stubbornness
   c. loyalty

2. Those big black clouds certainly look **ominous!** We'd better put off our picnic for another day.
   a. threatening
   b. breath-taking
   c. beautiful

3. It was opening night of the football season, and the feeling of happiness was **pervasive.** A sad face was not to be seen in the whole crowd.
   a. keeping a tight hold
   b. allowed to happen
   c. spreading throughout

When you read "Ride the Red Cycle," you may find some words you do not know, such as *physical therapist, rotation, stranded,* and *scowl.* Remember to look at the words and sentences around these words to help you figure out what they mean.

Ride
the Red Cycle

by Harriette Gillem Robinet

In spite of so many obstacles in his way, Jerome desperately wanted to learn to ride a cycle. Why was success so important to him?

"Jerome's got something to say. Listen!"

Jerome felt a warm blush rise up from his neck as Tilly, his fifteen-year-old sister, spoke for him. He wished she wouldn't do that. It made him feel as if he wasn't real.

The trouble was that people were always helping him. His speech was slow and slurred, and someone was always finishing what he wanted to say. When he played baseball, he would kneel to bat the ball, and someone would run the bases for him. When he tried to roll his wheelchair at school, one of the kids would insist on pushing it. Everything happened *to* him, but he never got a chance to make things happen himself. Like a chick breaking out of an egg, he wanted to break free.

Sitting at the breakfast table on that sunny spring morning, he felt a little dizzy; his heart beat faster, the room looked fuzzy to him. It was now or never, he thought. He had to make a break, and this was how he was going to do it. There was a dream that haunted him, and he had to do something about it. He wished he spoke more clearly; but since he couldn't, he asked very slowly.

"I wanna tricycle to ride!"

"How's Jerome gonna ride a cycle, when he can't walk yet, Papa?" Liza asked innocently. Jerome made a face at her.

"Jerome, you stop that!" Mama's fingers tapped on the table.

Round-faced Liza was only five, but already she could ride Tilly's big two-wheeler. She didn't mean to hurt anyone when she reminded the family that eleven-year-old Jerome, who was in the fifth grade, couldn't walk.

As a baby, he had walked at nine months. By his first birthday, he was running around strong. But when he was two years old, a disease had gone to his brain and left damage that affected his whole body. When he got better, he had to learn to support his head, turn over, and crawl all over again — but his legs remained too weak for him to walk.

Papa, a short stocky man with dark brown skin, cleared his throat. "What do *they* say, Mary?"

Jerome felt angry tears springing into his eyes, but he couldn't blink or someone would notice. Why did he always have to hear what *they* had to say? All Jerome's life, *they* — all the people in his life that other boys never had to worry about — got to say things about him. *They* were the physical therapists who exercised his legs, the speech therapists, the bone doctors, the nerve doctors, and the eye doctors. *They* made all the decisions in his life, but just once he wanted to do something all by himself!

He had thought for a long time, and he had chosen carefully for himself. A teenager with cerebral palsy had told him that a two-wheeler was out of the question; it took balance to ride a two-wheeler — but three wheels. . . .

Of course he was pleased with the wheelchair. He was able to get around the neighborhood with it, except for curbs. Until he was six, his folks had to carry him everywhere.

The wheelchair was all right, but Jerome had a wonderful dream. In it, he was speeding fast, with the wind in his face, eyes squinted tightly, leaning forward like the leather-jacket guys on motorcycles. That was his dream; and in his dream hundreds of thousands watched as he raced along a track. Cheers and clapping sounded like thunder in the sky. He was reckless and calm and cool, and millions knew his name. As he stepped off his cycle, he walked with a casual swagger: Jerome Johnson, cycle rider!

All right, he couldn't race a motorcycle, but he had seen a man on a three-wheel cycle once, the kind of cycle he wanted. Summer vacation started in a few weeks, and with real wheels he would be able to go everywhere. Oh, for a set of wheels!

Mama answered Papa softly. "John, the physical therapist says it'll be good leg motion, good for his legs — but Dr. Ryan says that left leg is real stiff."

"Ha!" Papa jumped at the mention of Dr. Ryan. "Dr. Ryan didn't think he could learn to crawl either, but he did. I think the boy ought to have a tricycle!"

"Hey now, Papa!" Tilly said triumphantly. "Jerome and I'll be ready to go shopping when you come home." Saturdays Papa worked half-days at the post office.

Mama finished clearing the breakfast table and went to tell the news to Mrs. Mullarkey, the next-door neighbor. Liza, her round face grinning, and little brother, Gordon, ran out to play. Tilly, tall and thin, dug her hands in her skirt pockets and followed.

Whirling in his chair, Jerome saw a limp balloon on the kitchen sideboard. It was one Gordon had been playing with. He reached over, grabbed it, and tried to pop it with his broad clumsy hands. Straining violently, half-afraid but wanting to hear the loud bang, he grunted, "Break balloon."

It was too hard. His hands were too stiff to pop the silly old balloon — something else he couldn't do.

Outside, Gordon overheard Jerome say "break balloon" just as Papa was coming home from work.

"Papa, Papa," Gordon called. "Jerome's gonna make the moon — He's gonna ride his cycle to the moon, Papa?"

Papa smiled wearily and hugged Gordon. He didn't know where that little boy got his wild ideas! Inside, Tilly and Jerome were ready to go shopping. They were soon on their way.

In the bicycle shop window, Jerome saw what he wanted. The seat was higher than those on small three-wheelers, the wheels were really big, and the color was orange-red.

"Papa, I want that one," he called out. Oh! He could feel the wind whizzing through his black hair as he sped along the highways. Highways? Well, along the sidewalk anyway.

Tilly pushed his wheelchair straight up to the big three-wheel cycle, while Papa went to get a salesperson. There was no price tag on the cycle, and he was afraid to hope. His heart beat faster, and he felt breathless for the second time that day. He was so close. This was the cycle he wanted. Would it cost too much?

Papa came back and lifted his son onto the seat of the big red cycle. "It must be all right; he'll buy it for me," Jerome thought. He gripped the handles and noticed red and white streamers on the plastic handle grips — how they would fly in the wind as he rode! He felt shaky, though, up so high on the seat; and as he held on and looked around, Papa noticed.

"Never you mind, Son. I'll build up the pedals and make the seat broader," Papa told him. Then to the salesperson, he said, "We'll take this one."

Papa paid at the cash register, and soon Jerome was riding home, with his dream cycle tied down in the trunk of the car.

It took Papa almost a week of evenings after work to finish outfitting the cycle. He attached wooden blocks to the pedals and put leather straps on the blocks to hold his son's shoes. Since Jerome kept sliding off the seat, Papa made a new one. From a secondhand chair, he got a plastic seat and back, all in one piece. He drilled holes and screwed the new seat onto the cycle, then he put a seat belt around it.

On the first of June, Jerome sat on his cycle outdoors for the first time; but he didn't try riding until Papa came home. Everyone was excited. Kids and their mothers from the other houses on the block gathered on his front doorstep. Some kids were riding their bicycles in circles and then standing astride them. Liza, a proud grin across her face, rode up and down the block, calling people to come see her brother's new cycle.

One mother told Mama that Jerome was a brave boy, but for the millionth time Mama said, "Jerome ought to be grateful for just being alive. I never thought he'd be living

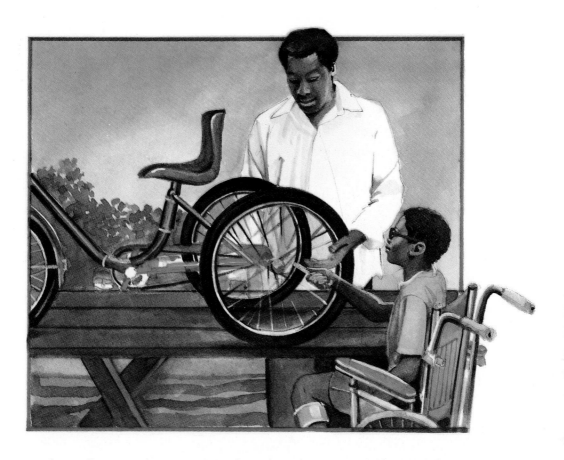

today, the way he was. He lay there two weeks and didn't know anybody. He was all but dead before he came to." Mama was always harping on how sick he had been.

Jerome didn't mind what Mama said. He knew she was scared he wouldn't be able to ride the cycle. He knew how his mother felt because he was scared himself. How would he ever find out, though, if he didn't try?

Jerome thought Mama looked a little proud of him in spite of what she said. She stood on the steps with her thin arms crossed tightly. He was glad people were calling it a cycle and not a tricycle. It was big enough not to look like the tricycles Gordon's friends rode.

When Papa came home, he pulled his son's handlebars slowly and showed him how to push from his knees to pedal.

Jerome leaned forward, panting — but his legs wouldn't move. His legs wouldn't move!

After a while the neighbors and kids grew tired of watching him, and they agreed it would be a long time before he learned to ride — if ever. As they began drifting away, he felt disappointment drape over him. He hadn't really expected to ride the first day, but somehow he had hoped. . . .

The kids went their different ways, calling noisily to each other and racing off on bicycles; but Papa and Tilly stayed, giving him pushes.

"Papa, look, they catch," Jerome whispered to his father. At each rotation of the wheel, the brace on his left leg caught in the front wheel. Papa shifted Jerome's foot further.

"I'll put a shield on the sides to keep those braces from catching," he told his son.

The shields did keep the braces from catching in the wheel, but they didn't make Jerome's legs turn the wheels of the cycle. He spent every afternoon after school sitting and trying to rock his cycle, but he never moved. Sometimes the kids came along and pulled or pushed him.

He had been able to get around by himself in the wheelchair, but now he often got stranded on his cycle. The kids would go in and leave him around the corner or down the street, and he couldn't follow them. When dinner time came, Mama or Tilly had to go looking for him.

Then something exciting happened. One day he was turning the handlebars and weaving back and forth, as some boys ran behind, pushing him. After one sharp turn, the red cycle fell over. Mama fussed about the bump on his forehead and his scraped knees, but Jerome felt happy and victorious.

"Look, Papa," he called later, when Papa came in from work. "I got a bandage. I hurt my knee."

He had had calluses on his hands and knees from crawling, but he'd never had a good hurt knee before. Now he had joined all those other kids who got to wear bandages on their knees. Somehow it made him feel as if he was really learning to ride. Other kids fell off bicycles when they were learning to ride, and he had fallen too. That night he thought and thought and came up with a plan.

"Hey, Tilly," he called the next day. "Take me up by the alley where it slants to the street."

"Trucks come in the alley by the factory, Jerome. You've gotta stay on the sidewalk," Tilly told him.

"But Tilly, you'll be with me," he begged. "I can ride there."

So Tilly pulled him along the block, not telling anyone where they were going. When they reached the alley, she sat in the uncut grass and chickweed, watching for cars and reading a book. She enjoyed the peace and quiet. No one was around, so Jerome could grunt and sway all he needed, trying to pedal.

Three weeks passed, and school was out. Every morning Tilly and Jerome went on their secret trip for a couple of hours. When Mama asked them where they went all morning, Jerome said, "I've been near."

Soon Jerome could shake the cycle enough on the slope so that his right leg got down fast enough for the left leg to reach the top of its pedal. Then he could push the stiff left leg down. He pedaled, but not always. He never could be sure. The dream of success was becoming a nightmare. He felt foolish and silly not being able to depend on his legs.

"Tilly, don't tell," he begged. Every day they went to the alley. Tilly pushed the cycle out of the way when trucks came up to the factory, then she put her brother back on the slope and sat, chin in hands, watching him struggle with the red cycle.

By July he could ride down the slant, but he fought and struggled to ride up. Soon his legs moved one after the other, and he was riding. Some days Jerome nearly burst with

triumph, and Tilly wanted to tell Mama and Papa right away. Other days, though, there was only failure. On those days his legs wouldn't push as he wished; in fact, they wouldn't move at all.

He had nightmares about his legs not working when he tried to show Mama and Papa. In his dreams, they were watching, and his legs wouldn't budge. His legs must learn to move one after the other all the time. He knew it wouldn't be easy, and he was fighting hard. Gradually he became more sure of being able to pedal. His legs worked more often than they didn't.

In August smothering heat arrived, but Jerome forced his legs to move in spite of the sweat pouring off him. Besides Tilly, no one else knew how hard he was trying.

At home Mama was afraid to hope; it broke her heart to watch him sit still out front on that red cycle. Papa was afraid not to hope.

By then the kids on the block had decided that Jerome would never ride. He had been fun to be with before — if only he would be satisfied with himself. What was so important about riding that cycle?

The summer before, Jerome had played baseball with the other kids, and Tommy had usually run bases for him. Now all Jerome did was sit alone on the big red cycle. The kids stopped playing with him. Why did he want that big cycle anyway?

But Jerome had his dream, and he had chosen it carefully. It was something he could do; it was possible, and he would do it. It was one thing he would get to do all by himself. Tilly, it was true, brought him to the slanted drive; but *he* was the one fighting his legs to ride. He'd show Tommy and David and all the kids. He'd even show Tilly . . . because there was something secret he was practicing late at night, all by himself.

By the end of August he could hardly wait to show off. As he became sure of himself, the perfect occasion came up. The neighbors planned a block party for Labor Day weekend.

That Saturday morning, police closed the street at both ends, and teenagers decorated trees with yellow crepe paper banners. Neighbors held brightly colored balloons, and marching music filled the air. Everyone was dressed in cool, colorful clothes for the hot summer day.

In the morning there was a pet parade, then games with water-filled balloons. Artists of all ages drew pictures on the sidewalk with colored chalk.

In the afternoon there was a program of local talent. Tommy played drums, Liza sang a funny song, and another girl arranged a mushroom dance with five little girls. Jerome knew that Tilly had put his name next on the program.

For the mushroom dance, the little girls held umbrellas covered with brown paper. Everyone liked the silly twirling dance. When they finished, Mrs. Mullarkey called out, "Next on our program is Jerome Johnson, who will, who will . . . Jerome Johnson, folks!"

Everyone clapped politely. Then there was an eerie quiet. Adults and kids looked at one another to see if anyone knew what was going to happen. What was he going to do?

Tilly pulled her brother out into the street at the end of the block and left him sitting on the shiny orange-red cycle. Her heart was pounding. She lowered her head and stuck her hands in her jean pockets as she strolled away from him. He was on his own.

Mama folded her arms to calm herself. Papa sat down on the curb because his knees grew weak. Liza hugged Gordon and waited. Gordon wondered if his brother would go to the moon now.

Jerome, frowning and gritting his teeth, struggled for what seemed like hours to get his legs moving. After two long

minutes, slowly but firmly, he began pedaling — gripping the handles and leaning forward as though he were speeding along. There was no wind whipping in his face, but that didn't matter. He was riding his cycle himself; he was riding. That was all he could think.

Jerome's progress down the street was slow, deliberate, and strangely rhythmic. People could hardly wait to applaud, and as he neared the end, clapping burst forth and the kids cheered. He remained calm and cool, though.

"Okay," he thought to himself, "with Tilly's help, I learned to ride. But now I'll really show them."

He stopped in the middle of the street, opened the seat belt, and bowed with a flourish to the people on his right. His hands trembled.

Tilly wondered why he had stopped in the middle. She started toward him, but he stopped her with an icy scowl. Papa stood up, but Jerome frowned at him too.

The neighbors got quiet again.

Carefully, Jerome slid his right leg around and off the cycle. He stood crouched on both feet, his knees and hips bent under his weight. He was grateful for the braces that kept his feet flat on the ground. At night when he had practiced this with his braces off, he'd stood on his toes.

He heard himself saying, "I wanna thank everybody that helped me, 'specially my sister Tilly, and my papa, and my mama."

Then, while eighty people held their breath, he let go of the cycle. His arms wavered at his sides, balancing him. His head was high; his chin jutted forward.

He slid his stiff left leg forward, with his feet and knees twisted in, then he stepped jerkily off on his right foot. He dragged his left leg and stepped with his right. Deliberate, slow, arms waving in the air, one leg after the other, Jerome Johnson walked. It was stiff and clumsy walking — but these were his first steps, practiced late at night.

Before he reached his wheelchair, he fell to the street. No one moved toward him. Clapping and cheering could be heard for blocks. It was almost like thunder in the sky. His dream had come true.

He didn't try to get to his feet again; he crawled to his wheelchair. He would work on walking with his physical therapist, now that it wasn't a secret anymore — now that he'd shown them how much he could do all by himself.

Mama couldn't believe her eyes. Papa cried and didn't care who saw him. Liza and Gordon were staring with their mouths hanging open. For Gordon, his brother's going to the moon had seemed a simple thing; his brother's walking was far more wonderful.

Tilly rolled on the grass, laughing and crying and hugging herself for joy. Her tough, stubborn little brother had learned to ride a cycle and had taught himself to walk.

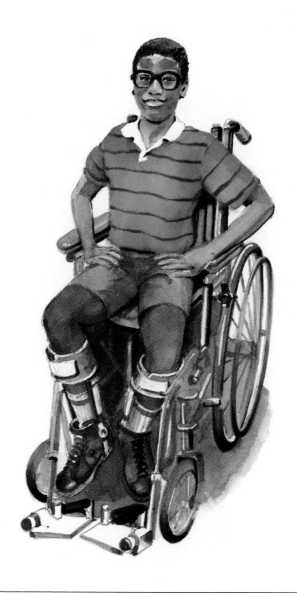

Author

Harriette Gillem Robinet, who has a son with cerebral palsy, has met many children with similar disabilities. For them she wanted to write a book that would reflect some of their dreams and victories. Dr. Robinet, who has a doctor's degree from Catholic University, has been a biology teacher and a research scientist.

Comprehension Questions

1. Why was learning to ride the cycle so important to Jerome?
2. How did Jerome's friends feel about his struggle to ride?
3. What event made Jerome realize he would have more chance of success if he practiced riding his cycle in the alley that slanted toward the street?
4. Why had Jerome felt it was important to keep it a secret that he was practicing walking?
5. What do you think the author meant by the following statement, which appears on page 487: "Jerome had his dream, and he had chosen it carefully"?

Vocabulary

Pick out the word that doesn't fit in each set, and tell why.

1. thick	thin	broad	wide
2. humid	damp	dry	moist
3. smooth	slick	glassy	rough
4. glared	scowled	frowned	grinned
5. curt	respectful	courteous	polite

Think of four more words, three of which go together. See if your classmates can figure out which word doesn't belong.

Writing a Journal Entry

Pretend that you are Tilly. Write what her journal entry might have been on the day Jerome demonstrated his achievements for his neighbors.

There Is Fear....
There Is Joy

An Inuit Chant
Translated by Knud Rasmussen

There is fear in
Feeling the cold
Come to the great world
And seeing the moon
 — Now new moon, now full moon —
Follow its old footprints
In the winter night.

There is joy in
Feeling the warmth
Come to the great world
And seeing the sun
Follow its old footprints
In the summer night.

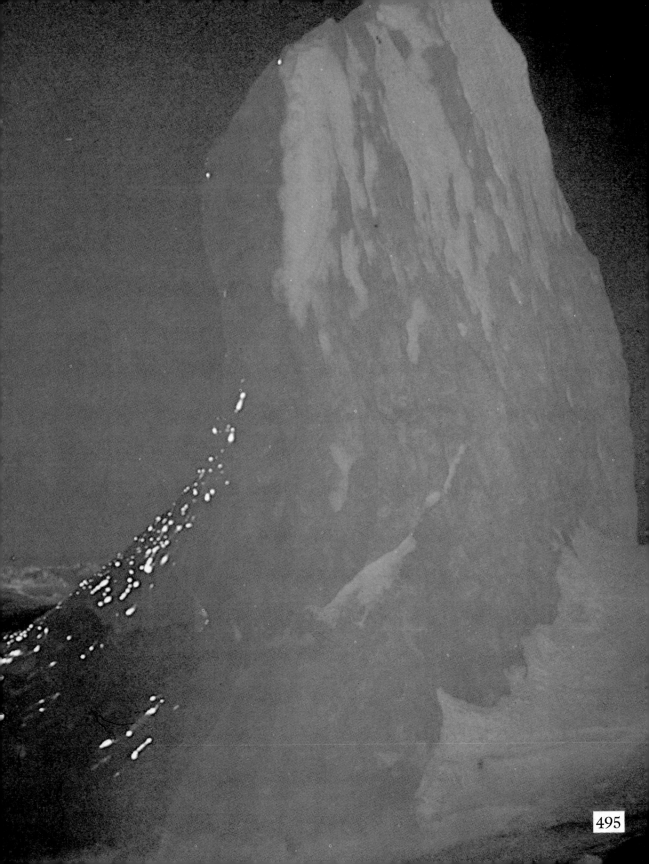

Graphs

For a science project, Juanita was studying the weather and how it changes. At the same time each day, she wrote down the temperature and described the weather. After doing this each day for two weeks, she had quite a bit of information.

Juanita wanted to show her classmates what the weather had been like. So she put the information on two graphs.

A **graph** is a drawing that helps you to compare numerical information. With a graph, you can clearly see how things are alike or different — or how things change. Textbooks, encyclopedias, magazines, and newspapers often have graphs, so it's important to know how to read them. There are several kinds of graphs: pictographs, bar graphs, line graphs, and circle graphs. This lesson will deal with line graphs and circle graphs.

Line Graphs

Juanita made a **line graph** to show how the temperature had changed. A line graph helps you see changes or differences that can be measured. Graph 1 is the line graph Juanita made. On a line graph, a line connects points that stand for numbers. The line is shown on a grid of thin lines, which are labeled to tell you what numbers and facts they stand for.

Like all graphs, a line graph has a **caption** that tells you what you should learn from it. Read the caption below Graph 1. You can see that Graph 1 tells you what the temperature was every afternoon at 4:00 for a two-week period. The thin lines that run straight up and down the graph stand for the days of the week. They are labeled *Sun, M, T, W, Th, F,* and *S.* Each line going across the graph stands for a temperature.

Most of the time, you will not need to look at every point on a line graph. You will look only at the points that give you the facts you need.

To find what the temperature was on Monday of the first week, find *M* at the bottom of the graph. Then follow the black line that runs up from it until you reach the point where the red line touches the black line. Then look across to the left to see which number the thin line stands for. You can see that the temperature was 60 degrees Fahrenheit that Monday and that it was also 60 degrees on Tuesday of the first week. What was the temperature on Wednesday of the first week?

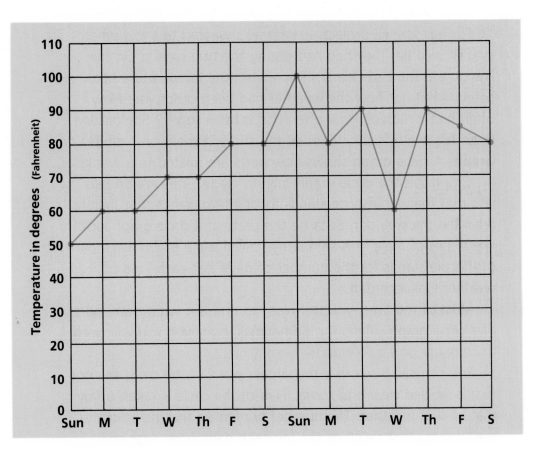

Graph 1. Daily temperatures at 4:00 P.M. during the two-week period June 2 to June 15

A quick look at the line graph gives you a good idea of how the temperature changed. As the red line goes across the graph from day to day, it sometimes goes up, sometimes goes straight across, and sometimes goes down. The red line shows that the temperature was not the same during these two weeks. You can see from the upward slant of the red line that the temperature either went up or stayed the same during the first week. It went up and down, though, during the second week. How often was the temperature the same two days in a row?

Circle Graphs

For her science project, Juanita also wanted to show what kind of weather they had had during the two weeks. On the line graph, she had clearly shown what the temperature had been — but not how the weather had been otherwise. How often had it rained? How often had it been sunny? She divided these facts into four categories and showed them on a **circle graph.** A circle graph shows how parts are related to a whole.

Graph 2 is the circle graph Juanita made. The caption tells you that the whole circle stands for the two weeks that Juanita recorded the weather. Because the parts of a circle graph look like pieces of a pie, it is sometimes called a *pie graph*. Each part of this pie stands for the number of days that each kind of weather was recorded.

Most of the time, you will want to find out what every part of a circle graph stands for. Sometimes, however, you will need to compare only a few parts.

You can easily see that the largest piece of the pie is the one that is labeled *clear and sunny*. Half of the circle is taken up by that kind of weather. The number printed on that piece of the pie tells you that seven of the fourteen days were clear and sunny. Even if no numbers were printed on the graph, you could compare the size of the pieces and see at once that *clear*

Graph 2. Number of days having each kind of weather during the two-week period June 2 to June 15

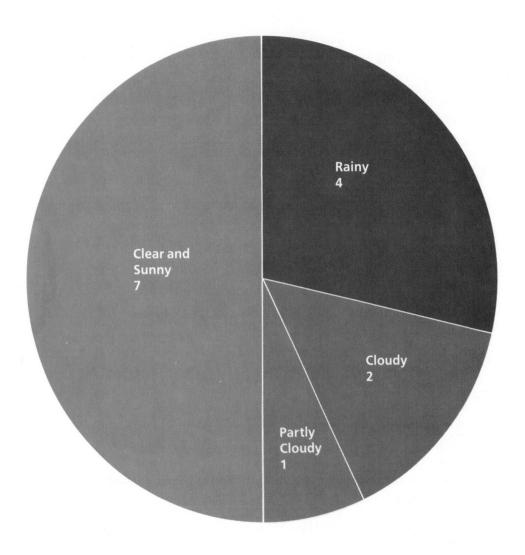

Rainy
4

Clear and
Sunny
7

Cloudy
2

Partly
Cloudy
1

and sunny was the kind of weather that happened most often. Anyone looking at the circle could also see that clear and sunny, cloudy, and partly cloudy days combined to make up about two thirds of the graph.

Reading Graphs

Use Graph 1 to answer the questions that follow.

1. What temperature occurred most often during the fourteen days?
2. What were the highest and lowest temperatures recorded on the graph?
3. Which day showed the greatest increase in temperature from the day before?
4. What is the difference between temperatures on the first and last days of the experiment?

Use Graph 2 to answer the following questions.

5. On how many days were there clouds in the sky?
6. How many more *clear and sunny days* than *rainy days* were recorded?
7. Which kind of weather occurred the least often?
8. Why could you say that the good and bad days of weather were about equally divided?

Skill Summary

- When numerical information is put on a graph, it is easier to make comparisons and to see changes.
- There are different kinds of graphs. A line graph helps you to see changes and to make comparisons. A circle graph helps you to see the relationship of a part to a whole.

- Always read the caption on a line graph to find out what you should learn from it. Then carefully read the labels that tell you what the lines going up and down and across the graph stand for.
- On a circle graph, carefully read the caption that tells what the whole circle represents; then read the labels that tell what each part of the circle stands for.

The Paper Caper

by Caroline B. Cooney

Why would anyone steal a computer program? When Lynn set out to solve this mystery, she didn't realize the obstacles — and danger — she would face. How could she find the solution in time?

Lynn and Victoria, twin sisters, were spending the summer with their aunt Camilla and uncle Steve. Uncle Steve had a computer business called Greer Data Systems, which he ran from an office in a spare room of the house.

Uncle Steve was designing a computer program for a local newspaper. Lynn was very interested in the computer, and Uncle Steve was teaching her a little bit about operating it. She had also taken on a job delivering newspapers for the same local paper. While on her route, she met Shad, who also delivered papers.

Just as he was about to finish the program for the newspaper, Uncle Steve discovered that his office had been robbed.

"Who came into my office?" shouted Uncle Steve. He bounced off the walls and desks of the little room like a bullet ricocheting on a TV cop show. "I go out to lunch with Camilla, and I come back and find somebody's gotten into my office! Was it one of you kids? Did you come in here, Lynn?"

Lynn, Victoria, and Shad shrank back against the wallpaper. "No, sir," said Lynn. "We didn't, honest."

Aunt Camilla bent over the file cabinets, her long dark hair swaying. "It isn't here, Steve," she said. "Where can it be? What could have happened?"

"Somebody stole it," he said. "That's what happened."

"We forgot to lock the outside door to the office," said Aunt Camilla. "It was stupid of us."

"Stole what?" said Lynn.

"Your uncle Steve's program for the newspaper circulation," said Aunt Camilla, pawing through piles of paper on the tops of the desks. "We did a trial run for Mr. Forio, the owner, this morning. It went perfectly. Your uncle called Mr. Hamill, the circulation manager, to say we can install tomorrow. Then we went out to lunch to celebrate getting the job over with."

"How could I have been so dumb?" said Uncle Steve. "I worked for three months on that program. How could I have gone off, leaving the disk in plain sight with the door unlocked?"

Lynn thought it most odd that anybody would steal a computer program. "What would they do with it?" she wondered. It wasn't like stealing a color television or a silver tea set.

Uncle Steve sighed and dropped onto the torn corduroy couch. Aunt Camilla sorted through the trash on the floor. Uncle Steve sifted through the stacks on the couch. Lynn tried to find the disk in the wastebasket.

The disk just wasn't in the office.

"What will you do, Uncle Steve?" said Victoria worriedly.

"I still have the flow charts," he said. "I can reconstruct. I told Mr. Forio I'd install tomorrow, though. Now we'll be lucky if I can do it next week."

Shad cupped his hands over Lynn's ear. "What are flow charts?" he whispered.

"The written-down program," she hissed. "You wouldn't believe how long the program is in writing. Not all of it is written down, either — just hints and clues to help him remember."

"Shall I call the police?" said Aunt Camilla.

Uncle Steve sighed. "I suppose you could." He rubbed his hands over his wrinkled forehead and dismally sat down at the screen. From a wide drawer he pulled two huge, thick notebooks of green and white striped paper: the flow charts. "Don't anybody bother me," he said. "Make yourselves scarce."

He turned on the computer. Aunt Camilla picked up the room. Shad and Victoria slipped outside. Lynn lingered. Over her uncle's shoulder, she could see the flow charts clearly.

250 IF LEN (D$) = 8 GOTO 240 said one line.

Uncle Steve flipped back to the first page, and there, in ordinary English, was a list of codes. Lynn memorized one of them. "Now," she thought, "I can access the personnel program!"

It was a long weekend. Aunt Camilla carried trays of food in to Uncle Steve, who hunched over his computer, stabbing at the keys. The girls played outdoors with Shad, delivered their papers, and stayed out of Uncle Steve's hair. Aunt Camilla called the police, and they said they'd look into it. Mr. Forio telephoned constantly, and after each phone call Uncle Steve was a little angrier.

Lynn almost wished her parents were back, so they could go home and be away from the tension at Greer Data Systems. She had never seen Uncle Steve so upset. Mr. Forio's plans were thrown off; and Mr. Hamill, who had from the beginning been opposed to the idea of a computer program, came in now and then, snarling.

Lynn walked down to the park with Victoria and Shad. The summer sun was very hot — too hot for bikes or ball games, almost too hot just to lie on the grass under the trees. "Who," said Shad, "would want to steal your uncle's computer program?"

"You don't steal unless you think you will be better off," said Victoria. "Who would be happier or richer if they had Uncle Steve's program?"

All they could think of was the *Daily News* — but that was where the program was going in the first place. "They wouldn't steal their own program, would they?" the children wondered.

"The disk had a label," said Victoria. "The thief knew it was a circulation program and not a gold brick or a George Washington autograph."

Lynn kept thinking, "Who would be happier or richer if they had that program?"

It was too hot to think. Her brain worked as clearly as chocolate pudding.

"Can you really run that computer, Lynn?" said Shad.

Lynn shrugged. "Sort of. One program, anyway. Personnel." Through the heat waves, she saw Shad's envy. She thought, "I wish I could show off. I promised Uncle Steve, though."

"Let's look me up," begged Shad, "the way you said you would last week. Your uncle said he'd be at the paper this afternoon, trying to work some bugs out of the system. You won't be bothering him."

"That's true," thought Lynn, aching to do it.

Victoria sat up fast and said, "Lynn, you'd better not."

"Uncle Steve says it's snooping," Lynn admitted. "He says it's trespassing on people's privacy to look them up in a computer."

"But it's *me* you're looking up," protested Shad. "It's *my* privacy, and I want you to snoop on it."

It would be fun to sit on the piano stool, swiveling a little, keeping Victoria and Shad in suspense, not letting them see how she did it. "I'm thirsty," she said. "Let's go back to Uncle Steve's and get something to drink."

They trudged down Eastern Avenue. There weren't many shade trees. The back of Lynn's T-shirt was sweaty wet, and she fanned herself by flapping it. Nobody said anything more about touching the computer, but everybody was thinking about it. When they got to the house, Aunt Camilla was busy in the greenhouse. Uncle Steve's car was gone. The children sat in the kitchen, which was dark and cool after being outdoors, and sipped ice water.

Finally, Lynn said, "Well, we could just go in and look."

They walked down the hall, past the bedrooms, and opened the door to Uncle Steve's office. The blinds were pulled, and it was musty and very, very hot. The outside door was locked and bolted. Lynn turned on the fluorescent light overhead and seated herself at the computer.

"Lynn, you shouldn't," said Victoria.

"I won't fool around. I know what I'm doing." She turned on the computer.

Victoria said, "I'm leaving"; but she didn't.

Lynn typed the access code in the right order. When the computer asked which file Lynn wanted, she typed 18. The personnel file was open. Lynn typed BAINBRIDGE CROSBY CURTIS. Shad grinned when his real name appeared in green letters on the screen.

Almost instantly the machine said NO SUCH EMPLOYEE. RETYPE IN CASE OF ERROR.

"I am not an error," said Shad huffily. "Retype me, Lynn."

Lynn typed his name again. Again the computer rejected it.

"Maybe it's under 'Shad,'" said Victoria.

SHAD CURTIS, Lynn typed. Nothing. She tried CURTIS, SHAD and then CURTIS, BAINBRIDGE CROSBY.

NO SUCH EMPLOYEE. RETYPE IN CASE OF ERROR, answered the computer.

"Uncle Steve said every single delivery person is in the file," said Lynn, puzzled. "What's your supplier's name?"

"Grant. He's Mr. Hamill's cousin. He has to be in there. He has about forty paperboys on his route."

The twins glared at him.

"And papergirls," he added.

"Thank you." Lynn typed GRANT.

"Mr. Grant couldn't have forgotten to give the newspaper my name," said Shad, "because I've been with him longer than anybody else on his string. Four years."

The computer rejected the name GRANT too.

"Maybe that's one of the bugs your uncle mentioned," said Shad. "Something's wrong with the program and——"

"There's nothing wrong with my uncle Steve's program," said Victoria icily.

Lynn was frowning. She knew she was using the computer correctly. "Who are some of the other kids who have routes with Mr. Grant?"

Shad gave her a long list. She tried them all. The computer had no records on Dick Thompson, none on Tom Kovach, P.M. Rose, or Donna Dominic. Shad said, "You don't know what you're doing. I'm getting out of here. Come on, Vic." He and Victoria went out of the office, flicking off the lights to be mean.

Lynn sat in the darkness and stared at the green letters on the screen, thinking and thinking.

The next day, the house was very quiet. Victoria was in the den watching television. Aunt Camilla was in her greenhouse. Uncle Steve was working hard in his office. The drapes and blinds were pulled to keep out the hot sun, and the whole place had a musty, hot feel. Two small window air conditioners puffed heavily at each end of the house, like beginning joggers about to faint.

Lynn fixed a lunch tray for her uncle. She carried it into the office and cleared a space for it on a table. "Uncle Steve," she said, "do you have every one of the delivery people in your data files? Is that list completely up to date?"

"I do, and it is," said Uncle Steve, cramming half a ham sandwich into his mouth and going right on typing. His cheeks squirreled out underneath his beard. "Good lunch. Thanks."

"Who gave you the list?" Lynn said.

"Mr. Hamill, of course. He's in charge of circulation, isn't he?"

Lynn had done some arithmetic yesterday. She earned three cents a paper. The customer paid fifteen cents. That left twelve cents that Lynn turned in to her supplier. The supplier paid five cents to the newspaper, which left him with a seven-cent profit. Seven cents wasn't enough to buy anybody anything.

"Does Mr. Hamill tell the press room how many papers to print?" she said.

"Of course he does," said Uncle Steve. "That's his job. Lynn, I'm sorry to be short with you. I'm all bent out of shape over that disk being stolen. Leave me alone and let me work, okay?"

"Okay." Lynn carried the tray back to the kitchen. With a felt-tipped marker on a paper napkin, she did some more figuring.

Shad had told her there were forty paperboys and girls on Mr. Grant's supply route. Lynn had ninety-eight papers; Shad had one hundred eleven.

"One hundred is easy to multiply with," Lynn said to herself. "So I'll say that each of those forty kids delivers one hundred papers every day. Seven cents is what Mr. Grant gets. Seven cents times forty times one hundred papers each is $280. So Mr. Grant is earning $280 a day times 365 days. That's ——" She made mistakes with the marker and started in on another napkin. "$102,200." Lynn was astonished. A little tiny seven cents that couldn't buy much of anything!

She perched on the kitchen counter to think better, with her legs swinging. "Isn't it wonderful what can happen to seven cents?" she said. "Over one hundred thousand dollars!" She drummed her heels slowly on the cabinets and looked out the kitchen window at the quiet street.

Suddenly she knew exactly why the program had been stolen. She knew who had stolen it too.

Uncle Steve spent the rest of the afternoon at the paper. "I'm so tired," he said at supper. "Let's do something pleasant tonight. How about a movie? Everybody want to go?"

"Yes," said Aunt Camilla and Victoria.

"No," said Lynn.

"No?" said her uncle. "Are you feeling sick, Lynn?"

She was feeling bad — bad that she had used the computer and bad about Mr. Grant and Mr. Hamill. "Yes, I have a headache," she said.

"Lock the door after us," called her uncle.

"Bye," said Victoria.

Lynn locked the kitchen door, and perched on the counter again, and did some more arithmetic. After a while she went into Uncle Steve's office and borrowed his pocket calculator. She hadn't made any mistakes on her napkin.

Just then, Mr. Hamill's yellow van drove up and parked in front of the house. "Oh, no!" thought Lynn. "They're going to steal it again!"

For a moment Lynn could not move. She was stuck to the counter. Only her heart leaped. Then she threw herself across the kitchen, reaching the telephone in two giant steps. With shaking fingers she dialed the number pasted on the receiver handle. Seven numbers had never taken so long to dial. Through the window she saw that Mr. Grant and Mr. Hamill were halfway across the lawn. They looked very much alike. They were cousins, Shad had told her. The telephone rang several times. Then a voice answered, "Police. Officer Mason here."

"This is Lynn Greer. Please come over to my uncle's house. We're in trouble. Hurry!"

"Is this a practical joke?"

"No, no! It's about the computer. The stolen disk." Lynn could no longer see the men. Faintly she heard them on the steps by the office door. "Greer Data Systems!" she cried. "Hurry!"

"A stolen what?" said Officer Mason. "What's this about computers?"

Lynn could not stay on the phone to explain. She rushed down the stuffy hall and burst through the door into the office to be sure the outside door was bolted. It wasn't. Mr. Hamill and Mr. Grant had already let themselves into the room.

They were horrified to see her. "You're the niece," said Mr. Hamill. "Didn't you all go to the movies? When your uncle was at the newspaper this afternoon, he said he wanted to take everybody out to the movies."

"I don't like movies. I'll tell him you came by." Lynn tried to show them out. "Good-by."

They didn't leave. They looked around the office. Lynn thought, "This time they'll take the disk *and* the flow charts. When Uncle Steve can't install the program by the second deadline, Mr. Forio will just shrug and give up on ever having computers. He'll say, 'It's easier the old way.' He'll cancel Uncle Steve's contract. We'll be broke, and Mr. Hamill and Mr. Grant will be safe."

"How did you get in?" she said.

"The door was open," said Mr. Grant. He gave Lynn a peculiar look, and she realized with a sick taste in her mouth that she had forgotten to tell Officer Mason the address. Even if he wanted to help her, he wouldn't know where to look.

"It's no good searching here," said Lynn. "There's nothing here but trash. My uncle left the program at the newspaper." Actually the new disk was on the couch, covering the split places. The flow charts were on Uncle Steve's piano stool.

"Looking?" said Mr. Grant. "For what?" He strolled around the room as if he were in a park. It wasn't easy, because of all the crumpled paper he had to wade through.

Lynn thought, "If I tell them I know what they've done, they'll give up and leave."

"I figured out what you two did," she said. "I'm going to tell Uncle Steve, and he'll tell Mr. Forio, so you'd better get out."

Mr. Hamill said, "What are you talking about, little girl?"

"I know that once the computer circulation program is installed, it will order the printers to print thirty thousand papers each day; but for at least four years, you've been printing four thousand more every day — four thousand Mr. Forio doesn't even know about. If you paid for those papers, you'd earn seven cents per paper, but you don't pay for them. You steal them; and after you pay the delivery people, you get twelve cents a paper. I worked it all out on a napkin. If you were honest, you'd have made a little over one hundred thousand dollars a year. This way, you're earning over one hundred seventy-five thousand dollars a year. That's practically three quarters of a million dollars you've stolen so far from the *Nearing River Daily News*."

They gaped at her.

Lynn said, "You didn't dare let my uncle's program run. The very first day, there'd be four thousand people without newspapers. They'd all telephone the newspaper to find out why. Mr. Forio would figure out right then that you two have been stealing."

Mr. Hamill said, "You haven't told your uncle this, have you, Lynn?"

"You thought if you stole the disk you'd be safe," she said. She could tell by their expressions that she was right about everything. "You thought it would take Uncle Steve months to rewrite the program. Now you've come back to get the flow charts as well, haven't you?"

Hamill and his cousin looked at each other. "What'll we do?" said Mr. Grant nervously.

Lynn was very pleased with herself.

Mr. Hamill began looking at Lynn again, and suddenly Lynn was afraid. She was between them and — and what? Money. Mr. Forio. Jail. They were angry, and they were dangerous.

"Oh, no," thought Lynn, her heart beginning to shiver in her chest. "What'll I do? I thought I was so smart!"

As she turned to run out of Uncle Steve's office, the quiet night was split by wailing sirens, coming closer and closer.

Officer Mason had decided Lynn's telephone call was no joke.

Victoria said, "I will never, never, NEVER forgive you for not telling me, for letting me go to see some two-hour movie, while you helped arrest two thieves."

"I thought you liked movies," said Lynn.

"I'd rather be in a movie than see one," said Victoria. "Weren't you scared?"

"Nope."

"I was," said Aunt Camilla. "I've never been so scared. We drove up to the house after a nice relaxing movie, and there were three police cars with their blue lights flashing."

Officer Mason plopped down tiredly on the old office couch. He sank right into the stuffing of the torn place. "The day your Aunt Camilla called about the disk being stolen, Lynn," he said, "we had no idea why anyone might want to take it. When you phoned the station, I remembered that theft and figured out who you were and what the address was. It took you to solve the mystery of why the disk was stolen, though. You're really something, Lynn."

Lynn beamed and strutted.

"Before we make you Delivery Person of the Year," said Uncle Steve, "there's still the problem of you sneaking in here and playing with my computer." Under his beard was a glare.

Victoria tried to rescue her twin. "Maybe we should all go to bed now and get a good night's rest."

"Rest?" said Aunt Camilla. "Is that allowed in Lynn's house?"

Lynn said, "I'm sorry, Uncle Steve. I knew I was wrong. I was showing off to Shad, and I knew I shouldn't, and Vic told me I shouldn't, and I did it anyway. I just accidentally discovered what Mr. Hamill and Mr. Grant were doing."

"It's all right to use my things," said Uncle Steve, "but it's not all right to sneak."

Everybody was silent for a minute, and Lynn felt awful, being scolded in front of Officer Mason and Mr. Forio. Then Mr. Forio thanked her, and Victoria said, "Next time I'm going to stay home with Lynn. We'll both have the excitement of figuring out things."

Author

Caroline B. Cooney is the author of several children's books, as well as short stories that have appeared in magazines. The computer background for her book *The Paper Caper* came from Mrs. Cooney's own experience as part owner of a data processing company and from her husband's experience as a computer analyst.

Thinking It Over

Comprehension Questions

1. How did Lynn figure out who had stolen Uncle Steve's disk? Why did they steal it?
2. Why was Lynn able to access the personnel file?
3. Why did the computer reject Shad's name?
4. How did Lynn feel when she told Grant and Hamill that she knew what they had done?

Vocabulary

The following words from "The Paper Caper" relate to computers and also have other meanings: **file, bug, program, screen**. Use these words to play a game with a group of two to four players.

First prepare a deck of sixteen cards. Print each word on four cards. Shuffle the cards and place them face down on the table. If three people are playing, remove one card.

Each player in turn draws a card and uses the word in a sentence. Players should try to use a different meaning for a word each time it is drawn. A player who repeats a meaning gets a point. When all of the cards have been played, the player with the *fewest* points wins.

Making Graphs

Make two circle graphs to illustrate how Lynn solved the mystery. Let each whole circle stand for the price a customer paid for a newspaper. On the first graph, show how the price per paper was divided (among the delivery person, the supplier, and the newspaper) when the supplier was honest. On the second graph, show how the price was divided if the supplier did not pay the newspaper publisher for the papers.

Computer Words

Uncle Steve was teaching Lynn and Shad to use his computer. On the screen below are some words they needed to learn.

Some computer words are borrowed from everyday English. What does the word *program* mean in each of the next two sentences?

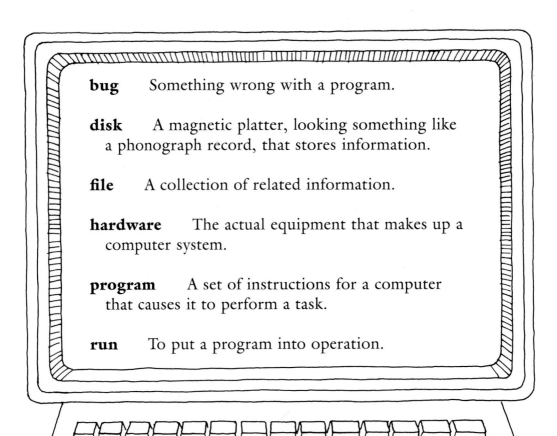

bug Something wrong with a program.

disk A magnetic platter, looking something like a phonograph record, that stores information.

file A collection of related information.

hardware The actual equipment that makes up a computer system.

program A set of instructions for a computer that causes it to perform a task.

run To put a program into operation.

Lynn is going to watch her favorite **program** tonight.
Lynn pressed the key to run the **program.**

In the first sentence, *program* means a television show. In the second sentence, it means a set of instructions for a computer.

Read each pair of sentences. Which sentence in each pair would you be more likely to find in a book on computers?

1. If you look at a **bug** under a microscope, it looks huge.
   A **bug** in the program might prevent it from working.
2. Information about the people who work for a company can be stored in the personnel **file.**
   The class marched in single **file** to the auditorium.
3. We bought a hammer and some nails at the **hardware** store.

The **hardware** for the new system includes a printer and a screen.
4. Take the dog with you when you go out to **run.**
   It can take many hours to write a program but only seconds to **run** it.

Use words from the computer dictionary to finish the story at the bottom of the page. Write the story on your paper.

Something Extra

Find some more computer words in books about computers or from people who know about them. Write each word on a card along with its meaning. If a word also has a meaning in everyday English, put that meaning on the card as well. Keep the words in a Computer Words file. See how many computer words your class can find.

Shad went to a computer store and bought a magnetic _____. It had a _____ on it that would help him use the computer to budget his paper route money.
When he tried to _____ the program, however, nothing happened. "Something's wrong with this program," said Shad to himself. "There must be a _____ in it."
Then Shad looked down at the floor and laughed. "No wonder it won't run! I accidentally unplugged the _____!"

Lovable Ladybug

by George Laycock

Many insects are thought of as pests — but not the ladybug. What makes ladybugs "lovable"?

522

A Useful Kind of Love

It seems strange to like a bug, but never step on a ladybug! It has friends everywhere.

The love between people and ladybugs, which are really not bugs but beetles, is not like young love in the springtime. It is a more useful kind of love. People love ladybeetles because they eat aphids. Aphids attack rose bushes and alfalfa plants. So if you have ladybeetles for neighbors, things can't be all bad.

A Big Job in the Citrus Groves

Who can forget the praise ladybeetles earned nearly one hundred years ago in the citrus groves of California? About that time, a parasite called the "cottony-cushion scale" slipped into the country from Australia. This insect had a great hunger for citrus leaves. Grapefruit, lemons, and oranges were more than breakfast food to it. It ate them hour after hour, until the whole California citrus business was in

A larger-than-life look at one of the four thousand varieties of ladybeetles. This one was photographed on Prince Edward Island, Canada.

danger. Grove owners asking banks for loans soon found that their bankers searched the trees for cottony-cushion scale. If the bankers found it, they refused to take a chance with their money. All the while, the cottony-cushion scale, unchecked by any of its natural enemies found in its native Australia, multiplied happily and marched forward through the citrus groves.

Word of the farmers' trouble reached Washington, D.C. The United States Department of Agriculture sent a team of specialists to Australia to seek out the natural enemy of the scale. What they found and brought back was a species of ladybeetle that ate cottony-cushion scale.

The little beetles, set free in California, had the scale in check in two years, and the state's great citrus business was saved. The cost had been less than five thousand dollars. No wonder people love the ladybeetle!

A Market for Ladybeetles

Those orange or red ladybeetles with the black spots are members of a large family. Around the world, there are some four thousand species of them. One of them, during its

Above: A hungry seven-spot ladybeetle larva eating an aphid. The ladybeetle larvae leave little food for the adults, who must then migrate to find food. Middle: An adult spotted ladybeetle feeding on marigold pollen, since the larvae have eaten all the aphids. Far right: A swarm of ladybeetles wintering in the mountains.

life, can eat as many as seven thousand aphids.

This fact has so impressed farmers that for many years there has been a strong market for ladybeetles. One California bug seller gathers ladybeetles while they are hibernating. Next he puts them into cold storage. Later he measures them by the gallon into sacks and packs them for shipping to his customers.

A gallon of ladybeetles, say those who have counted them, has seventy-five thousand of the busy little insects. What's more, the females will each lay about five hundred eggs. The eggs hatch in less than a week, and the larvae are just as hungry for aphids as are their parents.

Catching Ladybeetles

How do you catch seventy-five thousand ladybeetles? It's easier than it sounds, but it is important to understand the strange habits of these little six-legged predators. California ladybeetles are migratory insects. Their travels take them where there is the most food for them at different seasons.

In May and June, a new crop of adult ladybeetles appears in grain and hay fields. Almost at once, they face starvation. The larvae have already eaten most of the aphids. The adults do not just drift about. Instead, they fly straight upward into the sky for a mile or more. Here they find a tail wind that carries them off to the Sierra Nevada Mountains.

For nine months, the insects stay high in the mountains, where they feed on pollen. In February or March, they mate, and then they fly upward again until they are picked up by the winds. This time they are carried back to the valleys, where they are welcomed by the farmers, if not by the aphids.

During their days in the mountains, the ladybeetles often gather in great swarms. These are what draw the bug dealers. Some dealers report having gathered up as many as one hundred gallons of ladybeetles from a space the size of a ten-by-twelve-foot room.

There was even a time when the California Department of Agriculture gave out ladybeetles free to farmers. During the

A striped ladybeetle devouring one of its seven thousand aphids. This is what makes ladybeetles lovable!

winter, workers gathered beetles by the ton. The following spring, farm owners were given thirty thousand ladybeetles free for every ten acres farmed. This plan came to a halt when it was discovered, by marking them with paint, that the ladybeetles often flew out of the fields. However, the gains from transplanting ladybeetles were great enough that they are still bought and sold.

Be Kind to the Ladybeetle

No one, as far as we know, has ever figured out how ladybeetles learned to eat aphids in the first place; but it was a good thing they did. Without this skill, people might look upon the little beetle as just another bug. The ladybeetle is no everyday insect, though. Treat one kindly. Let it live. It has work to do yet, perhaps seven thousand aphids to eat. It's good to have at least one insect around that everybody loves.

Author

George Laycock is an award-winning author of over thirty books on nature and conservation, and he is a contributor to a number of magazines, including *National Wildlife* and *Boys' Life*. He also serves as field editor for *Audubon Magazine*. Animals and the outdoors are subjects of life-long interest to him.

Comprehension Questions

1. What makes ladybugs "lovable"?
2. What is the correct name for a ladybug?
3. Why was the cottony-cushion scale able to multiply so rapidly in California?
4. How did the ladybeetles help the California citrus farmers?
5. When is the best time for dealers to catch ladybeetles? Why?

Vocabulary

The title "Lovable Ladybug" is an example of alliteration — the repetition of beginning sounds. For each of the animals named below, make up a title that uses alliteration. Try to have at least three words in your title. Example: Absolutely Adorable Aardvark

elephant	**octopus**
chimpanzee	**kangaroo**
snail	**goat**
whale	**tiger**

Using Reference Sources to Find Information

You learned in this selection that ladybugs are not really bugs — they are beetles. Use an encyclopedia or a book about insects to find the answers to the questions listed below.

1. What is the difference between a bug and a beetle?
2. Why is a ladybug actually a beetle?
3. What are some other insects that are called "bugs" but are really beetles?
4. What are some other beetles that are helpful to people, as the ladybeetle is? How are they helpful?
5. What are some beetles that are harmful? Why?

Magazine Wrap-up

Literary Skill: Recognizing Main and Minor Characters

You have learned that the people in a story are called characters and that the most important character is called the main character. For example, Jerome was the main character in "Ride the Red Cycle" because the story was mostly about what he thought and did. The other characters in a story are called minor characters. Jerome's parents and his brother and sisters

were minor characters in "Ride the Red Cycle."

List the main and minor characters in each of these stories:

"Saukin!"

"The Boy Who Drew People Upside Down"

"The Paper Caper"

Vocabulary: Synonyms

Number your paper from 1 to 5. Read each set of words below, and decide which word does not belong with the others. Write the word beside the number on your paper.

1.	faintly weakly	softly boldly
2.	lingered departed	stayed waited
3.	alarmed calm	anxious panic-stricken
4.	manufacture produce	develop evaporate
5.	suspense burglary	theft robbery

Reference and Study Skill: Graphs

Look at the eight titles from Magazine Four listed below. Make a circle graph that shows how many of these selections are *fiction,* how many are *nonfiction,* and how many are *poetry.* Be sure to label your graph and write a caption for it.

"Making Dreams Come Alive: The Art of Marc Chagall"

"Ácoma: Pueblo in the Sky"

"Saukin!"

"Ride the Red Cycle"

"There Is Fear. . . . There Is Joy"

"Graphs"

"The Paper Caper"

"Lovable Ladybug"

Books to Enjoy

Bananas: From Manolo to Margie
by George Ancona
Excellent photos show how bananas are grown, harvested, and transported from Manolo's plantation home in Honduras to Margie's local market in the United States.

Susannah and the Blue House Mystery
by Patricia Elmore
Susannah and her friends try to piece together baffling clues to the location of a treasure.

Baseball's All-Time All-Stars
by Jim Murphy
The author selects two teams of the finest ballplayers and backs up his choices with facts and figures.

Keeping It Secret
by Penny Pollock
Mary Lou finds it difficult to make friends at her new school as she tries to keep her hearing aid a secret.

"The Open Road"

an excerpt from
*The Wind
in the Willows*

**written by
Kenneth Grahame**

**illustrated by
Stella Ormai**

Not an "animal story," but a
story whose characters just happen to be animals, *The Wind in
the Willows* recounts the adventures of the Mole, the Water Rat,
and the boastful and impetuous,
but warm-hearted, Toad. The
stories are told with an attention
to detail that transports the reader to the English countryside,
where the three friends row
about on the river, travel by caravan along "the open road," and
venture into the "Wild Wood."

The Wind in the Willows has
enchanted generations of readers,
young and old, since it was first
published in 1908. The book
that began as a father's bedtime
stories for his young son is now
recognized as a classic of children's literature.

HOUGHTON MIFFLIN · MEDALLION SELECTION

The Wind
in the Willows

by Kenneth Grahame

illustrated by Stella Ormai

The Open Road

"Ratty," said the Mole suddenly, one bright summer morning, "if you please, I want to ask you a favor."

The Rat was sitting on the river bank, singing a little song. He had just composed it himself, so he was very taken up with it and would not pay proper attention to Mole or anything else. Since early morning he had been swimming in the river in company with his friends the ducks. When the ducks stood on their heads suddenly, as ducks will, he would dive down and tickle their necks, just under where their chins would be if ducks had chins, till they were forced to come to the surface again in a hurry, spluttering and angry and shaking their feathers at him, for it is impossible to say quite *all* you feel when your head is under water. At last they begged him to go away and attend to his own affairs and leave them to mind theirs. So the Rat went away and sat on the river bank in the sun and made up a song about them.

"I don't know that I think so *very* much of that little song, Rat," said the Mole cautiously, after listening to the song.

"Neither do the ducks," replied the Rat cheerfully. "They say, '*Why* can't fellows be allowed to do what they like *when* they like and *as* they like, instead of other fellows sitting on banks and watching them all the time and making remarks and poetry and things about them? What *nonsense* it all is!' That's what the ducks say."

"So it is; so it is," said the Mole, with great heartiness.

"No, it isn't!" cried the Rat indignantly.

"Well then, it isn't; it isn't," replied the Mole soothingly. "What I wanted to ask you was, won't you take me to call on Mr. Toad? I've heard so much about him."

"Why, certainly," said the good-natured Rat, jumping to his feet and dismissing poetry from his mind for the day. "Get the boat out, and we'll paddle up there at once. It's never the wrong time to call on Toad. Early or late he's always the same fellow. Always good tempered, always glad to see you, always sorry when you go!"

"He must be a very nice animal," observed the Mole, as he got into the boat and took the sculls, while the Rat settled himself comfortably in the stern.

"He is indeed the best of animals," replied Rat. "So simple, so good natured, and so affectionate. Perhaps he's not very clever — we can't all be geniuses, and it may be that he is both boastful and conceited; but he has got some great qualities, has Toady."

Rounding a bend in the river, they came in sight of a handsome old house of red brick, with well-kept lawns reaching down to the water's edge.

"There's Toad Hall," said the Rat, "and that creek on the left, where the notice board says PRIVATE. NO LANDING ALLOWED leads to his boathouse, where we'll leave the boat. The stables are over there to the right. That's the banquet hall you're looking at now — very old, that is. Toad is rather rich, you know; and this is really one of the nicest houses in these parts, though we never admit as much to Toad."

They glided up the creek, into the shadow of a large boathouse. Here they saw many handsome boats, slung from the cross beams or hauled up on a slip, but none in the water. The place had an unused and a deserted air.

The Rat looked around him. "I understand," said he, "boating is played out. He's tired of it and done with it. I wonder what new fad he has taken up now? Come along, and let's look him up. We shall hear all about it quite soon enough."

They disembarked and strolled across the lawns in search of Toad, whom they presently happened upon resting in a wicker garden chair, with a preoccupied expression on his face and a large map spread out on his knees.

"Hooray!" he cried, jumping up on seeing them. "This is splendid!" He shook the paws of both of them warmly,

never waiting for an introduction to the Mole. "How *kind* of you!" he went on, dancing round them. "I was just going to send a boat down the river for you, Ratty, with strict orders that you were to be fetched up here at once, whatever you were doing. I want you badly — both of you. Now what will you take? Come inside and have something! You don't know how lucky it is, your turning up just now!"

"Let's sit quiet a bit, Toady!" said the Rat, throwing himself into an easy chair, while the Mole took another by the side of him and made some remark about Toad's "delightful residence."

"Finest house on the whole river," cried Toad boisterously. "Or anywhere else, for that matter," he could not help adding.

Here the Rat nudged the Mole. Unfortunately the Toad saw him do it and turned very red. There was a moment's painful silence. Then Toad burst out laughing. "All right, Ratty," he said. "It's only my way, you know; and it's not such a very bad house, is it? You know you

rather like it yourself. Now, look here. Let's be sensible. You are the very animals I wanted. You've got to help me. It's most important!"

"It's about your rowing, I suppose," said the Rat, with an innocent air. "You're getting on fairly well, though you splash a good bit still. With a great deal of patience, and any quantity of coaching, you may ——"

"O, pooh! Boating!" interrupted the Toad, in great disgust. "Silly, boyish amusement. I've given that up *long* ago. Sheer waste of time, that's what it is. It makes me downright sorry to see you fellows, who ought to know better, spending all your energies in that aimless manner. No, I've discovered the real thing, the only genuine occupation for a lifetime. I intend to devote the remainder of mine to it and can only regret the wasted years that lie behind me. Come with me, dear Ratty, and your amiable friend also, if he will be so very good, just as far as the stable yard, and you shall see what you shall see!"

He led the way to the stable yard, the Rat following with a most mistrustful expression; and there, drawn out of the coach house into the open, they saw a caravan, shining with newness, painted a canary yellow picked out with green, and red wheels.

"There you are!" cried the Toad, straddling and expanding himself. "There's real life for you, embodied in that little cart. The open road, the dusty highway! Camps, villages, towns, cities! Here today, up and off to somewhere else tomorrow! Travel, change, interest, excitement! The whole world before you and a horizon that's always changing! This is the very finest cart of its sort that was ever built, without any exception. Come inside and look at the arrangements. Planned 'em all myself, I did!"

The Mole was tremendously interested and excited, and he followed the Toad eagerly up the steps and into the caravan. The Rat only snorted and thrust his hands deep into his pockets, remaining where he was.

It was indeed very compact and comfortable. There were little sleeping-bunks, a little table that folded up against the wall, a cooking stove, lockers, bookshelves, a birdcage with a bird in it; and pots, pans, jugs, and kettles of every size and variety.

"All complete!" said the Toad triumphantly, pulling open a locker. "You see — biscuits, potted lobster, sardines — everything you can possibly want. Water here — bacon there — letter paper. You'll find," he continued, as they went down the steps again, "you'll find that nothing whatever has been forgotten, when we make our start this afternoon."

"I beg your pardon," said the Rat slowly, as he chewed a straw, "but did I overhear you say something about *'we,'* and *'start,' 'this afternoon'*?"

"Now, you dear, good old Ratty," said Toad imploringly, "don't begin talking in that stiff and sniffy sort of way, because you know you've *got* to come. I can't possibly manage without you; so please consider it settled, and don't argue — it's the one thing I can't stand. You surely don't mean to stick to your dull old river all your life and just live in a hole in a bank and *boat*? I want

539

to show you the world! I'm going to make an *animal* of you, my boy!"

"I don't care," said the Rat doggedly. "I'm not coming, and that's flat. I *am* going to stick to my old river *and* live in a hole *and* boat, as I've always done. What's more, Mole's going to stick to me and do as I do, aren't you, Mole?"

"Of course I am," said the Mole loyally. "I'll always stick to you, Rat, and what you say is to be — has got to be. All the same, it sounds as if it might have been — well, rather fun, you know!" he added wistfully. Poor Mole! The Life Adventurous was so new a thing to him and so thrilling, and this fresh aspect of it was so tempting, and he had fallen in love at first sight with the canary-colored cart and all its little furnishings.

The Rat saw what was passing in his mind and wavered. He hated disappointing people, and he was fond of the Mole and would do almost anything to oblige him. Toad was watching both of them closely.

"Come along in and have some lunch," he said diplomatically, "and we'll talk it over. We needn't decide anything in a hurry. Of course, *I* don't really care. I only want to give pleasure to you fellows. 'Live for others!' That's my motto in life."

During lunch — which was excellent, of course, as everything at Toad Hall always was — the Toad simply let himself go. Disregarding the Rat, he proceeded to play upon the inexperienced Mole as on a harp. He painted the prospects of the trip and the joys of the open life and the roadside in such glowing colors that the Mole could hardly sit in his chair for excitement. Somehow, it soon seemed taken for granted by all three of them that the trip was a settled thing; and the Rat, though still unconvinced in his mind, allowed his good nature to override his personal objections. He could not bear to disappoint his two friends, who were already planning out each day's separate occupation for several weeks ahead.

When they were quite ready, the now-triumphant Toad led his companions to the paddock and set them to catch the old gray horse, who, without having been asked, and to his own extreme annoyance, had been told off by Toad for the dustiest job in this dusty expedition. He frankly preferred the paddock and took a deal of catching. Meantime Toad packed the lockers still tighter with necessaries and hung nets of onions, bundles of hay, and baskets from the bottom of the cart. At last the horse was caught and harnessed, and they set off, all talking at once, each animal either trudging by the side of the cart or sitting on the shaft, as the humor took him. It was a

golden afternoon. The smell of the dust they kicked up was rich and satisfying; out of thick orchards on either side of the road, birds called and whistled to them cheerily; good-natured wayfarers, passing them, gave them "Good day" or stopped to say nice things about their beautiful cart; and rabbits, sitting at their front doors in the hedgerows, held up their forepaws, and said, "O my! O my! O my!"

Late in the evening, tired and happy and miles from home, they drew up on a remote common far from any habitation, turned the horse loose to graze, and ate their simple supper sitting on the grass by the side of the cart. Toad talked big about all he was going to do in the days to come, while stars grew fuller and larger all around them, and a yellow moon, appearing suddenly and silently, came to keep them company and listen to their talk. At last they turned into their little bunks in the cart; and Toad, kicking out his legs, sleepily said, "Well, good night, you fellows! This is the real life for a gentleman! Talk about your old river!"

"I *don't* talk about my river," replied the patient Rat. "You *know* I don't, Toad. But I *think* about it," he added pathetically, in a lower tone. "I think about it — all the time!"

The Mole reached out from under his blanket, felt for the Rat's paw in the darkness, and gave it a squeeze. "I'll do whatever you like, Ratty," he whispered. "Shall we run away tomorrow morning, quite early — *very* early — and go back to our dear old hole on the river?"

543

"No, no, we'll see it out," whispered back the Rat. "Thanks awfully, but I ought to stick by Toad till this trip is ended. It wouldn't be safe for him to be left to himself. It won't take very long. His fads never do. Good night!"

The end was indeed nearer than even the Water Rat suspected.

After so much open air and excitement, the Toad slept very soundly, and no amount of shaking could rouse him out of bed next morning. So the Mole and Rat turned to, quietly and gamely; and while the Rat saw to the horse and lit a fire and cleaned last night's cups and platters and got things ready for breakfast, the Mole trudged off to the nearest village, a long way off, for milk and eggs and other necessaries the Toad had, of course, forgotten to provide. The hard work had all been done, and the two animals were resting, thoroughly exhausted, by the time Toad appeared, fresh and gay, remarking what a pleasant, easy life they were all leading now, after the cares and worries of housekeeping at home.

They had a pleasant ramble that day over grassy downs and along narrow by-lanes and camped, as before, on a common, only this time the two guests took care that Toad should do his fair share of work. In consequence, when the time came for starting next morning, Toad was by no means so rapturous about the simplicity of the primitive life. Indeed, he attempted to resume his place in his bunk, whence he was hauled by force. Their way lay, as before, across country by narrow lanes, and it was not till the afternoon that they came out on the high road, their first high road; and there disaster sprang out on them — disaster momentous indeed to their expedition.

They were strolling along the high road easily, the Mole by the horse's head, talking to him, since the horse had complained that he was being frightfully left out of it, and nobody considered him in the least; the Toad and the Water Rat were walking behind the cart talking together — at least Toad was talking, and Rat was saying at intervals, "Yes, precisely; and what did *you* say to *him*?" — and thinking all the time of something very different, when far behind them they heard a faint warning hum, like the drone of a distant bee. Glancing back, they saw a small cloud of dust, with a dark center of energy, advancing on them at incredible speed, while from out of the dust a faint *toot-toot* wailed like an uneasy animal in pain. Hardly regarding it, they turned to resume their conversation, when in an instant (as it seemed) the peaceful scene was changed, and with a blast of wind and a whirl of sound that made them jump for the nearest ditch, it was

on them! The *toot-toot* rang with a brazen shout in their ears; they had a moment's glimpse of an interior of glittering plate glass and rich leather; and the magnificent motorcar, immense, breath snatching, passionate, with its pilot tense and hugging his wheel, possessed all earth and air for the fraction of a second, flung an enveloping cloud of dust that blinded and enwrapped them utterly, and then dwindled to a speck in the far distance, changed back into a droning bee once more.

The old gray horse, dreaming, as he plodded along, of his quiet paddock, in a new raw situation such as this simply abandoned himself to his natural emotions. Rearing, plunging back steadily, in spite of all the Mole's efforts at his head and all the Mole's lively language directed at his better feelings, he drove the cart backwards towards the deep ditch at the side of the road. It wavered an instant — then there was a heart-rending crash — and the canary-colored cart, their pride and their joy, lay on its side in the ditch, an irredeemable wreck.

The Rat danced up and down in the road, simply transported with passion. "You villains!" he shouted, shaking both fists. "You scoundrels, you robbers, you — you — road-hogs! — I'll have the law on you! I'll report you! I'll take you through all the courts!" His homesickness had quite slipped away from him, and for the moment he was the skipper of the canary-colored vessel driven on a shoal by the reckless jockeying of rival mariners, and he was trying to remember all the fine and biting things he used to say to masters of steam launches

when their wash, as they drove too near the bank, used to flood his parlor carpet at home.

Toad sat straight down in the middle of the dusty road, his legs stretched out before him, and stared in the direction of the disappearing motorcar. His breath was short; his face wore a placid, satisfied expression; and at intervals he faintly murmured, "Toot-toot!"

The Mole was busy trying to quiet the horse, which he succeeded in doing after a time. Then he went to look at the cart, on its side in the ditch. It was indeed a sorry sight: panels and windows smashed, axles hopelessly bent, one wheel off, sardine tins scattered over the wide world, and the bird in the birdcage sobbing pitifully and calling to be let out.

The Rat came to help him, but their united efforts were not enough to right the cart. "Hi! Toad!" they cried. "Come and bear a hand, can't you!"

The Toad never answered a word or budged from his seat in the road, so they went to see what was the matter with him. They found him in a sort of trance, a happy

smile on his face, his eyes still fixed on the dusty wake of their destroyer. At intervals he was still heard to murmur, "Toot-toot!"

The Rat shook him by the shoulder. "Are you coming to help us, Toad?" he demanded sternly.

"Glorious, stirring sight!" murmured Toad, never offering to move. "The poetry of motion! The *real* way to travel! The *only* way to travel! Here today — in next week tomorrow! Villages skipped, towns and cities jumped — always somebody else's horizon! O bliss! O toot-toot! O my! O my!"

"O *stop* it, Toad!" cried the Mole despairingly.

"And to think I never *knew*!" went on the Toad in a dreamy monotone. "All those wasted years that lie behind me, I never knew, never even *dreamt*! But *now* — but now that I know, now that I fully realize! O what a flowery track lies spread before me. What dust clouds shall spring up behind me as I speed on my reckless way! What carts I shall fling carelessly into the ditch in the wake of my magnificent onset! Horrid little carts — common carts — canary-colored carts!"

"What are we to do with him?" asked the Mole of the Water Rat.

"Nothing at all," replied the Rat firmly. "Because there is really nothing to be done. You see, I know him from of old. He is now possessed. He has got a new craze, and it always takes him that way, in its first stage. He'll continue like that for days now, like an animal walking in a happy dream, quite useless for all practical purposes. Never mind him. Let's go and see what there is to be done about the cart."

A careful inspection showed them that, even if they succeeded in righting it by themselves, the cart would travel no longer. The axles were in a hopeless state, and the missing wheel was shattered into pieces.

The Rat knotted the horse's reins over his back and took him by the head, carrying the birdcage and its hysterical occupant in the other hand. "Come on!" he said grimly to the Mole. "It's five or six miles to the nearest town, and we shall just have to walk it. The sooner we make a start the better."

"What about Toad?" asked the Mole anxiously, as they set off together. "We can't leave him here, sitting in the middle of the road by himself, in the state he's in! It's not safe. Supposing another Thing were to come along?"

"O, *bother* Toad," said the Rat savagely. "I've done with him!"

They had not proceeded very far, however, when there was a pattering of feet behind them, and Toad caught them up and thrust a paw inside the elbow of each of them, still breathing short and staring into vacancy.

"Now, look here, Toad!" said the Rat sharply. "As soon as we get to the town, you'll have to go straight to the police station and see if they know anything about that motorcar and who it belongs to, and you'll have to lodge a complaint against it. Then you'll have to go to a black-smith's or a wheelwright's and arrange for the cart to be

fetched and mended and put to rights. It'll take time, but it's not quite a hopeless smash. Meanwhile, the Mole and I will go to an inn and find comfortable rooms where we can stay till the cart's ready and till your nerves have recovered their shock."

"Police station! Complaint!" murmured Toad dreamily. "Me *complain* of that beautiful vision that has been granted me! *Mend* the *cart*! I've done with carts forever. I never want to see the cart or to hear of it again. O, Ratty! You can't think how obliged I am to you for agreeing to come on this trip! I wouldn't have gone without you, and then I might never have seen that — that swan, that sunbeam, that thunderbolt! I might never have heard that entrancing sound or smelt that bewitching smell! I owe it all to you, my best of friends!"

The Rat turned from him in despair. "You see what it is?" he said to the Mole, addressing him across Toad's head. "He's quite hopeless. I give it up — when we get to the town we'll go to the railway station, and with luck we may pick up a train there that'll get us back to River Bank tonight. And if ever you catch me going pleasuring with this provoking animal again ——!" He snorted, and during the rest of that weary trudge he addressed his remarks exclusively to Mole.

On reaching the town they went straight to the station and deposited Toad in the second-class waiting room, giving a porter two pence to keep a strict eye on him. They then left the horse at an inn stable and gave what directions they could about the cart and its contents.

552

Eventually, a slow train having landed them at a station not very far from Toad Hall, they escorted the spellbound, sleepwalking Toad to his door, put him inside it, and instructed his housekeeper to feed him, undress him, and put him to bed. Then they got out their boat from the boathouse, sculled home down the river, and at a very late hour sat down to supper in their own cosy parlor, to the Rat's great joy and contentment.

The following evening the Mole, who had risen late and taken things very easy all day, was sitting on the bank fishing, when the Rat, who had been looking up his friends and gossiping, came strolling along to find him. "Heard the news?" he said. "There's nothing else being talked about all along the river bank. Toad went up to town by an early train this morning. He has ordered a large and very expensive motorcar."

Comprehension Questions

1. Toad thought that traveling by cart was "the only genuine occupation for a lifetime" and that he would devote the rest of his life to it. Was he right? Explain.
2. What did Rat mean when he said, "Boating is played out"?
3. Why did Rat disagree when Mole suggested that they run away and go back to the river?
4. How did Rat's attitude toward the cart change after the cart was wrecked by the motorcar?

Author

Kenneth Grahame was born in 1859 in Edinburgh, Scotland, and was raised in England near the Thames River. There he learned about the types of river animals that appear in his book *The Wind in the Willows,* part of which you have just read. This book grew out of stories that Mr. Grahame made up for his son Alastair. Throughout Alastair's childhood, Mr. Grahame also wrote letters to his son with further adventures of Toad and his friends. *The Wind in the Willows* has delighted readers of all ages ever since its publication in 1908. Like another of Mr. Grahame's books, *The Reluctant Dragon*, it was made into a popular movie by Walt Disney.

In addition to writing, Mr. Grahame worked for the Bank of England and was Secretary of the Bank at the time of his retirement in 1908. He died in 1932.

Illustrator

Stella Ormai comes from rural Pennsylvania, where she spent her summers learning to love the forests and streams. She has written and illustrated many stories that show her special sensitivity to nature. If you enjoyed the illustrations in "The Open Road," you can see more of Stella Ormai's work in *Heartbeats,* by Alvin and Virginia Silverstein, and in Sandra Markle's *Kid's Computer Capers.*

Glossary

Some of the words in this book may have pronunciations or meanings you do not know. This glossary can help you by telling you how to pronounce those words and by telling you their meanings.

You can find out the correct pronunciation of any glossary word by using the special spelling after the word and the pronunciation key at the bottom of each left-hand page.

The full pronunciation key below shows how to pronounce each consonant and vowel in a special spelling. The pronunciation key at the bottom of each left-hand page is a shortened form of the full key.

Full Pronunciation Key

Consonant Sounds

b	**b**i**b**		p	**p**o**p**
ch	**ch**ur**ch**		r	**r**oa**r**
d	**d**ee**d**		s	mi**ss**, **s**au**ce**, **s**ee
f	**f**ast, **f**i**f**e, o**ff**, **ph**ase, rou**gh**		sh	di**sh**, **sh**ip
			t	**t**igh**t**
g	**g**a**g**		th	pa**th**, **th**in
h	**h**at		*th*	ba**the**, **th**is
hw	**wh**ich		v	ca**ve**, **v**al**v**e, **v**ine
j	**j**u**dg**e		w	**w**ith
k	**c**at, **k**i**ck**, pi**que**		y	**y**es
l	**l**id, need**l**e		z	ro**se**, si**z**e, **x**ylophone, **z**ebra
m	a**m**, **m**an, **m**u**m**			
n	**n**o, sudde**n**		zh	gara**g**e, plea**s**ure, vi**s**ion
ng	thi**ng**			

Vowel Sounds

ă	pat		ô	alter, caught, for, paw
ā	aid, they, pay		oi	boy, noise, oil
â	air, care, wear		ŏŏ	book
ä	father		ōō	boot, fruit
ĕ	pet, pleasure		ou	cow, out
ē	be, bee, easy, seize		ŭ	cut, rough
ĭ	pit		û	firm, heard, term, turn, word
ī	by, guy, pie		yōō	abuse, use
î	dear, deer, fierce, mere		ə	about, silent, pencil, lemon, circus
ŏ	pot, horrible		ər	butter
ō	go, row, toe			

Stress Marks

Primary Stress ′
bi·ol′o·gy   (bī ŏl′ə jē)

Secondary Stress ′
bi′o·log′i·cal   (bī′ə lŏj′i kəl)

a·bide by (ə **bīd′** bī) *v.* To live up to; to agree to.

a·bound (ə **bound′**) *v.* **1.** To be rich (in); to be plentiful: *Wildlife abounds in the region.*

a·buse (ə **byo͞os′**) *n.* **1.** Improper use. **2.** Mistreatment.

ac·cess code (ăk′sĕs′ kōd) *n.* A special code that allows one to get information from data that have been stored in a computer.

ag·ate (ăg′ĭt) *n.* A type of quartz that is cloudy in appearance and streaked with color.

a·gil·i·ty (ə **jĭl′**ĭ tē) *n.* The quality or condition of being able to move quickly and easily.

ail (āl) *v.* To be ill: *My mother is ailing.*

al·fal·fa (ăl **făl′**fə) *n.* A plant with cloverlike leaves and purple flowers, grown as feed for cattle and other livestock.

alfalfa

a·li·as (ā′lē′ əs) *n.* An assumed name used by a person wishing to conceal his or her identity.—*adv.* Otherwise named: *William Blake alias James Flynn.*

al·ler·gic rhi·ni·tis (ə **lûr′**jĭk rī **nī′**tĭs) *n.* A swelling of the tissue lining the nose, that may cause sneezing, watering eyes, or difficulty in breathing.

An·glo (ăng′ glō′) *n., pl.* **Anglos.** *Informal.* A white resident of the United States who is not of Latin descent. Short form of Anglo-American.

anx·ious·ly (ăngk′shəs lē)*or*(ăng′-) *adv.* **1.** In a worried manner. **2.** Eagerly.

a·phid (ā′fĭd) *or* (ăf′ĭd) *n.* A tiny, soft-bodied insect that sucks sap from plants.

ap·pall (ə **pôl′**) *v.* To fill with horror and amazement; shock: *The poor living conditions appalled me.*

ap·pren·tice (ə **prĕn′**tĭs) *v.* **ap·pren·ticed, ap·pren·tic·ing.** To place in a position to learn a craft or trade.

as·cend·ing (ə **sĕn′**dĭng) *adj.* Moving, going, or growing upward: *a tree with ascending branches.*

as·sert (ə **sûrt′**) *v.* To state or declare positively; claim: *reluctant to assert that his story is true.* **Idiom. assert (oneself).** To express oneself boldly or forcefully.

a·stride (ə **strīd′**) *prep.* With a leg on each side of: *She was sitting astride the horse.*

au·di·tion (ô **dĭsh′**ən) *n.* A test or trial performance, as of a person who is applying for a part in a play,

---

ă pat / ā pay / â care / ä father / ĕ pet / ē be / ĭ pit / ī pie / î fierce / ŏ pot / ō go / ô paw, for / oi oil / o͝o book / o͞o boot / ou out / ŭ cut / û fur / *th* the / th thin / hw which / zh vision / ə ago, item, pencil, atom, circus musical group, etc. — *v.* To perform in an audition: *He auditioned for a part in the play.*

bale (bāl) *n.* A large bound package or bundle of raw or finished material: *a bale of hay.* — *v.* **baled, bal·ing.** To wrap in bales.

bal·last (**băl′**əst) *n.* Any heavy material carried in a vehicle mainly to provide weight: *Submarines use water as ballast.*

bank (băngk) *v.* **1.** To pile (earth, snow, etc.) in a ridge or sloping surface. **2.** To pile ashes or fuel onto (a fire) to make it burn slowly.

bar·way (**bär′**wā) *n.* A gateway that is closed by bars that fit into posts.

bask (băsk) *or* (bäsk) *v.* To lie or rest and enjoy a pleasant warmth: *turtles basking on a log in the sun.*

bell·bird (**běl′**bûrd′) *n.* A tropical bird having a bell-like call.

bil·ious (**bĭl′**yəs) *adj.* Reminding one or suggestive of the bitter greenish liquid (bile) produced by the liver, especially in color: *a bilious complexion.*

bin·na·cle (**bĭn′**ə kəl) *n.* A stand on which a ship's compass case is supported.

bleak (blēk) *adj.* **bleak·er, bleak·est.** Gloomy; somber; dreary: *bleak thoughts.*

blub·ber (**blŭb′**ər) *n.* The thick layer of fat under the skin of whales, seals, and certain other sea animals.

blus·ter (**blŭs′**tər) *v.* To speak in a loud manner.

boar (bôr) *or* (bōr) *n.* **1.** A male pig. **2.** Also **wild boar.** A wild pig with dark bristles.

wild boar

brash (brăsh) *adj.* **1.** Hasty and unthinking; rash. **2.** Shamelessly bold; saucy.

bra·zen (**brā′**zən) *adj.* Insolent; rudely bold.

buff (bŭf) *adj.* Yellowish tan.

ca·nine teeth (**kā′**nīn′ tēth) *pl. n.* The pointed teeth located in the upper jaw; also called eyeteeth.

cap·size (**kăp′**sīz′) *or* (kăp **sīz′**) *v.* **cap·sized, cap·siz·ing.** To overturn: *A huge wave capsized our boat.*

car·a·van (**kăr′**ə văn′) *n.* **1.** A big covered vehicle; van. **2.** A home on wheels, as a trailer, a wagon, etc.

car·i·bou (**kăr′**ə boo′) *n., pl.* **car·i·bou** *or* **car·i·bous.** A deer of arctic regions of North America, with large, spreading antlers in both males and females.

charge (chärj) *n.* Electrical energy.

Chi·hua·hua (chĭ **wä′**wä) *or* (-wə) *n.* A very small dog of a breed that originated in Mexico.

ci·ca·da (sĭ **kā′**də) *or* (-kä-) *n.* An insect with a broad head and see-through wings. The males make a high-pitched sound.

cir·cu·la·tion (sûr′kyə **lā′**shən) *n.* The distribution of printed materials, such as newspapers and magazines.

com·pli·ments (**kŏm′**plə mənts) *pl.n.* Good wishes; regards.

con·fi·den·tial (kŏn′fĭ **dĕn′**shəl) *adj.* Secret.

course (kôrs) *or* (kōrs) *n.* The lowest sail on any mast of a square-rigged ship.

cove (kōv) *n.* A small, sheltered bay or inlet.

cov·ey (**kŭv′**ē) *n., pl.* **cov·eys.** A group or small flock of birds: *a covey of partridges.*

cow·er (**kou′**ər) *v.* To crouch or draw back, as from fear or pain.

crev·ice (**krĕv′**ĭs) *n.* Any narrow crack or opening.

crim·son (**krĭm′**zən) *or* (-sən) *n.* A vivid purplish red. — *adj.* Vivid purplish red.

cringe (krĭnj) *v.* **cringed, cring·ing.** To shrink back.

cro·chet (krō **shā′**) *v.* **cro·cheted** (krō **shād′**), **cro·chet·ing** (krō **shā′**ĭng). To make (a piece of needlework) by looping thread or yarn into connected links with a hooked needle called a **crochet hook.**

cross·tree (**krôs′**trē) *or* (**krŏs′**-) *n.* One of two crosspieces of wood or metal at the upper ends of the masts.

crown (kroun) *n.* The summit or highest point of something.

cu·mu·lus (**kyoo′**myə ləs) *n., pl.* **cu·mu·li** (**kyoo′**myə lī′). A fluffy, white cloud that is rounded at the top and sides and has a flat base.

cu·ra·tor (kyoo **rā′**tər) *or* (**kyoor′**ā′-) *n.* A person in charge of a museum, library, zoo, etc.

cur·dled (**kûr′**dld) *adj.* Sour.

cur·lew (**kûr′**loo) *or* (-lyoo) *n.* A shore bird with brownish feathers and a long, downward-curving bill.

curlew

da·ta file (**dā′**tə *or* **dăt′**ə *or* **dä′**tə fīl) *n.* A list of specific information or names.

de·cree (dĭ **krē′**) *n.* An authoritative order; a law.

deft·ly (**dĕft′**lē) *adv.* Quickly and skillfully.

ă pat / ā **pay** / â **care** / ä **father** / ĕ **pet** / ē **be** / ĭ **pit** / ī **pie** / î **fierce** / ŏ **pot** / ō **go** / ô **paw, for** / oi **oil** / oo **book** /
oo **boot** / ou **out** / ŭ **cut** / û **fur** / *th* **the** / th **thin** / hw **which** / zh **vision** / ə **ago, item, pencil, atom, circus**

de·fy (dǐ **fī′**) *v.* **de·fied, de·fy·ing, de·fies.** To oppose or challenge openly or boldly: *defy the law, defy tradition.*

de·lib·er·ate (dǐ **lǐb′**ər ǐt) *adj.* **1.** Done or said on purpose. **2.** Careful or cautious.

des·o·late (dĕs′ə lǐt) *adj.* **1.** Having little or no vegetation. **2.** Having few or no inhabitants; deserted: *a desolate wilderness.*

dig·ging (dǐg′ǐng) *n.* A search; an excavation site.

dis·mal·ly (dǐz′məl ē) *adv.* In a manner that causes sadness.

dog·ged·ly (dô′gǐd lē) or (dŏg′ǐd lē) *adv.* Stubbornly.

do·ry (dôr′ē) or (dōr′ē) *n., pl.* **do·ries.** A flat-bottomed boat with high flaring sides.

down (doun) *n.* Often **downs.** An expanse of rolling, grassy upland used for grazing, especially in southern England.

drive (drīv) *v.* **drove** (drōv), **driv·en** (drǐv′ən), **driv·ing.** To round up and make animals move from one place to another.

ear·nest·ly (ûr′nĕst lē) *adv.* Expressing or showing one's feelings in a sincere manner.

eb·on·y (ĕb′ə nē) *n., pl.* **eb·on·ies.** The hard black or blackish wood of a tropical tree. — *adj.* Black.

eel (ēl) *n.* Any of several long, slippery, snakelike fishes.

elk (ĕlk) *n., pl.* **elks** or **elk.** **1.** A large North American deer, the wapiti. **2.** The European moose.

elk (wapiti)

em·bank·ment (ĕm **băngk′**mənt) *n.* A mound of earth or stone built up to hold back water.

en·dur·ance (ĕn **dŏŏr′**əns) or **(-dyŏŏr′-)** *n.* The ability to withstand strain, stress, hardship, use, etc.: *Climbing that mountain is a real test of a person's endurance.*

ep·ic (ĕp′ǐk) *adj.* Like a long story or adventure with heroic characters.

ex·panse (ǐk **spăns′**) *n.* A wide and open extent, as of land, air, or water: *a vast expanse of desert; a majestic expanse of ocean.*

feed·back (fēd′băk′) *n.* Any information about the result of something.

flan (flăn) or (flän) *n.* **1.** A tart with a filling of custard, fruit, or cheese. **2.** A molded custard with a burnt-caramel topping.

flat[1] (flăt) *n.* A level surface.

flat[2] (flăt) *n.* An apartment on one floor of a building.

flax (flăks) *n.* A plant with blue flowers, seeds that yield linseed oil, and stems that yield a light-colored fiber from which linen is made.

floe (flō) *n.* A large, flat mass of ice formed on the surface of a body of water.

flour·ish (flûr′ĭsh) *or* (flŭr′-) *n.* An act of waving something vigorously or dramatically.

flue (floō) *n.* A pipe, tube, etc., through which smoke, steam, etc., may pass, as in a chimney or boiler.

flu·o·res·cent light (floō′ə rĕs′ənt līt) *n.* A type of light fixture having a gas-filled tube with a special coating on the inside.

fore·deck (fôr′dĕk′) *or* (fōr′-) *n.* The forward part of a deck, usually the main deck, of a ship.

forth·right (fôrth′rīt′) *or* (fōrth′-) *adj.* Straightforward; frank: *ask a forthright question.*

frame (frām) *n.* A single picture on a roll of movie film.

fran·tic (frăn′tĭk) *adj.* Very excited with fear, anxiety, etc.; desperate; frenzied: *a frantic mob scene; a frantic scream.*

fren·zy (frĕn′zē) *n., pl.* **fren·zies.** Wild excitement or a display of emotion, often accompanied by vigorous or violent activity: *sharks in a feeding frenzy.*

fri·jol, also **fri·jole** (frē hōl′) *n., pl.* **fri·jo·les** (frē hō′lēz) *or* (-lās). Any of certain beans grown and used for food, especially in Mexico and southwestern United States.

fri·vol·i·ty (frĭ vŏl′ĭ tē) *n.,pl.* **fri·vol·i·ties.** The condition of not being serious; silliness: *wasting their time on frivolity.*

fume (fyoōm) *v.* **fumed, fum·ing** To feel or show anger.

game·ly (gām′lē) *adv.* Willingly and readily.

gate·house (gāt′hous′) *n.* A small structure that is part of a gate where guards are usually found.

gaunt (gônt) *adj.* **gaunt·er, gaunt·est.** Thin and bony; haggard; emaciated; *a gaunt face.*

gen·er·a·tor (jĕn′ə rā′tər) *n.* A machine or device that converts mechanical energy into electricity.

Gi·la wood·peck·er (hē′lə woŏd′pĕk′ər) *n.* A woodpecker that is found in southwestern United States.

gin·ger·ly (jĭn′jər lē) *adv.* Cautiously; carefully.

gorge (gôrj) *n.* A deep, narrow passage with steep, rocky sides, as between mountains.

gourd (gôrd) *or* (gōrd) *or* (goōrd) *n.* **1.** The fruit of a vine related to the pumpkin, squash, and cucumber. **2.** The dried, hollowed out shell of such a fruit.

guin·ea pig (gĭn′ē pĭg) *n.* An animal related to the woodchucks,

---

ă pat / ā pay / â care / ä father / ĕ pet / ē be / ĭ pit / ī pie / î fierce / ŏ pot / ō go / ô paw, for / oi oil / oŏ book /
oō boot / ou out / ŭ cut / û fur / *th* the / th thin / hw which / zh vision / ə ago, item, pencil, atom, circus

mice, and squirrels, having short ears, short legs, and a tail so short as to be considered nonexistent.

gul·let (**gŭl′**ĭt) *n.* The throat.

haugh·ti·ly (**hô′**tə lē) *adv.* Proudly and vainly.

haunch (hônch) *or* (hänch) *n.* The hip part of a person or animal.

heave to (hēv tōō) *v.* **heaved** or *chiefly nautical.* **hove, heaving.** To bring a ship at sea to a standstill.

hedge·row (**hěj′**rō′) *n.* A row of bushes or trees forming a fence.

helm (hělm) *n.* The steering gear of a ship, especially the tiller or wheel.

helms·man (**hělmz′**mən) *n., pl.* **-men** (-mən). A person who steers a ship.

hem·i·sphere (**hěm′**ə sfîr′) *n.* Either of the halves into which the earth is divided by the equator or by a great circle that passes through the poles.

hem·lock (**hěm′**lŏk′) *n.* An evergreen tree with short, flat needles and small cones.

hemlock

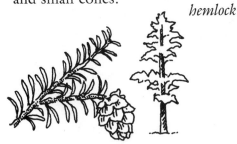

her·o·ine (**hěr′**ō ĭn) *n.* The main female character in a novel, movie, play, etc.

ho·mog·e·nize (hə **mŏj′**ə nīz′) *v.* **ho·mog·e·nized, ho·mog·e·niz·ing.** To spread evenly through a fluid, especially to make (milk) uniform by breaking the fat it contains into tiny particles.

hole (hōl) *n.* An opening or hollow made by or as if by digging, boring, cutting, poking, etc., into or through something. — *v.* **holed, hol·ing.** To put a hole or holes in.

huff·y (**hŭf′**ē) *adj.* **huff·i·er, huff·i·est.** Easily angered.

hull (hŭl) *n.* The framework of a ship or plane.

hutch (hŭch) *n.* A pen or coop for small animals, especially rabbits.

i·bis (**ī′**bĭs) *n.* A large wading bird with a long, downward-curving bill.

il·lu·sion (ĭ **lōō′**zhən) *n.* An appearance or impression that has no real basis: *The artist created the illusion of depth in the painting.*

in·con·sid·er·ate (ĭn′kən **sĭd′**ər ĭt) *adj.* Not taking into account other people's feelings; thoughtless.

in·flate (ĭn **flāt′**) *v.* **in·flat·ed, in·flat·ing.** To fill with gas or air and expand: *Did he inflate the tires? The balloon inflated quickly.*

in·let (**ĭn′**lět′) *or* (-lĭt) *n.* A bay, cove, estuary, or other recess along a coast.

in·ten·tion (ĭn **tĕn′**shən) *n.* Something intended; a plan, purpose, etc.

in·ter·est (ĭn′trĭst) *or* (-tər ĭst) *n.* A right, claim, or legal share in something: *an interest in the catering business.*

ir·re·deem·a·ble (ĭr′ĭ dē′mə bəl) *adj.* Not capable of being saved.

is·sue (ĭsh′ōō) *v.* **is·sued, is·su·ing. 1.** To put out; announce: *issue orders.* **2.** To come out; flow out: *Water issued from the broken pipe.*

jerk·y (jûr′kē) *n.* Meat, such as beef, that has been cut into strips and dried in the sun or cured with smoke.

jest (jĕst) *n.* Something said or done for fun or amusement.

jock·ey (jŏk′ē) *v.* To move in order to gain an advantage: *jockeyed the car into a tight space.*

jut (jŭt) *v.* **jut·ted, jut·ting.** To project sharply upward or outward; stick out.

keel ov·er (kēl ō′vər) *v.* To fall or lose one's balance.

keen·eyed (kēn′īd′) *adj.* Eager.

ker·o·sene (kĕr′ə sēn′) *or* (kăr′-) *or* (kĕr′ə sēn′) *or* (kăr′-) *n.* A thin, light-colored oil that is obtained mainly from petroleum and used chiefly as a fuel. — *modifier: a kerosene lamp.*

kit fox (kĭt fŏks) *n.* A kind of fox that has large ears and runs very fast.

kit fox

knoll (nōl) *n.* A small, rounded hill.

lab·y·rinth (lăb′ə rĭnth′) *n.* A network of winding, connected passages through which it is difficult to find one's way without help.

la·goon (lə gōōn′) *n.* A body of water, usually connecting with the ocean, especially one bounded by sandbars or coral reefs.

lamb (lăm) *n.* A young sheep.—*v.* **lambed, lamb·ing.** To give birth to a lamb.

lar·va (lär′və) *n., pl.* **lar·vae** (lär′vē) *or* **lar·vas.** An insect in an early form, when it has just hatched from an egg. A larva has a soft body that looks like a worm's.

laugh·ing·stock (lăf′ĭng stŏk′) *or* (lä′fĭng-) *n.* An object of mocking laughter, jokes, or ridicule.

ă pat / ā pay / â care / ä father / ĕ pet / ē be / ĭ pit /ī pie /î fierce / ŏ pot / ō go / ô paw, for / oi oil / ŏŏ book / ōō boot / ou out / ŭ cut / û fur / *th* the / th thin / hw which / zh vision / ə ago, item, pencil, atom, circus

leg·a·cy (lĕg′ə sē) *n., pl.* **leg·a·cies.** Money or property left to someone in a will.

lie to (lī tōō) *v. Nautical.* To remain stationary while facing the wind.

line (līn) *n.* The words said by an actor in a play.

list (lĭst) *v.* To tilt to one side, as a ship.

list·less·ly (lĭst′lĭs lē) *adv.* In a tired, unenthusiastic manner.

log·i·cal (lŏj′ĭ kəl) *adj.* **1.** Reasonable: *a logical choice.* **2.** Able to reason clearly and rationally: *a logical mind.*

lush (lŭsh) *adj.* **lush·er, lush·est. 1.** Having or forming a thick, plentiful plant growth: *lush green lawns; lush grass.* **2.** Luxurious; sumptuous: *a lush carpet.*

lyr·i·cal (lĭr′ĭ kəl) *adj.* Songlike; poetic.

main·stay (mān′stā′) *n.* **1.** A strong rope or cable that holds in place the mainmast of a sailing vessel. **2.** A main support: *He is the mainstay of the team.*

make·shift (māk′shĭft′) *adj.* Something that serves as a temporary substitute: *They lived in a makeshift shelter until their house was finished.*

mat·ter-of-fact·ly (măt′ər əv făkt′ lē) *adv.* Stating the facts without showing any emotion.

me·sa (mā′sə) *n.* A flat-topped hill or small plateau with steep sides, common in the southwestern United States.

mesa

mo·men·tous (mō mĕn′təs) *adj.* Of the utmost importance or significance: *a momentous occasion.*

mot·tled (mŏt′ld) *adj.* Covered with spots or streaks of different colors.

Mount Gambier (mount găm′ bē ā) *n.* A town on the southern coast of Australia, about 125 miles west of Melbourne.

mow[1] (mō) *v.* **mowed, mowed** *or* **mown** (mōn), **mow·ing. 1.** To cut down (grass, grain, etc.): *Mow the grass before it gets too high.* **2.** To cut the grass, grain, etc. from: *mow the lawn.*

mow[2] (mou) *n.* **1.** A place for storing hay or grain. **2.** Feed that is stored, especially in a barn.

mud flat (mŭd flăt) *n.* Land covered at high tide and exposed at low tide.

must·y (mŭs′tē) *adj.* **must·i·er, must·i·est.** Stale or moldy: *a musty smell.*

mys·ti·cal (mĭs′tĭ kəl) *adj.* **1.** Based on spiritual thoughts or practices. **2.** Inspiring a sense of mystery or wonder.

nar·ra·tion (nă rā′shən) *n.* The act of telling a story.

nour·ish (nûr′ĭsh) *or* (nŭr′ĭsh) *v.* To provide (a living thing) with the food or other substances it needs to grow and remain alive. — **nour′ish·ing** *adj.: a nourishing meal.*

nui·sance (nōō′səns) *or* (nyōō′-) *n.* A source of inconvenience or annoyance; a bother.

o·blige (ə blīj′) *v.* **o·bliged, o·blig·ing.** To make grateful or thankful: *They were obliged to her for her help.*

o·co·ti·llo (ō′kə tē′yō) *or* (-tēl′-) *n.,pl.* **o·co·ti·llos.** A prickly, cactuslike tree of desert regions of the southwestern United States and Mexico, having clusters of tube-shaped red flowers.

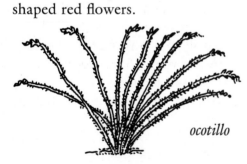

ocotillo

o·men (ō′mən) *n.* A thing or event regarded as a sign of future good or bad luck.

out·lan·dish (out lăn′dĭsh) adj. Strange in appearance or manner: *outlandish clothes.*

o·ver·hang (ō′vər **hăng′**) *n.* A projecting part of something, as a rock formation.

pad·dock (păd′ək) *n.* A fenced field or area in which horses are kept for grazing or exercising.

pain·ter (pān′tər) *n.* A rope attached to the bow (front) of a boat, used for tying up.

pa·lo·ver·de (păl′ō vûr′dē) *or* (-**vûrd′**) *n.* A spicy, nearly leafless shrub, of the southwestern United States, with yellow flowers.

par·a·site (păr′ə sīt′) *n.* An animal or plant that lives in or on a different kind of animal or plant.

par·lia·ment (pär′lə mənt) *n.* **1.** An assembly of persons that makes the laws for a nation. **2. Parliament.** The national legislature of the United Kingdom, made up of the House of Commons and the House of Lords.

pa·thet·i·cal·ly (pə thĕt′ĭk lē) *adv.* Sadly; pitifully.

pep·per mill (pĕp′ər mĭl) *n.* A container to grind peppercorns into pepper.

per·i·lous (pĕr′ə ləs) *adj.* Full of danger; hazardous.

per·son·nel (pûr′sə nĕl′) *n.* The division of a company or other organization concerned with the selection, placement, and training of employees.

ă pat / ā pay / â care / ä father / ĕ pet / ē be / ĭ pit / ī pie / î fierce / ŏ pot / ō go / ô paw, for / oi oil / ŏŏ book / ōō boot / ou out / ŭ cut / û fur / *th* the / th thin / hw which / zh vision / ə ago, item, pencil, atom, circus

pitch pipe (pĭch′ pīp′) *n.* A small pipe that, when sounded, gives the standard musical tone for a piece of music or for tuning an instrument.

plac·id (plăs′ĭd) *adj.* Peaceful; calm.

plain·tive (plān′tĭv) *adj.* Mournful; sad: *a plaintive song.*

pneu·mo·nia (nŏŏ mōn′yə) *or* (nyŏŏ-) *n.* Any of several usually serious diseases of the lungs, caused by bacteria, viruses, chemicals, or irritation.

political party (pə lĭt′ĭ kəl pär′tē) *n.* A group organized to advance its ideas about government and usually to nominate and support candidates for public office.

pol·li·wog (pŏl′ē wŏg′) *or* (-wôg′) *n.* A tadpole; a frog or toad in its early, newly hatched stage, when it lives in the water and has a tail.

polliwog

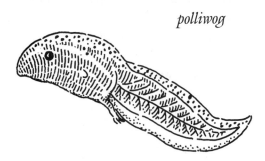

port (pôrt) *or* (pōrt) *n.* The left side of a ship or aircraft facing forward.

poul·tice (pōl′tĭs) *n.* A soft, moist, sticky mixture, usually heated, spread on cloth and applied to an aching part of the body.

pred·a·tor (prĕd′ə tər) *or* (-tôr′) *n.* An animal that lives by capturing and feeding on other animals.

prem·ise (prĕm′ĭs) *n.* An idea that forms the basis for action.

pre·oc·cu·pied (prē ŏk′yə pīd′) *adj.* Deep in thought.

prim·i·tive (prĭm′ĭ tĭv) *adj.* Simple or crude.

probe (prōb) *n.* A long, slender tool used to reach into or touch something in order to examine it.

prog·ress (prŏg′rĕs′) *or* (-rĭs) *n.* **1.** Onward movement; advance: *made slow progress through traffic.* **2.** Steady improvement: *a baby making progress in learning to talk.* —*v.* **pro·gress** (prə grĕs′). **1.** To move along, advance, proceed. **2.** To make steady or regular improvements.

pros·per·ous (prŏs′pər əs) *adj.* **1.** Vigorous and healthy; thriving: *a prosperous garden.* **2.** Economically successful; enjoying wealth or profit: *prosperous cities; a prosperous business.*

pulse (pŭls) *n.* A short burst of electrical energy.

put up (pŏŏt ŭp) *v.* To startle birds so that they fly away.

rap·tur·ous (răp′chər əs) *adj.* Feeling or expressing overwhelming delight; joyful.

rav·age (răv′ĭj) *v.* **rav·aged, rav·ag·ing.** To bring heavy destruction upon; devastate: *a hurricane ravaging the coast.*

ra·vine (rə **vēn′**) *n.* A deep, narrow cut in the earth's surface.

re·flect (rĭ **flĕkt′**) *v.* To give back an image as does a mirror or clear water.

re·fuge (**rĕf′**yo͞oj) *n.* **1.** Protection; shelter: *seeking refuge in the castle.* **2.** A place of protection or shelter: *a wildlife refuge.*

rep·ri·mand (**rĕp′**rĭ mănd′) *n.* A severe scolding.

res·er·voir (**rĕz′**ər vwär′) *n.* **1.** A chamber or container used for storing a fluid: *the reservoir of a fountain pen.* **2.** A large supply of something built up over a long period of time: *a reservoir of good will.*

re·tort (rĭ **tôrt′**) *v.* To make a quick, clever, or angry reply.

rheu·ma·tism (**ro͞o′**mə tĭz′əm) *n.* Any of several diseased conditions that affect the muscles, tendons, bones, joints, or nerves, causing pain and disability.

ric·o·chet (**rĭk′**ə shā′) *v.* **ric·o·cheted** (**rĭk′**ə shād′) or **ric·o·chet·ted** (**rĭk′**ə shĕt′ĭd), **ric·o·chet·ing** (**rĭk′**ə shā′ĭng) or **ric·o·chet·ting** (**rĭk′**ə shĕt′ĭng). To rebound at least once from a surface or surfaces.

rig·a·ma·role (**rĭg′**ə mə rōl′) *n.* Variant of **rig·ma·role** (**rĭg′**mə rōl′) *n.* Confused and rambling speech; nonsense.

rig·ging (**rĭg′**ĭng) *n.* The system of ropes, chains, and pulleys used to support and control the masts, sails, and yards of a sailing vessel.

ring·tailed "cat" (**rĭng′**tāld kăt) *n.* An animal, similar to a raccoon, found in the southwestern United States.

ringtailed "cat"

rip tide (rĭp tīd) *n.* A current of water disturbed by an opposing current. Also called **rip current.**

rit·u·al (**rĭch′**o͞o əl) *n.* **1.** The form or order of events followed during a religious or other ceremony. **2.** Any procedure faithfully and regularly followed.

rou·tine (ro͞o **tēn′**) *n.* A series of activities performed regularly; standard or usual procedure.

rub·ble (**rŭb′**əl) *n.* **1.** Irregular, broken pieces of rock. **2.** Fragments of stone or other material left after the destruction or decay of a building: *a cannon shot that reduced the tower to rubble.*

run (rŭn) *n.* A course or track along or down which something can travel.

ă pat / ā pay / â care / ä father / ĕ pet / ē be / ĭ pit / ī pie / î fierce / ŏ pot / ō go / ô paw, for / oi oil / o͞o book / o͞o boot / ou out / ŭ cut / û fur / *th* the / th thin / hw which / zh vision / ə ago, item, pencil, atom, circus

sa·gua·ro (sə **gwär′**ō) *or* (**-wär′**ō) *n., pl.* **sa·gua·ros.** A very large cactus of the southwestern United States and Mexico, having upward-curving branches, white flowers, and edible red fruit.

sal·low (**săl′**ō) *adj.* **sal·low·er, sal·low·est.** Of a sickly yellowish color or complexion.

salt·cel·lar (**sôlt′**sĕl′ər) *n.* A small dish or shaker for giving out salt.

sar·cas·ti·cal·ly (sär **kăs′**tĭk əl lē) *adv.* In a bitterly joking way, so as to make fun of someone or something.

scorn·ful·ly (**skôrn′** fəl lē) *adv.* In a manner expressing a feeling that someone or something is inferior.

scull (skŭl) *n.* **1.** An oar used for rowing a boat from the stern. **2.** A kind of short-handled oar. **3.** A small, light racing boat.—*v.* To move (a boat) with a scull or sculls.

se·crete (sĭ **krēt′**) *v.* **se·cret·ed, se·cret·ing.** To produce something from cells or bodily fluids.

serial number (**sîr′**ē əl **nŭm′**bər) *n.* A number that identifies one of a series of similar machines, per-sons grouped together, etc.: *the serial number of a car.*

set (sĕt) *n.* A structure on a stage, designed to represent the place where the action or scene of a play occurs.

se·vere·ly (sə **vîr′**lē) *adv.* Harshly: *scolded the dog severely.*

shaft (shăft) *or* (shäft) *n.* One of the two parallel poles between which an animal drawing a vehicle is hitched.

shed (shĕd) *v.* **shed, shed·ding.** To lose, drop, or cast off by natu-ral process: *trees that shed their leaves in autumn.*

shirk·er (**shûrk′**ər) *n.* One who avoids an unpleasant task because of laziness.

shoal (shōl) *n.* **1.** A shallow place in a body of water. **2.** A sandbank or sandbar.

skein (skān) *n.* A length of yarns, thread, etc., wound in a long, loose coil.

skew·er (**skyōō′**ər) *n.* A long pin of wood or metal, used to hold meat during cooking.

sledge (slĕj) *n.* A vehicle on run-ners, drawn by horses, dogs, or reindeer and used for transporting loads across snow and ice.

slough (slōō) *or* (slou) *n.* **1.** A hollow or depression in the ground, usually filled with mud or mire. **2.** A stagnant swamp, bog, marsh, etc.

snipe (snīp) *n., pl.* **snipe** *or* **snipes.** A brownish wading bird with a long bill.

snipe

569

soar (sôr) *or* (sōr) *v.* To rise, fly, or move in the air with ease, like an eagle or a hawk.

sol·emn·ly (sŏl′əm lē) *adv.* In an impressive or serious manner.

spunk (spŭngk) *n.* *Informal.* Spirit; courage.

squall (skwôl) *n.* A brief, sudden, and violent windstorm, often accompanied by rain or snow. — *v.* To storm violently for a short time.

stack·yard (stăk′yärd′) *n.* A yard where grain or straw is stacked.

star·board (stär′bôrd′) *or* (-bōrd′) *n.* The right side of a ship or aircraft facing forward.

stat·ic (stăt′ĭk) *n.* Hissing or crackling noise from a radio.

staves (stāvz) *n.* A plural of **staff** (a long stick carried as an aid in walking).

steth·o·scope (stĕth′ə skōp′) *n.* An instrument used to listen to sounds made within the body.

stew·ard (stoo′ərd) *or* (styoo′-) *n.* **1.** A person who manages another's property, finances, etc. **2.** A person in charge of the household affairs of a large estate, club, hotel, or resort.

stilt (stĭlt) *n.* **1.** Either of a pair of long, slender poles, each with a foot support part way up, enabling the wearer to walk elevated above the ground. **2.** Any of various types of posts or pillars used as supports for a building, dock, etc. **3.** A long-legged wading bird with a long bill.

stilt

stock (stŏk) *n.* Domestic animals such as horses, cattle, sheep, pigs, etc.

store (stôr) *or* (stōr) *n.* **1.** A place where merchandise is offered for sale; a shop. **2.a.** A stock or supply reserved for future use. **b. stores.** Supplies, as of food, clothing, or arms.

stout·ly (stout′ lē) *adv.* In a determined, bold, or brave manner.

sulk·i·ly (sŭlk′ ĭ lē) *adv.* In a gloomy manner.

sum·mon (sŭm′ən) *v.* To send for; request to appear.

sus·pense (sə spĕns′) *n.* The condition of being uncertain about what will happen.

swag·ger (swăg′ər) *v.* To walk with a superior or proud attitude.

swale (swāl) *n.* A piece of land that is moist and marshy.

swamp (swŏmp) *v.* To soak, fill or cover with water or other liquid: *The waves swamped the boat and sank it.*

ă pat / ā pay / â care / ä father / ĕ pet / ē be / ĭ pit / ī pie / î fierce / ŏ pot / ō go / ô paw, for / oi oil / ŏŏ book /
ōō boot / ou out / ŭ cut / û fur / *th* the / th thin / hw which / zh vision / ə ago, item, pencil, atom, circus

swiv·el (swĭv′əl) *v.* **swiv·eled** or **swiv·elled, swiv·el·ing** or **swiv·el·ling.** To turn freely.

syn·a·gogue (sĭn′ə gŏg′) *or* (-gôg′) *n.* A building or place of meeting for Jewish worship and religious instruction.

tack (tăk) *n.* **1.** A small nail with a sharp point and a flat head. **2.** A course of action or an approach: *try a new tack.*

tail wind (tāl′ wĭnd′) *n.* A wind whose direction is the same as that of the course of a bird or vehicle.

ta·lus (tā′ləs) *n., pl.* **ta·lus·es. 1.** A slope formed by a collection of debris. **2.** A sloping mass of debris that collects at the base of a cliff.

tear duct (tîr dŭkt) *n.* A tube in the body through which tears flow.

tech·ni·cian (tĕk nĭsh′ən) *n.* A person who is skilled in a certain scientific subject or process.

tet·a·nus shot (tĕt′n əs shŏt) *n.* A shot often given to prevent a disease that enters the body through an open wound.

thong (thông) *or* (thŏng) *n.* A strip of leather used to fasten something, such as a sandal.

thresh·er (thrĕsh′ər) *n.* A machine that separates the seeds from grain-bearing plants.

thrive (thrīv) *v.* **throve** (thrōv) or **thrived, thrived** or **thriv·en** (thrĭv′ ən), **thriv·ing.** To grow or do well; be or stay in a healthy condition: *Some plants thrive in damp, sandy soil.*

tim·ber (tĭm′bər) *n.* A beam or similarly shaped piece of wood, such as those used in building a house or forming a ship's frame.

tit·ter (tĭt′ər) *v.* To utter a restrained, nervous giggle.

to-do (tə dōō′) *n. Informal.* Commotion or bustle; stir; fuss.

tol·er·ance (tŏl′ər əns) *n.* The capacity for or practice of recognizing and respecting the opinions, practices, or behavior of others.

tongue de·pres·sor (tŭng dĭ **prĕs′** sər) *n.* A thin wooden stick used to hold the tongue down so a doctor can see into the throat.

trem·u·lous (trĕm′yə ləs) *adj.* Trembling; quivering: *speaking with a tremulous voice.*

tuft (tŭft) *n.* A cluster of hair, feathers, grass, yarn, etc., growing or held close together at the base.

turn of the cen·tu·ry (tûrn ŭv thə **sĕn′** chə rē) *n.* The time within a few years of a new century, especially from the late 1800's to the early 1900's.

un·at·tain·able (ŭn ə tān′ə bəl) *adj.* Not able to be accomplished or achieved by effort.

un·der·tow (ŭn′dər tō′) *n.* The current beneath the surface of a body of water running in a direction opposite to that of the current at the surface.

un·furl (ŭn fûrl′) *v.* To spread or open out; unroll: *unfurl a flag.*

vict·uals (vĭt′lz) *pl.n.* Food supplies; provisions.

vine·yard (vĭn′yərd) *n.* A piece of ground on which grapevines are grown and tended.

vise (vīs) *n.* A device of metal, usually consisting of a pair of jaws that are opened and closed by means of a screw or lever, used in carpentry or metalworking to hold work in place.

vise

wake (wāk) *n.* **1.** The visible track of waves, ripples, or foam left behind something moving through water. **2.** The course or route over which anything has passed: *The hurricane left destruction in its wake.*

ware (wâr) *n.* **1.** Manufactured articles or goods of the same general kind, such as glassware or hardware. **2.** Pottery or ceramics, such as earthenware or stoneware. **3. wares.** Goods for sale.

wash (wŏsh) *or* (wôsh) *n.* A flow of water or air caused by the passage or action of a boat, aircraft, oar, propeller, etc.

whet (hwĕt) *or* (wĕt) *v.* **whet·ted, whet·ting.** To make more keen; stimulate: *The exciting book whetted my interest.*

whim·si·cal (hwĭm′sĭ kəl) *or* (wĭm′-) *adj.* Playful, fanciful.

winch (wĭnch) *n.* A machine for pulling or lifting, consisting of a drum around which a rope or cable attached to the load is wound as the load is moved.

work·shop (wûrk′shŏp′) *n.* A group of people studying or working together in a special field or subject.

yard (yärd) *n.* **1.** A unit of length equal to 3 feet or 36 inches. **2.** A long pole attached crosswise to a mast to support a sail.

ă pat / ā pay / â care / ä father / ĕ pet / ē be / ĭ pit / ī pie / î fierce / ŏ pot / ō go / ô paw, for / oi oil / ŏŏ book / ōō boot / ou out / ŭ cut / û fur / *th* the / th thin / hw which / zh vision / ə ago, item, pencil, atom, circus

Reading and Writing Aids

Reading Aids

Use these aids to help you read words you have not seen before.

1. Use the letter sounds and the context, the sense of nearby words, phrases, and sentences.

    *   Sometimes the general sense of the passage may be the best context clue.

        "If you **heed** my advice," said Mr. Phelps, "you will surely succeed." (follow)

    *   A synonym, a word with nearly the same meaning, can be a context clue.

        In fairy tales, foxes are often sly. Are real foxes that **cunning**? (sly, clever)

    *   A contrast word such as *but* or *although* will sometimes let you know that a word of opposite meaning follows.

        Although the painting contains many **angular** lines, it has some soft, curved shapes too. (sharp-cornered)

2. Look for a base word with a prefix, a suffix, or both. Use the context and the meanings of the base word and its prefix, suffix, or both to figure out the meaning of a word.

    If you **mislabel** these packages, they will be sent to the wrong place.

Prefix	Base Word	Meaning
mis-	label	"label wrongly"

    The speaker became **famous** for her wise sayings.

Base Word	Suffix	Meaning
fame	-ous	"having fame"

    When the friends shook hands, their **disagreement** was over.

Prefix	Base Word	Suffix
dis-	agree	-ment

    Meaning
    "action of not agreeing"

3. If you cannot figure out the meaning, use a glossary or a dictionary.

Study Aid

Use the SQRRR method to learn and remember information.

Step One: Survey. Look over the main headings and summary statements.

Step Two: Question. Turn the headings into questions you expect the material to answer.

Step Three: Read. Read the material under the headings to answer your questions.

Step Four: Recite. Answer your questions in your own words.

Step Five: Review. Look again at each heading, and recite the answers to your questions.

Writing Aids

Step One: Choose a topic.
Think about a topic. Choose a topic about which you already know something or about which you can easily find information.

Step Two: Write your first draft. Just get your ideas down on paper; you will have a chance to make changes later.

Step Three: Revise your first draft. *Revise* means "to make changes." Use these questions to help you revise:

- Did you stick to your topic?
- Did you include all important information?
- Did you present information in the correct order?
- Did you include necessary details and descriptions?
- Did you include necessary dialogue?

Step Four: Proofread your first draft. *Proofread* means "to read over and correct mistakes." Use these questions to help you proofread:

- Did you indent all paragraphs?
- Did you use capital letters correctly?
- Did you include all necessary punctuation marks?
- Did you spell all words correctly?
- Did you write each sentence to express a complete thought?

Step Five: Make a final copy.
Make a final copy to share with someone. Prepare a neat, clean copy that shows all revisions and corrections. Then proofread your final copy to see that you have not made additional mistakes.

Continued from page 2.

Bibliographical Note

The study method described in part of the lesson "Organizing Study Time" and in "Reading and Writing Aids" is based on the widely used SQ3R system developed by Francis P. Robinson in *Effective Study*, 4th ed. (New York: Harper & Row, Publishers, Inc., 1961, 1970).

Credits

Cover and title page illustrated by D. J. Simison
Magazine openers illustrated by William Giese

Illustrators: **8–9** William Giese **12–25** David Biedrzycki **30–41** Ian Robertson **53–58** Chris Demarest **62** Bill Ogden **64–79** David Wenzel **89–90** Susanah Brown **94–105** Mary Beth Schwark **109–112** Bill Ogden **114–115** Laura Cornell **116–137** (illustrations) Higgins Bond (borders) © Mitchell & Malik **142–143** William Giese **146–162** John Shipperbottom **165** Jan Brett **168–169** Bill Ogden **170–181** Graham Humphreys **171** (map) Susanah Brown **183** Cecilia von Rabenau **192–201** Nick Harris **224–225** Carol Schwartz **226** Bill Ogden **228–240** Ben F. Stahl **253** Susanah Brown **256–260** Josette Gourley **262–279** Alan Baker **282–283** Lynne Cherry **285** Bill Ogden **286–287** William Giese **290–302** Mou-Sien Tseng **304–320** Collette Slade **322** Susanah Brown **337** K. Christopher Schuh **344–358** Donna Diamond **367–370** Susanah Brown **372–380** Mike Codd **385** Susanah Brown **392** Bill Ogden **394–415** Cherie Wyman **420–421** William Giese **436–438** Laura Cornell **442–454** Jan Wills **458–474** Arvis Stewart **478–492** Larry Raymond **502–518** Eric Jon Nones **520** Bill Ogden **530–553** (illustrations) Stella Ormai (borders) © Mitchell & Malik **556–572** George M. Ulrich

Photographers: **28** © G. Schaller/Bruce Coleman Inc. **29** © Bo Hong Jin/Bruce Coleman Inc. **47** © Mike Yamashita/Woodfin Camp **50** © Bill Melendez Productions, Inc. **51** © United Features Syndicate Inc. **54** (left) "Ungloved Hand" film/ © Lisa Crafts **54** (right) "Opening New Frontiers" film/NASA **60** © Bill Melendez Productions, Inc. **82–83, 86** Dan Morrill/Reese-Gibson **87** © David C. Fritts/Animals Animals **88, 90** © Ted Levin/Animals Animals **91** © Ron Austing/Bruce Coleman Inc. **92** © Charles Palek/Animals Animals **107** "MOON AND WILD GEESE" from the series of Wakan Roe Shu Hiroshige, 1797–1858/Courtesy Museum of Fine Arts, Boston, Ross Collection, gift of Denman Waldo Ross. **166–167** "TWO FIGURES BY THE SEA" (detail) by Winslow Homer, 1882 /Courtesy of the Denver Art Museum, Denver, Colorado **184** © Stella Hardee/Bruce Coleman Inc. **185** (top) James David Brandt/Earth Scenes **185** (bottom), **186** © Dr. E. R. Degginger **187** (top) © Francisco Erize/Bruce Coleman Inc. **187** (right, bottom) M. P. Kahl/Tom Stack & Assoc. **187** (bottom, left), **188** (top) © Dr. E. R. Degginger **188** (bottom) © Stella Hardee/Bruce Coleman Inc. **188–189** © Jen & Des Bartlett/Bruce Coleman Inc. **189** (top) © Doug Allan/Animals Animals **189** (bottom) © Dr. E. R. Degginger **190, 191** Russ Kline/National Science Foundation Polar Information Program **205** Grant Heilman Photography **210–222** © Hartmann/Dutton **243** © Wallin/Taurus Photos **248–249** Dan Morrill/Reese-Gibson **250–254, 324–334** Ken O'Donoghue/Reese-Gibson **340** © Zig Leszczynski/Animals Animals **342** © Ernest Manewal/Black Star **360** Ralph Mercer **384, 386** (left) © G. R. Roberts **386** (right) Robert Frerck/Odyssey Photos **388–391** © G. R. Roberts **393** © Bill Binzen **424–425** "THE MARKET PLACE" by Marc Chagall, 1917/ Metropolitan Museum of Art, New York, Bequest of Scofield Thayer, 1982 **427** "I AND THE VILLAGE" by Marc Chagall, 1911/Collection of The Museum of Modern Art, New York/Mrs. Simon Guggenheim Fund **429** "VITEBSK FROM MOUNT ZADUNOV" by Marc Chagall, 1917, Private Collection/photo by Bruce Jones **433** "SELF-PORTRAIT WITH SEVEN FINGERS" by Marc Chagall, 1912/Stedelijk Museum Amsterdam **434** "PEASANT VILLAGE" by Marc Chagall, 1925/Albright-Know Gallery, Room of Contemporary Art Fund **435** "GREEN VIOLINIST" by Marc Chagall, 1918/Solomon R. Guggenheim Museum, NY **456–457** Paul Logsdon/Fotowest **457** (top) © Dr. E. R. Degginger **457** (bottom) Jack Parsons/Fotowest **476** Michael Heron **494–495** © Bryan Alexander/Black Star **522** © Raymond A. Mendez/Animals Animals **524** (left) © Kim Taylor/Bruce Coleman Inc. **524–525** © C. W. Perkins/Animals Animals **525** (right) © Keith Gunnar/Bruce Coleman Inc. **526** © Dr. E. R. Degginger